Introduction to

Computer Hardware and Data Communications

Introduction to

Computer Hardware and Data Communications

P.-A. Goupille

Translated and revised by G. M. Loadwick

Prentice Hall

MASSON

This edition published 1993 by
Prentice Hall International (UK) Ltd
Campus 400, Maylands Avenue
Hemel Hempstead
Hertfordshire HP2 7EZ
A division of
Simon & Schuster International Group

© 1990 Masson, Paris

This book was originally published under the title *Technologie des Ordinateurs: Pour les I.U.T. et B.T.S. informatique* by P.-A. Goupille.

© 1993 Masson and Prentice Hall International (UK) Ltd

Typeset in 10/12 Times with Helvetica
by Mathematical Composition Setters Ltd, Salisbury, Wiltshire

Printed and bound in Great Britain
by Redwood Books, Trowbridge, Wiltshire

Library of Congress Cataloging-in-Publication Data

Goupille, P.-A. (Pierre-Alain)
    [Technologie des ordinateurs (pour les IUT et BTS informatiques).
English]
    Introduction to computer hardware and data communications/by P.
-A. Goupille.
        p.   cm.
    Translation of: Technologie des ordinateurs (pour les IUT et BTS
informatiques)
    Includes bibliographical references and index.
    ISBN 0-13-896838-1
    1. Microcomputers. 2. Data transmission systems.   I. Title.
TK7888.3.G6513   1993   92-33171
004.16–dc20   CIP

British Library Cataloguing in Publication Data

A catalogue record for this book is available from
the British Library

ISBN 0-13-896838-1

2   3   4   5   97   96   95   94   93

Contents

Preface

This book on computer hardware and data communications is unashamedly oriented towards microcomputers because these are the most widely available computers and the easiest to understand. Originally written for students of computing in France, the book will be particularly useful for first- and second-year degree students in the UK studying computing or information technology, and will also be useful for students following Higher National BTEC courses in computing studies.

The book has thirty chapters covering five main themes but not all of the chapters need to be studied on a first reading; some of them, for example the chapters covering logic circuits, can easily be omitted entirely.

Chapters 1 to 6 cover the way in which data are represented in a computer system.

Chapters 7 to 13 show the functioning of the elementary circuits constituting the machine.

Chapters 14 to 20 present the way in which the central processor and the main memory work.

Chapters 21 to 26 present a wide range of peripheral devices which can be attached to the system.

Chapters 27 to 30 consider data communications, wide area networks and local area networks.

The text is supplied with numerous examples and exercises. Many of the exercises (self-assessed questions, or SAQs) have fully worked solutions included at the end of the chapters. These worked solutions can serve a dual purpose: they can be used by students to check their own solutions or they can be used as additional examples.

It is not possible to treat all topics to the same depth in a book of this size bearing in mind the diversity of the subject and the speed with which advances are still being made. Students should not hesitate to seek help from their lecturers or to consult other texts if they feel that they need more information on any of the topics.

Some additional material has been specially written for this UK edition to acknowledge the popularity of the 68000 processor and to introduce some recent developments in UK telecommunications networks.

I would like to express my gratitude to Peter Cheetham of Staffordshire University School of Computing and to two anonymous reviewers for reading the original translation and for their very helpful comments and suggestions for improving the text. I am also very grateful to Dave Irwin for sharing with me his very up-to-date knowledge of developments in the UK telecommunications industry.

G. M. Loadwick
Stafford 1992

Chapter 1

Introduction to computer architecture

1.1 Definition of information processing

Information processing has been defined as the 'science of organising, manipulating, and distributing information with the aid of automatic machines'.

Although the words used in this definition would serve equally well to define the term computing, they have not been chosen lightly.

Information processing is primarily a **science**: it obeys rules and precise laws and its processes are performed in a completely rational way.

The **automatic machines** mentioned in the definition are the computers whose architecture we will be studying in more detail in the following chapters.

Information is the meaning given to data by the way in which it is interpreted. **Data** is the raw material that computers manipulate and process.

1.2 Analogy of an information system

Let us begin by introducing a simple analogy illustrating what a computer is and how it works.

Consider an employee working in an office. While working the employee is at the centre of the processing and we can think of her as the **central processing unit** (see Figure 1.1). Her in-tray contains the work to be processed (**input data**) while her out-tray holds the results of processing (**output results**). We can think of this system as an information processor which accepts input data, processes it and produces output results, as in the diagram below:

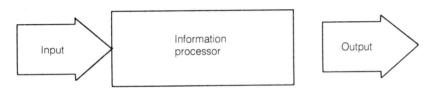

To carry out her work the employee needs to perform calculations (mathematical operations, comparisons, etc.). To help her she uses a calculator (or **arithmetic unit**).

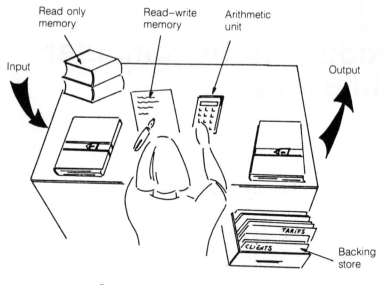

Central processing unit (CPU)

Figure 1.1   An office worker

So as not to forget what she has been asked to do, she writes down the instructions she has been given. They constitute her **program of work**. In the same way she writes down certain details about the data she is going to process. These actions are analogous to **storing** or **memorising** in the computer memory the instructions to be executed and the **data** to be processed by the computer.

The memory can be **updated** by **writing** to it and its contents can be examined by **reading** it. This kind of memory is called a **read–write** memory or **RWM** (pronounced rum):

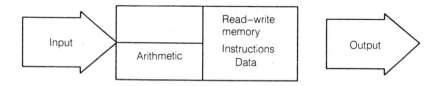

In contrast the employee might need to refer to data such as tax tables, for example, which does not change. This kind of data need only be written once but can be read as often as required. Data like this is known as **read only** data and may be stored in read only memory or **ROM**.

The volume of information held in, say, a price catalogue or a list of customers' addresses, is often too large for an employee to remember. Large volumes of data will be kept in filing cabinets containing **files** of customer details or prices of goods. These cabinets form an **auxiliary memory** or **backing store**.

All these elements, shown in the diagram below, are to be found in computers and we are going to study them in more detail in the following pages:

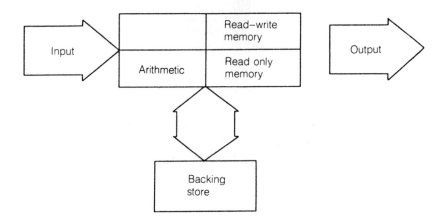

The computer we are most likely to meet nowadays is a microcomputer like the one shown in Figure 1.2. Let us remove its cover and look inside:

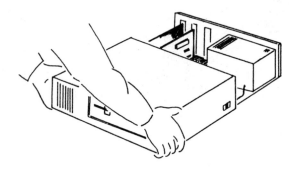

A number of parts can be identified immediately (see Figure 1.3). The heaviest and most obvious is usually the power supply generally accompanied by a cooling fan.

A number of electric cables leave the power supply to feed the various components. We can distinguish, in particular, a number of circuit boards covered with electronic components. These boards are generally plugged into a larger circuit board called a **mother board** situated at the base of the machine. The mother board generally includes the processor, more commonly called the **microprocessor chip**.

One of the cards plugged into the mother board carries a large number of identical components and is the central memory (read only memory and read–write memory) of the computer. In some microcomputers it is often the mother board itself that carries the central memory. Some of the other boards have cables leading to modules at the front of the machine. These modules house the built-in backing stores such as hard disks, floppy disks, tape streamers, etc.

Figure 1.2   A microcomputer

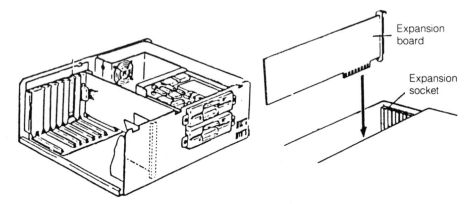

Expansion
board

Expansion
socket

Figure 1.3   With the covers removed

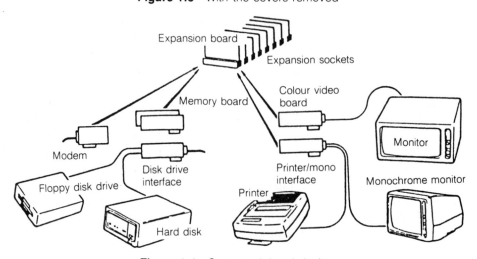

Expansion board

Expansion sockets

Colour video
board

Memory board

Monitor

Modem

Disk drive
interface

Printer/mono
interface

Monochrome monitor

Floppy disk drive

Printer

Hard disk

Figure 1.4   Some peripheral devices

It is equally possible for modules to be placed outside the main box (see Figure 1.4) and you will already have noticed that the screen or **monitor** is connected to the box via a plug and socket. So too is the keyboard which enables data for processing to be entered into the computer.

In the following chapters we are going to study all these computing terms more closely and we will look at the way computers are organised and at their various peripherals (printers, monitors etc.). But before that we must first of all study how data is represented in the computer, to see how data can be assimilated or 'understood' by information systems.

1.3 **Note on SAQs**

The chapters in this book have been designed to allow the student to study at his or her own pace. Wherever it has been appropriate, we have set SAQs. Sometimes we have supplied solutions to SAQs at the end of the chapter; at other times we have simply suggested how the answers can be verified. By doing these SAQs students can check just how much knowledge they have acquired.

Do not hesitate to use other books if you have any doubts or questions unresolved and do not forget that your teacher or lecturer is there to answer your questions.

EXERCISES

1.1 Without the aid of the book redraw the schematic diagram of a simplified information processor such as the one we have presented in this chapter.

1.2 Name the various parts of the microcomputer shown below:

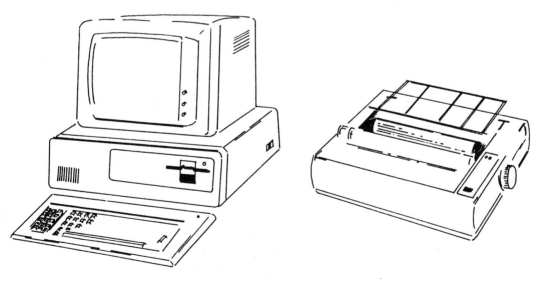

Chapter 2

The representation of data

Modern computer systems are built from integrated circuits, which are electronic components containing several tens or even several hundreds of thousands of transistors on a single chip of silicon. They function according to a two-state logic which corresponds, in simple terms, to current flowing or not flowing through a transistor.

The two logic states, conventionally denoted by **0** and **1** define a logic called **binary**. The two states correspond to two voltage levels, which for simplification we will call 0 volts and +5 volts, as shown below:

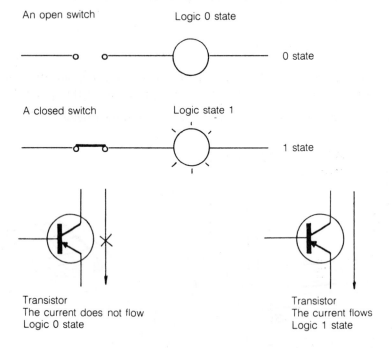

An open switch   Logic 0 state

                                              0 state

A closed switch   Logic state 1

                                              1 state

Transistor   Transistor
The current does not flow   The current flows
Logic 0 state   Logic 1 state

All data to be processed must be capable of being represented in a form the machine can use, that is to say for present purposes, in **binary**. The transformation from a form understandable by human-beings to a form understandable to the computer is called **coding**.

We shall see that there are numerous ways of coding data; we will consider **binary, hexadecimal, BCD, ASCII. . . .** .

2.1 **Binary notation (pure binary)**

In binary there are just two symbols, 0 and 1, which when combined together in different patterns allow all data to be represented for processing.

The base of binary numbers is 2 (because we use just two symbols); calculations are performed in **base 2**. A number n in base 2 is conventionally written n_2.

Example 2.1 **Binary notation: 101_2**

A number in base 10, such as we normally use, should be written in the form n_{10}; for example 135_{10}. Generally such notation is not used for base 10, but beware: in certain cases there can be confusion (101_2 and 101_{10} do not have the same value).

2.2 **Conversions**

To make learning easier we will only consider positive integers for the time being. Fractions will be studied later.

It is possible to convert from a number in base 10 to a number in base 2 by successive division.

Example 2.2 **Converting 135_{10} to base 2**

$$
\begin{array}{llll}
135/2 & = 67 & \text{remainder} & 1 \\
67/2 & = 33 & \text{remainder} & 1 \\
33/2 & = 16 & \text{remainder} & 1 \\
16/2 & = 8 & \text{remainder} & 0 \\
8/2 & = 4 & \text{remainder} & 0 \\
4/2 & = 2 & \text{remainder} & 0 \\
2/2 & = 1 & \text{remainder} & 0 \\
1/2 & = 0 & \text{remainder} & 1 \\
\end{array}
$$

The arrow pointing towards the top indicates the direction for reading the answer. The number 135_{10} would thus be equivalent in pure binary to 10000111_2.

Each binary element, being able to take the value 0 or 1, is called a binary digit, or more usually **bit** (an abbreviation for **binary digit**).

A group of four bits is called a **nibble** or a **quartet**; a group of eight bits is called a **byte** or an **octet**.

Conversely it is easy to convert a number in base 2 to a number in base 10 by successive multiplications.

Starting at the right, each element (or bit) of the binary number is multiplied by 2 raised to a power. The power starts at zero on the right and increases by 1 for each successive bit. The resulting values are then added together to obtain the answer.

Example 2.3   Converting 10011_2 to decimal

$$
\begin{array}{ccccc}
1 & 0 & 0 & 1 & 1 \\
\times & \times & \times & \times & \times \\
2^4 & 2^3 & 2^2 & 2^1 & 2^0 \\
= & = & = & = & = \\
16 & 0 & 0 & 2 & 1
\end{array}
$$

and adding these values gives 19_{10}.

Notice that each of the bits, starting from the right, is multiplied by the successive values 1, 2, 4, 8, 16, 32, 64, 128, ...

This indicates another technique for converting decimal numbers to binary. This consists of subtracting from the number the greatest power of 2 possible and then continuing to subtract decreasing powers of 2 in sequence down to 2^0 for integers.

If the power of 2 can be subtracted at a particular stage a 1 is written down if not, a 0 is written.

Example 2.4 135_{10} to base 2 again

$$
\begin{array}{llll}
\text{From} & 135 \text{ we can} & (1) \text{ subtract} & 128 \text{ remainder } 7 \\
& 7 \text{ we cannot} & (0) \text{ subtract} & 64 \text{ remainder } 7 \\
& 7 \text{ we cannot} & (0) \text{ subtract} & 32 \text{ remainder } 7 \\
& 7 \text{ we cannot} & (0) \text{ subtract} & 16 \text{ remainder } 7 \\
& 7 \text{ we cannot} & (0) \text{ subtract} & 8 \text{ remainder } 7 \\
& 7 \text{ we can} & (1) \text{ subtract} & 4 \text{ remainder } 3 \\
& 3 \text{ we can} & (1) \text{ subtract} & 2 \text{ remainder } 1 \\
& 1 \text{ we can} & (1) \text{ subtract} & 1 \text{ remainder } 0
\end{array}
$$

Beware: the direction of reading is reversed! The result is still (happily!) 10000111_2.

The first ten binary numbers

1_{10}	$\to$	1_2	
2_{10}	$\to$	10_2	
3_{10}	$\to$	11_2	
4_{10}	$\to$	100_2	
5_{10}	$\to$	101_2	
6_{10}	$\to$	110_2	
7_{10}	$\to$	111_2	
8_{10}	$\to$	1000_2	
9_{10}	$\to$	1001_2	
10_{10}	$\to$	1010_2	

SAQs

2.1 Convert to binary (a) 397_{10}, (b) 133_{10} and (c) 110_{10}.

2.2 Convert to decimal (a) 101_2, (b) 0101_2 and (c) 1101110_2.

Verify your answers by reconverting them to their original base.

2.3 **Binary operations**

Operations on binary numbers are performed in just the same way as operations on decimal numbers. Remembering that the only symbols used are 0 and 1, we have the following fundamental operations.

2.3.1 *Addition*

$$0 + 0 = 0$$
$$0 + 1 = 1$$
$$1 + 0 = 1$$
$$1 + 1 = 0 \text{ and 'carry 1' or } \quad 1$$
$$\frac{+1}{}$$
$$\text{carry } \rightarrow \quad 10$$

2.3.2 *Subtraction*

$$0 - 0 = 0$$
$$0 - 1 = 1 \text{ and 'borrow 1' or } \quad 0$$
$$\frac{-1}{}$$
$$1 - 0 = 1 \qquad \text{borrow } \rightarrow \quad 11$$
$$1 - 1 = 0$$

Example 2.5 Addition and subtraction

$$1010 + 1011 \qquad\qquad 1011 - 0101$$

1010	1011
+ 1011	−0101
1010 ← carries	100 ← borrows
10101	0110

SAQ

2.3 Working in binary, perform the following calculations and check your answers by repeating the calculations after converting to decimal:

(a) 1100 + 1000
(b) 1001 + 1011
(c) 1100 - 1000
(d) 1000 - 101
(e) 1 + 1 + 1 + 1

2.3.3 *Multiplication*

Binary multiplication is performed in the same way as decimal multiplication. The multiplicand is multiplied by each bit of the multiplier in turn to produce the partial products. Each new partial product is shifted one place relative to the previous one and then the partial products are added together to form the result.

Example 2.6   Multiplication

```
         1000              1011
       × 1010            ×  111
         0000              1011
         1000              1011
         0000              1011
         1000              1111  ← carries
       1010000           1001101
```


SAQ

2.4 Perform the following calculations:
(a) 1011 × 11
(b) 1100 × 101
(c) 100111 × 0110
Verify your answers by performing the necessary conversions.

2.3.4 *Division*

We have seen that multiplication is based on a series of additions; conversely division is based on a succession of subtractions and uses the same methods as ordinary decimal division.

Example 2.7 1100_2 divided by 100_2

$$
\begin{array}{r}
11 \\
100 \overline{\smash{\big)}\ 1100} \\
-\ 100 \\
\hline
0100 \\
-\ 100 \\
\hline
000
\end{array}
$$

The result is thus 11_2.

Example 2.8 101100_2 divided by 100_2

$$
\begin{array}{r}
1011 \\
100 \overline{\smash{\big)}\ 101100} \\
-\ 100 \\
\hline
110 \\
-\ 100 \\
\hline
100 \\
-\ 100 \\
\hline
0
\end{array}
$$

The result is thus 1011_2.

SAQ

2.5 Perform the following calculations:

(a)   100100/11

(b)   110000/110

Verify your answers by performing the necessary conversions.

2.4 Negative numbers

Numbers used in the text up to now, even the results obtained to subtractions, have all been positive. What about negative numbers?

2.4.1 *Sign and magnitude representation*

The most obvious method of representing negative numbers would be to reserve a bit to represent the sign, and allow the other bits to represent the absolute value of the number.

The usual convention is to make the first bit (that is the one in the leftmost position, which we call the **M**ost Significant **B**it or **MSB**), a 0 to represent a positive number and a 1 to represent a negative number. We refer to this convention as **sign and magnitude** representation. Thus using a six-bit representation:

$$0{:}11011 \text{ would represent } 27_{10}$$
$$1{:}11011 \text{ would represent } -27_{10}$$

Here we have placed a ' : ' between the first bit (representing the sign), and the other bits (representing the magnitude); in practice the colon does not exist and we will not use it from now on.

Such a representation of signed numbers means that the sign bit has to be treated differently to the other bits and requires different electronic circuits to be used according to whether the operation being performed is addition or subtraction. This problem is avoided by using another form of representation called **complement** representation.

2.4.2 *Complement representation*

2.4.2.1 1's complement
The 1's complement of a binary number is obtained by inverting the value of the bits of the number.

Thus consider the binary number 00010, which represents the number $+2_{10}$. It has a 1's complement of 11101.

2.4.2.2 2's complement
The 2's complement of a number is obtained by adding 1 to the 1's complement. Thus in the preceding example:

$$\begin{array}{ll} 11101 & \text{1's complement} \\ +\quad 1 & \\ \hline 11110 & \text{2's complement} \end{array}$$

2.4.2.3 Working in 1's complement
In a machine working in 1's complement, subtraction is achieved by adding the 1's complement of the number to be subtracted. Any carry which emerges from the most significant (or left-hand) end is then added back at the least significant (right-hand) end. This is called **end-around carry**.

Example 2.9   End-around carry

Normal form   1's complement form
                00111111   00111111 63_{10}
            − 00011100   + 11100011 $− 28_{10}$
                    carries →   1111111
                                100100010
end-around carry →   └────→ 1
                                00100011 35_{10}

If there is no carry from the most significant end this means that the answer is a negative number represented in 1's complement form. The magnitude of the answer can be determined by finding its 1's complement.

Example 2.10   Subtract 63_{10} from 28_{10}

First we find the 1's complement of the number to be subtracted (here 63_{10}):

Normal form   1's complement form
        00011100   00011100 28_{10}
    − 00111111   + 11000000 $− 63_{10}$
no end-around carry → 11011100

We have no end-around carry from the left-hand end; the result is therefore a **negative** number in **1's complement**. We must determine its 1's complement to obtain its magnitude; in this case it is 00100011 or 35_{10}.
The actual result was therefore $− 35_{10}$.

Note: The same principle is used for 2's complements. The only difference is that if a carry occurs from the most significant end it is not fed back to be added in at the least significant end. Instead of using 1's complements, 2's complements are used.

EXERCISE

2.1   Use the 2's complement method to repeat the subtractions given in Examples 2.9 and 2.10.

SAQ

2.5   Perform the calculation $20_{10} − 30_{10}$ in binary: (a) first using 1's complement; and (b) 2's complement.

2.5 **Fractions**

The numbers we have used so far have been negative or positive integers. We are equally likely to meet fractions and so we also need to be able to code them in binary.

We have seen in Section 2.2 that the integer part of a number can be expressed in positive powers of 2; now we will see that the fractional part can be expressed in **negative** powers of 2. The binary number obtained in this way is written with the integer part on the left of the point and the fractional part on the right of the point. The point should now be called the **binary point**.

Example 2.11   Representation of fractions

100.01 will be equivalent to:

$$(1 \times 2^2) + (0 \times 2^1) + (0 \times 2^0) \cdot (0 \times 2^{-1}) + (1 \times 2^{-2})$$
$$(1 \times 4) + (0 \times 2) + (0 \times 1) \cdot (0 \times \tfrac{1}{2}) + (1 \times \tfrac{1}{4})$$

that is 4.25_{10}.

Binary to decimal conversion is thus easily achieved. So too is conversion from decimal to binary. We showed in Section 2.2 how to convert decimal integers to binary by successive division by 2.

To convert decimal fractions to binary fractions we multiply the decimal fraction by 2. The integer part thus obtained represents the value (1 or 0) of the first bit to the right of the point. The remaining fractional part is again multiplied by 2 to obtain the value of the next bit. The process is repeated until either all the fraction has been converted or the precision of the result is judged to be sufficient.

Example 2.12 0.6875_{10} into binary

$$
\begin{array}{llll}
0.6875 & \times\ 2 & =\ 1.375 & \text{giving } 1 \times 2^{-1} \\
0.375 & \times\ 2 & =\ 0.750 & \text{giving } 0 \times 2^{-2} \\
0.750 & \times\ 2 & =\ 1.500 & \text{giving } 1 \times 2^{-3} \\
0.500 & \times\ 2 & =\ 1.000 & \text{giving } 1 \times 2^{-4}
\end{array}
$$

Since there is no remaining fraction to multiply, the conversion is complete and the result shows that 0.6875_{10} converts to 0.1011_2.

The following table showing some decimal equivalents of negative and positive powers of 2 will be useful in the work that follows.

2^{-n}	n	2^n
1	0	1
0.5	1	2
0.25	2	4
0.125	3	8
0.0625	4	16
0.03125	5	32
0.015625	6	64
0.0078125	7	128
0.00390625	8	256
0.001953125	9	512
0.0009765625	10	1024

SAQ

2.7 Convert (a) 127.75_{10} and (b) 307.18_{10} to binary.
You should note that in (b) the conversion of .18 is quite long. With this type of conversion, it often happens that the fractional part does not terminate; the length of the binary fraction depends on the precision required.

EXERCISES

2.2 Convert 507_{10} and 4025_{10} to binary.

2.3 Convert 100001_2 and 1011101_2 to decimal.

2.4 Add 1000101_2 to 1111_2, then add 1011111_2 to 10011_2.

2.5 Subtract 111_2 from 11000001_2, then subtract 1111_2 from 110000_2.

2.6 Subtract 27_{10} from 45_{10} then subtract 75_{10} from 64_{10}, using first 1's complement and then 2's complement.

2.7 Multiply 111011_2 by 1001_2 then multiply 11010110_2 by 111_2.

2.8 Divide 1000100_2 by 11_2 then divide 1010101_2 by 100_2.

Solutions to SAQs

2.1 (a) Convert to binary: 397_{10}

$$397/2 = 198 \quad \text{remainder} \quad 1$$
$$198/2 = 99 \quad \text{remainder} \quad 0$$
$$99/2 = 49 \quad \text{remainder} \quad 1$$
$$49/2 = 24 \quad \text{remainder} \quad 1$$
$$24/2 = 12 \quad \text{remainder} \quad 0$$
$$12/2 = 6 \quad \text{remainder} \quad 0$$
$$6/2 = 3 \quad \text{remainder} \quad 0$$
$$3/2 = 1 \quad \text{remainder} \quad 1$$
$$1/2 = 0 \quad \text{remainder} \quad 1$$

The result is read from the bottom to the top and gives us therefore 110001101_2.

(b) $133_{10} = 10000101_2$

(c) $110_{10} = 1101110_2$

2.2 (a) $101_2 = 1 \times 2^2 + 0 \times 2^1 + 1 \times 2^0$
$= 1 \times 4 + 0 \times 2 + 1 \times 1 = 5_{10}$

(b) $0101_2 = 5_{10}$. Comparing with 2.2(a) we see that a zero in front of the number has no more significance in binary than it has in decimal.

(c) $1101110_2 = 110_{10}$

2.3 Perform the following calculations in binary:

(a) $1100 + 1000$

```
      1100
 +    1000
      1
     10100
```

(b) $1001 + 1011 = 10100$

(c) $1100 - 1000$

```
    1100
 - 1000
    0100
```

(d) $1000 - 101$

```
    1000
 -   101
    111    ← borrows
    0011
```

(e) $1 + 1 + 1 + 1$

```
        1
 +    1     10
 +    1     11
 +    1    100
      100
```

2.4 Perform the following calculations in binary:

(a) 1011×11

```
        1011
 ×        11
        1011
       1011
        111
      100001
```

(b) 1100 × 101

$$
\begin{array}{r}
1100 \\
\times \quad 101 \\
\hline
1100 \\
. \ . \ . \ . \\
1100 \\
\hline
111100
\end{array}
$$

(c) 100111 × 0110 = 11101010

2.5 Perform the following calculations in binary:

(a) 100100/11

$$
\begin{array}{r}
1100 \\
11 \overline{\smash)\ 100100} \\
-11 \\
\hline
11 \\
-11 \\
\hline
00
\end{array}
$$

(b) 110000/110 = 1000

2.6 Perform the calculation 20_{10} − 30_{10} in binary.

decimal	Binary	1's complement	2's complement
20	00010100	11101011	11101100
30	00011110	11100001	11100010

(a) By 1's complement

$$
\begin{array}{l}
00010100 \quad (+20) \\
+ \ 11100001 \quad (-30) \ \text{in 1's complement} \\
\hline
11110101
\end{array}
$$

There is no end-around carry.
   If there is no end-around carry it means that it is a negative number in 1's complement form. Inverting, we have

$$00001010 \quad (-10)$$

(b) By 2's complement

$$
\begin{array}{l}
00010100 \quad (+20) \\
+ \ 11100010 \quad (+30) \ \text{in 2's complement} \\
\hline
11110110
\end{array}
$$

This is a negative number in 2's complement form. Complementing it we have

$$
\begin{array}{l}
00001001 \\
+ \qquad \ 1 \\
\hline
00001010 \quad (-10)
\end{array}
$$

2.7 Convert the following to binary:

(a) 127.75_{10}

$$
\begin{array}{lll}
127/2 &= 63 & \text{remainder} \quad 1 \\
63/2 &= 31 & \text{remainder} \quad 1 \\
31/2 &= 15 & \text{remainder} \quad 1 \\
15/2 &= 7 & \text{remainder} \quad 1 \\
7/2 &= 3 & \text{remainder} \quad 1 \\
3/2 &= 1 & \text{remainder} \quad 1 \\
1/2 &= 0 & \text{remainder} \quad 1
\end{array}
$$

The integer part is 1111111_2:

$$
\begin{array}{l}
.75 \times 2 = 1.50 \\
.50 \times 2 = 1.00
\end{array}
$$

At this point there is no more fractional part left so we stop. The number 127.75_{10} is equal to 1111111.11_2.

(b) 307.18_{10}

$$
\begin{array}{lll}
307/2 &= 153 & \text{remainder} \quad 1 \\
153/2 &= 76 & \text{remainder} \quad 1 \\
76/2 &= 38 & \text{remainder} \quad 0 \\
38/2 &= 19 & \text{remainder} \quad 0 \\
19/2 &= 9 & \text{remainder} \quad 1 \\
9/2 &= 4 & \text{remainder} \quad 1 \\
4/2 &= 2 & \text{remainder} \quad 0 \\
2/2 &= 1 & \text{remainder} \quad 0 \\
1/2 &= 0 & \text{remainder} \quad 1
\end{array}
$$

$$
\begin{array}{l}
.18 \times 2 = 0.36 \\
.36 \times 2 = 0.72 \\
.72 \times 2 = 1.44 \\
.44 \times 2 = 0.88 \\
.88 \times 2 = 1.76 \\
.76 \times 2 = 1.52 \\
.52 \times 2 = 1.04 \\
\text{etc.}
\end{array}
$$

The number 307.18_{10} gives $100110011.0010111 \ldots_2$.

Chapter 3

Hexadecimal and octal notation

Binary has the advantage of being directly understandable by the machine (and it is therefore said to be at **machine language** level), but is by contrast difficult for human-beings to assimilate. In consequence we use other systems of notation, notably **octal**, base 8 and **hexadecimal**, base 16.

3.1 Hexadecimal notation

In hexadecimal notation we use an **alphabet** of sixteen symbols. The figures we use in the decimal system comprise only ten symbols (0 to 9), and we have to use six extra symbols to complete the hexadecimal alphabet. We use the letters A B C D E F.

Hexadecimal alphabet: 0 1 2 3 4 5 6 7 8 9 A B C D E F
Decimal equivalent: 0 1 2 3 4 5 6 7 8 9 10 11 12 13 14 15

3.1.1 Conversions to and from hexadecimal

A number in base 10 can be converted to a number in base 16 by successive divisions.

Example 3.1 Convert the number 728_{10} to base 16

$$728_{10}/16 = 45 \quad \text{remainder} \quad 8$$
$$45_{10}/16 = 2 \quad \text{remainder} \quad 13$$
$$2_{10}/16 = 0 \quad \text{remainder} \quad 2$$

Since we are working in hexadecimal notation, numbers greater than 10 have to be replaced by letters, thus our 13 has to be replaced by the letter D. We can write $728_{10} = 2D8_{16}$.

Conversely it is easy to change a hexadecimal number to a decimal number by successive multiplications just as we did when changing from binary to decimal. This time we do not use powers of 2 but powers of 16 because the base is now 16.

Example 3.2   Convert $13D_{16}$ to base 10

$$1 \times 16^2 + 3 \times 16^1 + 13 \times 16^0$$
$$1 \times 256 + 3 \times 16 + 13 \times 1$$
$$13D_{16} = 317_{10}$$

SAQs

3.1 Convert (a) 3167_{10}, (b) 219_{10} and (c) 6560_{10} to hexadecimal.

3.2 Convert (a) $3AE_{16}$, (b) FFF_{16} and (c) $6AF_{16}$ to decimal.

3.1.2 *Direct binary/hexadecimal conversions*

Each of the sixteen symbols of the hexadecimal alphabet can be represented in four bits. We can convert directly from binary to hexadecimal by splitting the binary number into groups of four bits, starting at the right of the number, and noting the hexadecimal value of each group.

Example 3.3 732_{10} is 101101111002_2

Splitting the binary number into groups of four bits starting on the right, we obtain

	0010	1101	1100
	2	13	12
that is	2	D	C_{16}

Conversion from hexadecimal to binary can be performed by reversing this procedure, that is, we convert the hexadecimal digits to their binary equivalents.

Example 3.4   Convert $10C_{16}$ to binary

1	0	C_{16}
0001	0000	1100_2

SAQs

3.3 Convert (a) 128_{10}, (b) 101_{10}, (c) 256_{10}, (d) 110_2 and (e) 1001011_2 to base 16.

3.4 Convert (a) $C20_{16}$ and (b) $A2E_{16}$ to base 10.

3.5 Convert (a) $F0A_{16}$ and (b) $C01_{16}$ to base 2.

3.2 **Octal notation**

There is a third base which is used in computing but it is used much less frequently than binary or hexadecimal. It is base 8, or octal notation.
The alphabet uses just eight symbols: 0 1 2 3 4 5 6 7.

3.2.1 *Conversions to and from octal*

A number can be converted from base 10 to base 8 using successive division by 8 according to the same principles we used above.

Example 3.5 Convert 304_{10} to octal

$$304_{10}/8 = 38 \quad \text{remainder} \quad 0$$
$$38_{10}/8 = 4 \quad \text{remainder} \quad 6$$
$$4_{10}/8 = 0 \quad \text{remainder} \quad 4$$

As usual, the result is read from bottom to top and we obtain $304_{10} = 460_8$.

Conversely we can convert a number in octal to a number in decimal by successive multiplications just as we have done before for binary and hexadecimal, but this time using powers of 8.

Example 3.6 Convert 13_8 to decimal

$$1 \times 8^1 + 3 \times 8^0$$
$$1 \times 8 + 3 \times 1$$
$$13_8 = 11_{10}$$

SAQs

3.6 Convert (a) 3167_{10}, (b) 219_{10} and (c) 6560_{10} to octal.

3.7 Convert (a) 317_8, (b) 7021_8 and (c) 677_8 to decimal.

3.2.2 *Direct binary/octal conversions*

Each of the eight symbols of the octal alphabet can be represented in three bits. So we can convert directly from binary to octal by splitting the binary number into groups of three bits, starting at the right of the number, and noting the octal value of each group.

Example 3.7 $732_{10} = 1011011100_2$

Splitting this number into groups of three starting from the right we obtain:

010	011	011	100
1	3	3	4

giving 1334_8.

The conversion from octal to binary is done in the opposite way, that is we convert the octal digits to their respective binary equivalents.

Example 3.8 **Convert 107_8 to binary**

1	0	7
001	000	111_2

SAQs

3.8 Convert (a) 128_{10}, (b) 101_{10}, (c) 256_{10}, (d) 110_2 and (e) 1001011_2 to base 8.

3.9 Convert (a) 20_8 and (b) 125_8 to base 10.

EXERCISES

3.1 Convert directly to base 16: 1245_{10}, 2347 and 975_{10}.

3.2 Convert directly to base 10: $2ABBC_{16}$, $3F0C_{16}$ and $2AF_{16}$.

3.3 Convert to base 16 by first converting to binary: 624_{10}, 412_{10} and 6752_{10}.

3.4 Convert to base 10 by first converting to binary: $3E1_{16}$, $16F_{16}$ and $FFFF_{16}$.

3.5 Convert directly to base 8: 1245_{10}, 2347_{10} and 975_{10}.

3.6 Convert directly to base 10: 276_8, 3700_8 and 2771_8.

3.7 Convert to base 8 by first converting to binary: 52_{10}, 652_{10} and 892_{10}.

3.8 Convert to base 10 by first converting to binary: 31_8, 160_8 and 2001_8.

Solutions to SAQs

3.1 Convert to hexadecimal:

(a) 3167_{10}

$$3167/16 = 197 \quad \text{remainder} \quad 15 \quad \text{that is F}$$
$$197/16 = 12 \quad \text{remainder} \quad 5$$
$$12/16 = 0 \quad \text{remainder} \quad 12 \quad \text{that is C}$$

Reading upwards we obtain the answer $C5F_{16}$.

(b) $219_{10} = DB_{16}$

(c) $6560_{10} = 19A0_{16}$

3.2 Convert to decimal:

(a) $3AE_{16}$

$$3 \qquad\qquad A \qquad\qquad E_{16}$$
$$3 \times 16^2 + A \times 16^1 + E \times 16^0$$
$$3 \times 256 + 10 \times 16 + 14 \times 1$$

that is 942_{10}.

(b) $FFF_{16} = 4095_{10}$

(c) $6AF_{16} = 1711_{10}$

3.3 Convert to base 16:

(a) 128_{10}

$$128/2 = 64 \quad \text{remainder} \quad 0$$
$$64/2 = 32 \quad \text{remainder} \quad 0$$
$$32/2 = 16 \quad \text{remainder} \quad 0$$
$$16/2 = 8 \quad \text{remainder} \quad 0$$
$$8/2 = 4 \quad \text{remainder} \quad 0$$
$$4/2 = 2 \quad \text{remainder} \quad 0$$
$$2/2 = 1 \quad \text{remainder} \quad 0$$
$$1/2 = 0 \quad \text{remainder} \quad 1$$
$$128_{10} = 10000000_2$$

We split this binary result into groups of four bits starting on the right to obtain:
$1000 \quad 0000_2$.

Then we write down the hexadecimal equivalents of these groups:

$$1000 \rightarrow 8 \quad \text{and} \quad 0000 \rightarrow 0$$
$$128_{10} = 80_{16}$$

    (b) $101_{10} = 65_{16}$

    (c) $256_{10} = 100_{16}$

    (d) 110_2

We extend the group to four bits by placing an extra 0 on the left to give 0110_2 and thus 6_{16}.

    (e) $1001011_2 = 4B_{16}$

3.4 Convert to base 10:

    (a) $C20_{16}$

        We reconstruct the groups of four bits:

$$
\begin{array}{ccc}
C & 2 & 0_{16} \\
1100 & 0010 & 0000_2
\end{array}
$$

        Then we convert the binary number obtained to decimal:

$$110000100000_2 = 3104_{10}$$

    (b) $A2E_{16} = 2606_{10}$

3.5 Convert to base 2:

    (a) $F0A_{16}$
        We reconstruct the groups of four bits:

$$
\begin{array}{ccc}
F & 0 & A_{16} \\
1111 & 0000 & 1010_2
\end{array}
$$
$$F0A_{16} = 111100001010_2$$

    (b) $C01_{16} = 110000000001_2$

3.6 Convert to octal:

    (a) 3167_{10}

$$
\begin{array}{llll}
3167/8 = & 395 & \text{remainder} & 7 \\
395/8 = & 49 & \text{remainder} & 3 \\
49/8 = & 6 & \text{remainder} & 1 \\
6/8 = & 0 & \text{remainder} & 6
\end{array}
$$

        Reading upwards we obtain the result 6137_8.

    (b) $219_{10} = 333_8$

    (c) $65601_{10} = 146408_8$

3.7 Convert to decimal:

(a) 317_8

$$3 \times 8^2 + 1 \times 8^1 + 7 \times 8^0$$

with labels 3, 1, 7_8 above the terms.

that is 207_{10}.

(b) $7021_8 = 3601_{10}$

(c) $677_8 = 447_{10}$

3.8 Convert to base 8:

(a) 128_{10}

$$
\begin{aligned}
128/2 &= 64 &\text{remainder}\quad 0\\
64/2 &= 32 &\text{remainder}\quad 0\\
32/2 &= 16 &\text{remainder}\quad 0\\
16/2 &= 8 &\text{remainder}\quad 0\\
8/2 &= 4 &\text{remainder}\quad 0\\
4/2 &= 2 &\text{remainder}\quad 0\\
2/2 &= 1 &\text{remainder}\quad 0\\
1/2 &= 0 &\text{remainder}\quad 1\\
128_{10} &= 10000000_2
\end{aligned}
$$

Now we split the binary number into groups of three starting from the right to obtain:

$$010 \quad 000 \quad 000_2$$

Then we note the octal equivalents of these groups:

$$2 \quad 0 \quad 0_8$$

$128_{10} = 200_8$

(b) $101_{10} = 145_8$

(c) $256_{10} = 400_8$

(d) 110_2
We take groups of three bits, giving $110_2 = 6_8$.

(e) $1001011_2 = 113_8$

3.9 Convert to base 10:

(a) 20_8

$$
\begin{array}{cccc}
2 & & & 0_8 \\
2 \times 8^1 & + & 0 \times 8^0 \\
2 \times 8 & + & 0 \times 1
\end{array}
$$

that is 16_{10}.

(b) $125_8 = 85_{10}$

Chapter 4

The representation of data

Information to be processed by computers is composed of letters, figures or special symbols. It is, at the present time, too costly to build electronic systems having as many stable states as there are characters to be represented. Present hardware uses only two states (e.g. presence or absence of an electric current, existence or not of a pulse of current or of a magnetic field).

We must therefore find a way to represent all data to be processed, be it figures, letters or other characters such as exclamation marks, inverted commas, etc., in a way that the machine can use. For this purpose we have to code the data so that what can be understood by human-beings can be assimilated by machine.

With a one-bit code we can represent two states, which we call **0** and **1**, that is 2^1 combinations. We must therefore use a code of four bits to represent the 10 figures (0 to 9) used in the decimal system; but if we also wish to represent letters of the alphabet we need a code which has enough combinations to represent 26 letters and 10 numbers, that is 36 different combinations. This implies using a code of six bits ($2^5 = 32$ combinations being insufficient; $2^6 = 64$ combinations being sufficient even to allow coding of certain other information such as new line, new page, etc.). We shall meet several codes which allow alphabets of various sizes to be represented.

4.1 The Binary Coded Decimal (BCD) code or 8421 code

The **Binary Coded Decimal** or **BCD** code is also known as **Natural Binary Coded Decimal (NBCD)**, or **8421** code from the fact that it uses powers of 2 to weight the values of its bit positions.

We noted above that we need a four-bit code to represent the figures 0–9 ($9_{10} = 1001_2$). In Binary Coded Decimal **each figure** of the number to be coded is represented by its four-bit **binary equivalent**. We will see that in fact there are several ways to represent a number using BCD. The table below shows how numbers are represented in BCD or 8421:

Number	Bit position			
	2^3	2^2	2^1	2^0
	8	4	2	1
0	0	0	0	0
1	0	0	0	1
2	0	0	1	0
3	0	0	1	1
4	0	1	0	0
5	0	1	0	1
6	0	1	1	0
7	0	1	1	1
8	1	0	0	0
9	1	0	0	1

Example 4.1 317_{10} in BCD

$$0011 \quad 0001 \quad 0111$$
$$3 \qquad 1 \qquad 7$$

This simple code is often used for storing numbers and will be met quite frequently, especially when using the language COBOL. Very infrequently the four-bit code is extended to a six-bit BCD code to allow additional, non-numeric, characters to be coded.

SAQ

4.1   Code the numbers (a) 826_{10}, (b) 1807_{10} and (c) 2905_{10} in BCD.

4.2   The ASCII seven-bit code

ASCII (American Standard Code for Information Interchange) is one of the most frequently used codes in computing. It was defined in 1963 in the United States of America and taken up by standards institutes throughout the world for international data transmission. The **International Standards Organisation (ISO)** used it for their **ISO seven-bit** code, and the CCITT (Commission Consultative Internationale des Téléphones et Télécommunications) used it to produce **CCITT No. 5**.

The ASCII code is listed in Figure 4.1. We can convert a symbol in the Figure to its ASCII equivalent by noting the hexadecimal values of the coordinates of the symbol.

	0	1	2	3	4	5	6	7
0	NUL	DLE	SP	0	@	P		p
1	SOH	DC1	!	1	A	Q	a	q
2	STX	DC2	"	2	B	R	b	r
3	ETX	DC3	#	3	C	S	c	s
4	EOT	DC4	$	4	D	T	d	t
5	ENQ	NAK	%	5	E	U	e	u
6	ACK	SYN	&	6	F	V	f	v
7	BEL	ETB	'	7	G	W	g	w
8	BS	CAN	(	8	H	X	h	x
9	HT	EM	)	9	I	Y	i	y
A	LF	SUB	*	:	J	Z	j	z
B	VT	ESC	+	;	K	[	k	{
C	FF	FS	,	<	L	\	l	!
D	CR	GS	−	=	M	]	m	{
E	SO	RS	.	>	N	ˆ	n	~
F	SI	US	/	?	O	−	o	DEL

NUL	NULl	DLE	Data Link Escape
SOH	Start Of Heading	DC1	...
STX	Start of TeXt	DC4	Device Control
ETX	End of TeXt	NAK	Negative AcK
EOT	End Of Transmission	SYN	SYNchronous
ENQ	ENQuiry	ETB	End Transmission Block
ACK	ACKnowledge	CAN	CANcel
BELL	BELL	EM	End of Medium
BS	BackSpace	SUB	SUBstitute
HT	Horizontal Tabulation	ESC	ESCape
LF	Line Feed	FS	File Separator
VT	Vertical Tabulation	GS	Group Separator
FF	Form Feed	RS	Record Separator
CR	Carriage Return	US	United Separator
SO	Shift Out	SP	SPace
SI	Shift In	DEL	DELete

Figure 4.1   The ASCII code

Example 4.2   Coding 'A' in ASCII

In Figure 4.1 A lies at the intersection of the column with a hexadecimal value
4 and the row with a hexadecimal value 1. The ASCII code for A is therefore
41 in **hexadecimal** (sometimes written 41H).

DEC	0	16	32	48	64	80	96	112
HEX	0	1	2	3	4	5	6	7
0 0	BLANK	► 16	BLANK SPACE	Ø	@	P	`	p
1 1	↑ ☺ 1	◄ 17	!	1	A	Q	a	q
2 2	↓ ● 2	⋈ ↕ 18	"	2	B	R	b	r
3 3	→ ♥ 3	■ ‼ 19	#	3	C	S	c	s
4 4	← ♦ 4	¶ 20	$	4	D	T	d	t
5 5	■ ♣ 5	§ 21	%	5	E	U	e	u
6 6	◤ ♠ 6	↕ ▬ 22	&	6	F	V	f	v
7 7	◆ • 7	↨ 23	'	7	G	W	g	w
8 8	✓ ■ DEL ←	↑ 24	(	8	H	X	h	x
9 9	◷ ○	↓ 25	)	9	I	Y	i	y
10 A	⌂ ☺ 10	→ 26	*	:	J	Z	j	z
11 B	♪ ♂ 11	← 27	+	;	K	[	k	{
12 C	▲ ♀ 12	∟ 28	,	<	L	\	l	|
13 D	▼ ♪ ↵	↔ 29	−	=	M	]	m	}
14 E	► ♫ 14	▲ 30	.	>	N	^	n	~
15 F	◄ ☼ 15	▼ 31	/	?	O	_	o	△ 127

Figure 4.2

DEC	128	144	160	176	192	208	224	240
HEX	8	9	A	B	C	D	E	F
0 0	Ç 128	É 144	á 160	ã ‖ 176	ij 192	208	∝ 224	≡ 240
1 1	ü 129	æ 145	í 161	õ ▒ 177	IJ 193	209	β 225	± 241
2 2	é	Æ 146	ó 162	¥ ▓ 178	194	210	Γ 226	≥ 242
3 3	â 131	ð 147	ú 163	¢ │ 179	195	211	π 227	≤ 243
4 4	ä 132	ö 148	ñ 164	œ ┤ 180	196	212	Σ 228	⌠ 244
5 5	à	ò 149	Ñ 165	Œ ╡ 181	197	213	σ 229	⌡ 245
6 6	å 134	û 150	ª 166	À ╢ 182	198	214	µ 230	÷ 246
7 7	ç	ù	º 167	Ä ╖ 183	199	215	τ 231	≈ 247
8 8	ê 136	ÿ 152	¿ 168	Ö ╕ 184	200	216	Φ 232	° 248
9 9	ë 137	Ö 153	⌐ 169	╣ 185	201	217	Θ 233	∙ 249
10 A	è	Ü 154	¬ 170	║ 186	202	218	Ω 234	· 250
11 B	ï 139	ø ¢ 155	½ 171	+ ╗ 187	203	219	δ 235	√ 251
12 C	î 140	£	¼ 172	╝ 188	204	220	∞ 236	ⁿ 252
13 D	ì 141	Ø ¥ 157	¡ 173	© ╜ 189	205	221	φ 237	^{2} 253
14 E	Ä 142	₧ 158	<< 174	® ╛ 190	206	222	∈ 238	∎ 254
15 F	Å 143	ƒ 159	>> 175	™ ┐ 191	207	223	∩ 239	BLANK

Source: *Amstrad PC1512 User's Guide*.

Figure 4.2 ASCII codes for the Amstrad PC 1512

Certain languages and some software need ASCII characters to be given in decimal and not in hexadecimal (this is the case, for example, in some versions of BASIC). The character A of the preceding example would then be coded 65 and not 41H. For example, in BASIC the instruction PRINT CHAR(65) prints 'A' whereas PRINT CHAR(41) prints ')'.

Conversely, if we search the grid in Figure 4.1 to find the character corresponding to the ASCII code 2AH we find that the character ＊ lies at the intersection of column 2 with row A.

ASCII code is often extended to eight bits by adding a control bit (called a **parity** bit) to the usual seven bits. If parity checking is not used this bit may be kept at 0 or it may be used by designers to define their own range of symbols, especially graphics symbols. Certain characters such as **EOT, ENQ** or **ACK** are only used in particular applications. They are not in normal use but are defined for data transmission (for example between a computer and a printer).

As an example of an extended code we have included Figure 4.2 which gives the ASCII codes for the **Amstrad** PC 1512.

SAQs

4.2 Decode the following memory dump of the file that is given below in ASCII.

59 6F 75 20 68 61 76 65 20 73 75 63 63 65 65 64 65 64 2E

4.3 Code the following text in ASCII: 'To have a friend you must be one.'

4.3 **Viewdata videotex standard**

Videotex, which is used in the UK Prestel system, is a telecommunications procedure which enables a user to receive messages on a video screen.

To gain access to viewdata requires a terminal and a modem. The terminal can be a specially adapted television receiver, a special-purpose viewdata terminal, or a PC with the necessary communications software. In France, users of the public videotext service Teletel are provided with a free Minitel terminal.

The set of ASCII characters forms the basis of the code but it has had to be extended to accommodate all the graphics characters (mosaics) used by videotext.

Figures and letters are coded in videotex in the same way as in ASCII, but to the basic codes (grid G0) have been added some extra sets. The first set (grid G2) defines codes for accents and special symbols; another (grid G1) defines the characters for mosaics which are used to draw pictures on the screen. Finally, a fourth set (grid C0) encodes control signals used for controlling the communications and the screen. The videotex characters are shown in Figure 4.3.

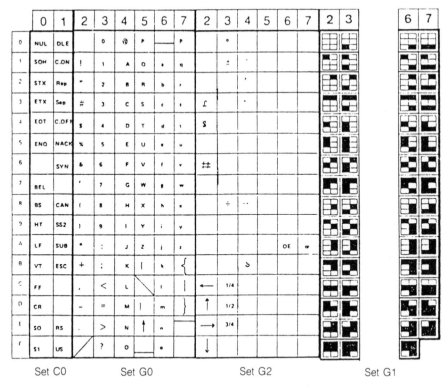

Source: P. Bourgault, *Minitels et micro-ordinateurs*, Editions Sybex.

Figure 4.3   Videotex characters

To access the characters defined in set G2, the control character 19H
(representing SS2 in C0) must first be sent, and to obtain characters from set G1 the
code 0EH (representing S0 in C0) must first be sent.

Example 4.3   To obtain 'é', and blank mosaic

To obtain the accented character 'é' the hexadecimal sequence 19 43 42 has to
be transmitted. Note that after obtaining the character from set G2 we return
automatically to set G0. This is not so for all the sets.

  If we wish to display the blank mosaic we send the sequence 0E 20 and,
to return to the character set G0, the code 0F. The complete sequence to
display a blank mosaic and return to the character mode is 0E 20 0F.

Each videotex character can have its appearance modified by various
attributes defining the foreground colour, the background colour, underlining,
blinking, inverse colours, etc. Each of these attributes can act in different ways:
either in **full screen mode** where they affect the whole display, or in **full row mode**

where they affect only the line of characters, or in **parallel mode** where they affect the characters positioned before the cursor, or in **serial mode** where they affect the characters positioned after the cursor.

Example 4.4   To obtain a yellow background

To obtain a yellow background on the screen in full screen mode, we send the hexadecimal sequence 1B 23 20 53. The code 1B corresponds to the escape character (ESC). To obtain a series of blue characters, we send the sequence 1B 44.

4.3.1   *Videotex control codes*

Just as it is possible to control the colour of a character or a background, the position of the cursor on the screen can also be controlled by giving the corresponding hexadecimal code, as indicated below:

Position cursor	1F, col,row
Move cursor left	08
Move cursor right	09
Move cursor down	0A
Move cursor up	0B
Cursor return	0D
Cursor home (top left)	1E
Clear screen	0C
Clear to end of line	18
Space	20
Repeat character	12,n times, 0E
Cursor on	11
Cursor of	14
. . .	

4.4   **Eight-bit codes**

The number of bits manipulated by some machines in one operation is a **byte** (eight bits, also known as an **octet**). Therefore eight-bit codes are very common in computing.

4.4.1   *Extended or unpacked BCD code*

We have seen that only four bits are needed to code a figure in the range 0–9. A group of four bits is known as a **nibble** (or sometimes as a **quartet**). Two nibbles can be accommodated in a byte and conventionally it is the nibble on the right which holds the BCD, the nibble on the left usually being filled with 0's (but some manufacturers use 1's).

Example 4.5 17_{10} coded in extended BCD

$$
\begin{array}{ccc}
1 & & 7 \\
0000 \quad 0001 & & 0000 \quad 0111 \\
\text{Nibble} \quad \text{Nibble} & & \text{Byte}
\end{array}
$$

SAQs

4.4   Convert (a) 125_{10}, (b) 256_{10} and (c) 45785_{10} to extended BCD.

4.5   Decode the following numbers represented in extended BCD:

00001000   00000111   00000101   00000000   00000001

4.4.2   *Condensed or packed BCD*

Half the byte is wasted whenever extended BCD is used to represent a figure because the four bits on the left are always occupied by 0's or 1's. In **condensed** or **packed** BCD both halves of the byte are used to hold figures represented in BCD (that is each nibble represents an 8421 code) and this allows twice as much data to be stored in each byte.

Example 4.6 17_{10} coded in packed BCD

$$
\begin{array}{cc}
1 & 7 \\
0001 & 0111
\end{array}
$$

SAQs

4.6   Convert (a) 125_{10}, (b) 256_{10} and (c) 45785_{10} to packed BCD.

4.7   Decode the following numbers represented in packed BCD:

00010000   00000000   01000111

4.4.3   *EBCDIC*

EBCDIC (**E**xtended **B**inary **C**oded **D**ecimal **I**nterchange **C**ode is mainly used by IBM. The code is sometimes classed as a nine-bit code when it makes use of an **odd**

Bits 4, 5, 6 and 7 \ Bits 0 and 1 → Bits 2 and 3 →	00				01				10				11			
	00	01	10	11	00	01	10	11	00	01	10	11	00	01	10	11
0000	NUL	DLE	DS		SP	&										0
0001	SOH	DC1	SOS				/		a	i			A	J		1
0010	STX	DC2	FS	SYN					b	k	s		B	K	S	2
0011	ETX	DC3							c	l	t		C	L	T	3
0100	PF	RES	BYP	PN					d	m	u		D	M	U	4
0101	HT	NL	LF	RS					e	n	v		E	N	V	5
0110	LC	BS	EOB	UC					f	o	w		F	O	W	6
0111	DEL	IL	PRE	EOT					g	p	x		G	P	X	7
1000		CAN							h	q	y		H	Q	Y	8
1001		EM							i	r	z		I	R	Z	9
1010	SMM	CC	SM		¢	'		:								
1011	VT	CU1	CU2	CU3	.	$	,	#								
1100	FF	IFS		DC4	<	*	%	@								
1101	CR	IGS	ENQ	NAK	(	)	—	'								
1110	SO	IRS	ACK		+	;	>	=								
1111	SI	IUS	BEL	SUB	|	¬	?	.								

Source: Phong Tuan Nghien, *Transmission de données*, Imfoprax.

Figure 4.4   EBCDIC

parity bit (an extra bit to check the validity of the associated eight bits). It is shown in Figure 4.4.

The command characters have virtually the same meaning as in ASCII. Thus SP indicates a space, CR carriage return . . .

SAQs

4.8 Decode the memory dump of the following file coded in EBCDIC:

> E3 88 89 A2 40 89 A2 40 81 40 94 85 94 96 99 A8 40
> 84 A4 94 97 40 89 95 40 C5 C2 C3 C4 C9 C3

4.9 Code the following message using EBCDIC:

> FICHE 1987 in EBCDIC$:EXO:$

EXERCISES

4.1 Code the text 'Message WX & KV *?' in ASCII.

4.2 Decode the ASCII text '47 43 53 45 20 31 39 39 32'.

4.3 Code the message '>-ASCII is simple +/'.

4.4 Code the numbers 123455_{10} and 3796_{10} in packed BCD.

4.5 Code the numbers 08712_{10} and 6754_{10} in unpacked BCD.

Solutions to SAQs

4.1 Code in BCD:

(a) We have to code each figure of the number in its equivalent four-bit binary thus:

$$
\begin{array}{ccc}
8 & 2 & 6 \\
1000 & 0010 & 0110
\end{array}
$$

(b) $1807_{10} = 0001$ 1000   0000   0111

(c) $2905_{10} = 0010$ 1001   0000   0101

4.2 Decode the following memory dump of the file that is given below in ASCII:

59 6F 75 20 68 61 76 65 20 73 75 63 63 65 65 64 65 64 2E

You have succeeded.

4.3 Code in ASCII 'To have a friend you must be one.'

22 54 6F 20 68 61 76 65 20 61 20 66 72 69 65 6E 64 20 79
6F 75 20 6D 75 73 74 20 62 65 20 6F 6E 65 2E 22

4.4 Convert to extended BCD:

(a) 125_{10}
Each figure of the number is converted to its equivalent in eight-bit binary knowing that the nibble on the left is filled with 0's (or 1's according to the manufacturer):

$$
\begin{array}{ccc}
1 & 2 & 5 \\
0000\ 0001 & 0000\ 0010 & 0000\ 0101
\end{array}
$$

(b) $256_{10} = 00000010$ 00000101   00000110

(c) $45785_{10} = 00000100$ 00000101   00000111   00001000   00000101

4.5 Decode the following numbers represented in extended BCD.

$$
\begin{array}{ccccc}
00001000 & 00000111 & 00000101 & 00000000 & 00000001 \\
8 & 7 & 5 & 0 & 1
\end{array}
$$

4.6 Convert to packed BCD:

(a) Each figure of the number is converted to its four-bit binary equivalent:
$125_{10} = 0001$ 0010   0101.

(b) 256_{10} = 0010   0101   0110

(c) 45785_{10} = 0100   0101   0111   1000   0101

4.7 Decode the following numbers coded in packed BCD:

0001 0000 0000 0000 0100 0111
 1   0   0   0   4   7

4.8 Decode the memory dump of the following file coded in EBCDIC:

E3 88 89 A2 40 89 A2 40 81 40 94 85 94 96 99 A8 40
84 A4 94 97 40 89 95 40 C5 C2 C3 C4 C9 C3

This is a memory dump in EBCDIC.

4.9 Code the following message using EBCDIC:

FICHE 1987 in EBCDIC$:EXO:$

C6 C9 C3 C8 C5 40 F1 F9 F8 F7 40 89 95 40 C5 C2 C3 C4 C9
C3 40 5B 7A C5 E7 D6 7A 5B

Chapter 5

Error detection and prevention

Data is constantly being moved around inside the computer; from keyboard to memory, from memory to screen, etc. We must therefore ensure that this movement has not caused any errors in the data. Several methods are used for this purpose, ranging from simple parity control, to sophisticated codes which can correct the errors they detect.

5.1 Error control using parity

To the n bits which form the original character we add one extra bit. The bit is chosen so that the total number of 1 bits will be even (a code with **even parity**) or odd (a code with **odd parity**).

Example 5.1   Odd and even parity

00111001   **even** parity
↑ parity bit

10111001   **odd** parity
↑ parity bit

This method, although generally satisfactory, is only useful if errors do not change two or four or six bits at the same time because an even number of errors will not affect the parity of the data.

Example 5.2   Error detection

If we transmit the group 10010000 with even parity and we receive 01010000, it is impossible to say whether or not it is the data which was sent because the parity remains even.

SAQs

5.1 Complete the following bytes by including an even parity bit:

(a)   – 1010001

(b)   – 0111111

5.2 Complete the following bytes by including an odd parity bit:

(a)   – 0111001

(b)   – 0001101

5.2 **Self-checking and self-correcting codes**

A simple parity check is not always sufficient for data which is constantly being moved from one location to another, especially in the case of data transmission over long distances (for example when two computers are connected over a telephone circuit) where transmitted signals are subject to electrical interference.

This has led to the development of codes which check for more than just single errors, and even to codes which correct the errors they find. Some of these techniques have been developed by the American engineer R.W. Hamming, and are called **Hamming Codes**.

In practice we distinguish two types of self-checking and self-correcting codes: block codes and cyclic codes.

5.2.1 *Block codes*

The principle used in block codes consists of structuring the data into fixed length **blocks** and adding to each block a certain number of check bits called redundancy bits.

This creates a **block code**, where only certain combinations of bits are acceptable and form a collection of valid code words. When the data is transmitted and arrives at the receiver two possibilities can arise: the *n*-bit word received is a valid code and the block which was transmitted can be reconstructed; or the *n*-bit word received is not a valid code and the receiver can then either recreate the original block (in the case of a **self-correcting code**) or ask for the block to be retransmitted (in the case of a **self-checking code**).

The effectiveness of such codes depends on the difference between one valid code word and another. The greater this difference, the less the possibility of one valid code being transformed into another valid code by a series of errors.

We define this difference, which we call the **Hamming distance**, to be the number of bits which have to be changed to transform one valid code word into the next code word in sequence. The greater the Hamming distance the more effective the code.

Example 5.3   Hamming distance

Between the two binary numbers 01010101 and 00001111 we can see a difference (distance) of four bits, which means that it would take four single errors to change one word into the other.

The block codes most commonly encountered are: **vertical parity checking** also called **VRC** (Vertical Redundancy Checking) the principle of which we described above; and **longitudinal parity checking** or **LRC** (Longitudinal Redundancy Checking) which we will consider next; and also a code called '*i* in *n*'.

In *i* in *n* codes, only combinations which have *i* bits with a value of 1 are valid from among the 2^n possible codes. An example is the **4 out of 8** code where out of a possible 256 combinations, only 70 are valid, such as:

```
00001111
00010111    2 bits have changed their value
00011011    2 bits have changed their value
00011101    . . .
00011110
00101110
00110110
00111010
00111100
01011100

. . .
11110000
```

The Hamming distance of such a code is equal to 2. In fact we can see from the progression of valid code words that two bits change from one valid code word to the next. Such a code ensures the detection of single errors, that is of errors which only affect a single bit of the character transmitted.

A common binary code with a Hamming distance of 1 is the **reflected binary** code (or **Gray** code). It is not used for data transmission but we will be meeting it again in the chapters on logic:

```
00000000
00000001
00000011
00000010
00000110
00000111
00000101
00000100
00001100
00001101
00001111
00001110

. . .
```

For a more general approach consider the following:

Hamming distance	Detectable errors	Correctable errors
1	0	0
2	1	0
3	2	1
4	3	1
5	4	2
. . .		

In fact a Hamming distance of 1 means that only one bit changes from one code word to the next (as is the case in reflected binary), and therefore if a transmission error affects one bit or even several bits, it is not possible to detect because all combinations of bits are valid code words.

With a Hamming distance of 2, such as we have in the 4 out of 8 code, if a transmission error transforms a bit from a 0 to a 1 we will have five 1-bits and three 0-bits and it is very easy to detect the error (because by definition there must be four 1-bits). On the other hand, we do not know which bit is wrong. The reasoning is the same if a transmission error changes a 1 to a 0, in which case we will have three 1-bits and again the error can be detected but not corrected.

Some block codes use a combination of **horizontal** and **vertical** parity checking (Longitudinal and Vertical Redundancy Checking, **LRC/VRC**) to detect errors.

For this purpose the characters to be transmitted are grouped into blocks and an additional character called the horizontal parity check character is added to the end of the block.

The horizontal parity check and the vertical (or character) parity check are used in combination to detect errors.

Example 5.4 Error checking in ASCII

Suppose we wish to transmit the characters PAG in ASCII code.

	PAG	LRC	
VRC	0 0 0	0	← crossed parity bit
	1 1 1	1	
	0 0 0	0	
	1 0 0	1	
	0 0 0	0	
	0 0 1	1	
	0 0 1	1	
	0 1 1	0	

The VRC character is the vertical parity check while the LRC is the horizontal parity check.

The hexadecimal values of the characters transmitted will therefore be, in this example, 50 41 47 56.

The Hamming distance in this example is 4; in fact changing a single bit of data leads to the changing of a bit in the VRC, a bit in the LRC, and the changing of the crossed parity bit, that is, a total of four bits will be changed.

Such a code will detect all single errors, double errors, and triple errors and can correct all single errors.

So, returning to the previous example of the characters PAG, suppose that a transmission error affects one of the bits:

	PAG	LRC	
VRC	000	0	← crossed parity bit
	111	1	
	000	0	
	100	1	
bit in error →	100	0	
	001	1	
	001	1	
	011	0	

SAQs

5.3 Think about how the system can **detect** and **correct** a single error like the one in the example above.

5.4 Consider the same problem but this time with two incorrect bits being received.

	PAG	LRC	
VRC	000	0	← crossed parity bit
bit in error →	101	1	
	000	0	
	100	1	
bit in error →	100	0	
	001	1	
	001	1	
	011	0	

Why can we no longer correct the error but only detect its presence?

5.2.2 *Cyclic codes*

Cyclic codes, also known as **CRC (Cyclic Redundancy Codes)** or **polynomial codes**, are a particular type of block code that is widely used in practice because of the ease with which it can be implemented in hardware. These codes are based on the use of a generator polynomial $G(X)$ and the principle that n bits of binary data can be treated as a polynomial in the dummy variable x. For example the data block 10111 can be treated as the polynomial:

$$X^4 + X^2 + X^1 + X^0$$

Starting with the i bits of data $I(X)$ to be transmitted we are going to derive r bits of redundant data $R(X)$ to place at the end of $I(X)$ so that the resulting polynomial $I'(X)$ will be divisible by the generator polynomial $G(X)$, without producing a remainder.

If the data received at the receiver is the same as the data $I'(X)$ that was transmitted, we should be able to divide it by the generator polynomial $G(X)$ again without a remainder being produced. If a remainder is produced it means that the transmitted data has been received incorrectly.

Example 5.5   Error checking by cyclic codes

Let us consider the message 10011011 $(i = 8)$ that we can represent by the following polynomial $I(X)$:

$$1 \times X^7 + 0 \times X^6 + 0 \times X^5 + 1 \times X^4 + 1 \times X^3 +$$

$$0 \times X^2 + 1 \times X^1 + 1 \times X^0$$

or more simply:

$$I(X) = X^7 + X^4 + X^3 + X^1 + X^0$$

The polynomial generator chosen here (arbitrarily) is $G(X) = X^3 + 1$ with $r = 4$ (r being equal to the number of bits in the polynomial generator). We next multiply $I(X)$ by X^{r-1}

$$
\begin{array}{rl}
10011011 & I \\
\times \quad 1000 & X^{r-1} \\
\hline
10011011000 &
\end{array}
$$

Next we divide the polynomial thus obtained by the generator polynomial, that is we divide

$$X^{10} + X^7 + X^6 + X^4 + X^3 \quad \text{by} \quad X^3 + 1$$

but instead of using binary division we work in modulo 2 arithmetic. The rules are the same except that in modulo 2 arithmetic,

$$1 + 1 = 0 \qquad \text{(there is no carry)}$$
$$\text{and} \quad 0 - 1 = 0 + 1 = 1$$

Working in modulo 2 we have:

```
              10001010  ← quotient not required
      1001│10011011000
           1001
           00001011
             1001
             1000
             1001
              010  ← remainder
```

Then we append the remainder to the original dividend I (10011011) to obtain what we set out to produce – a polynomial which is divisible by the generator polynomial without producing a remainder.

The data transmitted is 10011011 (I), to which we append the remainder to obtain:

10011011010 I'

At the receiver the message which is received is divided by the generator polynomial. The remainder will be zero if I' is received correctly, and then we need only take the top i bits of I' obtain the original message polynomial $I(X)$.

Let us do this second division.

```
              10001010  ← quotient not required
      1001│10011011010
           1001
           00001011
             1001
             1001
             1001
              000  ← zero remainder
```

So we can conclude that the data was received correctly.

The choice of a good generator polynomial is essential if we are to detect most of the errors that could occur. One of the most frequently used polynomials, and one which is a CCITT standard is:

$$X^{16} + X^{12} + X^5 + 1$$

This polynomial allows the detection of

100%	of single errors
100%	of double errors
100%	of errors with an odd number of bits
100%	of burst errors affecting 16 bits or fewer
99.99%	of burst errors affecting 18 bits or more

Such a code reduces the average rate of undetected errors by a factor of 100 or 1000 according to the type of error and only requires 16 redundancy bits for messages of the order of 1000 bits.

These codes are currently used for data transmission over telephone lines.

SAQ

5.5   Using the generator code $X^3 + 1$ determine the hexadecimal values that will actually be transmitted to send the binary message 10110110.

EXERCISES

5.1   Complete each of the following by including its even parity value: 10010001_2, 000010101_2 and 10111101_2

5.2   Complete each of the following by including its odd parity value: 01100001_2, 0111110_2 and 10111000_2.

5.3   The text 'Message correct' is to be transmitted in ASCII code with VRC and LRC. Construct the hexadecimal codes that must actually be transmitted.

5.4   Using the generator polynomial $X^3 + X^2 + 1$ determine the original binary message knowing that the code transmitted is 10001010011101_2.

Solutions to SAQs

5.1   Complete the following bytes by including their even parity:

(a)   For even parity the number of 1-bits must be even. In this case the parity bit is 1:

11010001

(b)   For the second case of even parity the number of 1-bits must be even. In this case the parity bit is 0:

00111111

5.2 Complete the following bytes by including their odd parity:

(a)   **1**0111001

(b)   **0**0001101

5.3

		PAG	LRC	
VRC		000	0	← crossed parity bit
		111	1	
		000	0	
		100	1	
bit in error	→	1**0**0	0	
		001	1	
		001	1	
		011	0	

How can the error be detected and corrected?

The solution to this problem is relatively simple. First we have to check that the crossed parity bit is correct for LRC and VRC. In this case the crossed parity bit is 0 and it is correct so the error is not in VRC or LRC. However by checking the bits of LRC we can readily identify a row with the wrong parity. In the same way we can check the bits of VRC and identify an incorrect column. The intersection of the row with the column shows us where the wrong bit must be and thus we can correct it.

5.4 The same problem but this time two incorrect bits are received.

		PAG	LRC	
VRC		000	0	← crossed parity bit
bit in error	→	1**0**1	1	
		000	0	
		100	1	
bit in error	→	1**0**0	0	
		001	1	
		001	1	
		011	0	

Why can we no longer correct the error but only detect its presence?

In the second case the crossed parity again verifies that LRC and VRC are correct. But when we go on to check the bits of LRC and VRC we discover two wrong rows and two wrong columns, which means there are four intersections and therefore it is impossible to locate exactly the two wrong bits. Which two would we choose? We are thus able to detect that there has been an error but we are unable to correct it.

5.5 Using the generator code $X^3 + 1$ determine the hexadecimal values that will actually be transmitted to send the binary message 10110110.

The first thing to do is to multiply the block by X^{r-1}, i.e. by 1000 to obtain:

$$10110110000$$

Next we divide this binary string by the generator polynomial:

```
              10100010
      ┌─────────────────
1001  │10110110000
       1001
       ────
       001001
         1001
         ────
         00001000
            1001
            ────
            0010  ←  remainder
```

Then we have to append the remainder to the original binary string, that is: **101101100**010. This will be the binary string finally transmitted. Converted to hexadecimal it is B62$_{16}$.

Chapter 6

The representation of numbers

6.1 The concept of a computer word

Computer systems manipulating binary data normally work on fixed-length strings of bits. This fixed length of bits is known as a **word**. The size of the word will depend on the machine being considered; usual sizes are 8, 16, 32 or 64 bits.

For example the BULL DPS6 which is based on the 8086 microprocessor, has a word length of 16 bits, whereas the IBM 360 and machines based on the 80386 microprocessor use 32-bit words. The terms **half-word** and **double-word** are also in common use. These formats are shown in the diagram:

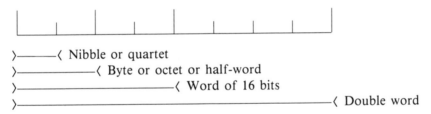

```
>———< Nibble or quartet
>————< Byte or octet or half-word
>——————————< Word of 16 bits
>————————————————————< Double word
```

Note: here a half-word is made of 8 bits and a word of 16 bits; on some machines (IBM 360 for example) a word could be 32 bits and a half word 16 bits.

In general, mainframe systems currently use a word size of 32 or 64 bits, and microcomputers use words of 16 or 32 bits but in these times of rapid development of microcomputer technology it is difficult to give definitive figures.

It is now common practice to call a group of 8 bits a byte and a group of 4 bits, a nibble.

Real numbers in computers can be represented in one of two forms, fixed point or floating point.

6.2 Numbers in fixed point form

A fixed point number is a signed number stored either as a binary integer or as a number in BCD.

Such a number is called a fixed point number because the responsibility to place the point lies with the programmer and not with the machine. That is to say

49

that the point does not appear in the stored number but is positioned by the programmer to separate the number into an integer part and a fractional part. (This is the role of the V indicator in COBOL data descriptions such as 99999V99.)

6.2.1 *Integer binary numbers*

An integer binary number is stored in binary form, the sign being indicated by the leftmost bit (the most significant bit) of the word, the other bits serving to define the number itself.

Example 6.1   Number stored in a byte

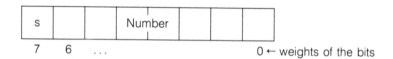

7   6   . . .   0 ← weights of the bits

The following conventions are widely adopted by manufacturers.

If the sign bit is **zero** the data is **positive**. The value **zero** is considered to be positive.

If the sign bit is **one** the data is **negative**. **Negative** numbers are usually coded in **2's complement** form.

Example 6.2   Negative and positive number storage in a byte

(a)   A byte containing the number $+45_{10}$

0	0	1	0	1	1	0	1

Sign   Number

(b)   A byte containing the number -23_{10}

As stated above we must first express the number in 2's complement form:

Original number	0010111
1's complement	1101000
+	1
2's complement	1101001

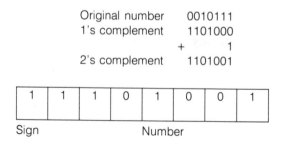

Sign   Number

These formats allow only a limited number of values to be stored depending on the size of the word being used.

Example 6.3   Number storage with a 16-bit word

The greatest positive value is: 0111111111111111_2

that is: $+ 32767_{10}$

The most negative value in 2's complement form is:

$$1000000000000000_2$$

that is: $- 32768_{10}$

Number of bytes	Values in pure binary	Values in 2's complement
1	0 to $+255$	-128 to $+127$
2	0 to $+65535$	-32768 to $+32767$
4	0 to $+4\ 294\ 967\ 295$	$-2\ 147\ 483\ 648$ to $+2\ 147\ 483\ 647$

6.2.2   *Numbers in BCD*

There are two possibilities of representing numbers in BCD depending on whether it is extended BCD or condensed BCD.

6.2.2.1   Extended BCD
In the case of extended BCD, each decimal figure is represented by a byte as explained earlier. Whenever this extended form is used, the four bits on the right of the byte are sufficient to code the numbers 0–9 while the four bits on the left or zone bits serve no purpose.

In one form of extended BCD, the zone part of the least significant byte is used to indicate the sign of the number.

Example 6.4   To represent the number $+341$ in extended BCD

1111	0011	1111	0100	0000	0001
Zone	3	Zone	4	Sign +	1

6.2.2.2   Condensed BCD

In this case each figure occupies a nibble. The sign is then generally stored in the least significant nibble:

0011	0100	0001	0000
3	4	1	Sign +

The method used to code the sign depends on the manufacturer; sometimes 0000 is used for a plus sign and 1111 for a minus sign (or the opposite), at other times, B_{16} (i.e. 1011_2) is used for plus and D_{16} (i.e. 1101_2) for minus (B and D are abbreviations for 2B and 2D the ASCII codes for + and − respectively).

To summarise, a number in fixed point form can be represented:

- In binary integer form.
- In condensed BCD.
- In extended BCD.

The choice is generally made by the programmer and is achieved by using special instructions from the programming language (for example the clause COMP in COBOL). It is important to understand how numbers are represented in these different forms so as to minimise the space required to store them on backing store.

Large numbers represented in fixed point form can sometimes occupy too much space. Representation in a form known as floating point might then be preferred.

SAQs

6.1   Code the number -357_{10} as a 16-bit binary integer.

6.2   Code (a) 38867_{10}, (b) 34.675_{10} and (c) -34.45_{10}, in extended BCD.

6.3   Code (a) 387_{10}, (b) 35.47_{10} and (c) -35.99_{10} in condensed BCD.

6.3   **Numbers in floating point form**

A number in floating point form has two values associated with it. The first, the **mantissa**, represents the significant figures of the number. The second, the **characteristic** or **exponent**, indicates the power to which the base is raised.

For example when we write in decimal 12×10^8 or simply 12 E 8:

- 12 is the **mantissa**.
- 8 is the **exponent**.

● 10 is the **base**.

and 12 E 8 = 1 200 000 000.

The most obvious and most compact way to represent a number in floating form is therefore to use a signed exponent and a signed mantissa.

Example 6.5   Representing a number with signed exponent and signed mantissa

$$-123.45 = -0.12345 \times 10^{+3}$$
$$0.0000678 = +0.678 \times 10^{-4}$$

However as a general rule we use a biased exponent instead of a simple exponent.

Example 6.6   Representing a number with a biased exponent

Consider a bias of 5 (which means that we systematically add 5 to the true value of every exponent), the numbers above will be represented in the following way:

-123.45	Sign of exponent	$+$ (10^{+3})
	Biased exponent	8 (5 + 3)
	Mantissa	0.12345
	Sign of number	$-$
$+0.000678$	Sign of exponent	$-$ (10^{-4})
	Biased exponent	1 (5 − 4)
	Mantissa	0.67800
	Sign of number	$+$

The technique of the biased exponent is very useful because it avoids using negative exponents (provided of course that the chosen bias is sufficiently large).

It should be noted that the representation of a number in floating point form is not necessarily unique.

Example 6.7   Number in floating point form

$$0.1234000 \times 10^2 = 0.0123400 \times 10^3 = 0.0001234 \times 10^5 \ldots$$

For this reason numbers in floating point are often shown in a **normalised** form.

A normalised floating point number is a number in which **the figure immediately to the right of the point** (on the left of the mantissa), **is not a zero** while the number to the left of the point is a zero. This zero is omitted when the number is stored as a fraction.

So, in our examples above, 0.01234000×10^3 is not normalised while 0.123400×10^2 is normalised and will be represented as $.123400 \times 10^2$.

There are several standards used by manufacturers to represent numbers in floating point (e.g. IEEE, IEE, DEC, IBM) but here we will just present the IEE and the IBM standards.

The **IBM standard** is as shown below:

Bit 31 30 29 28 27 26 25 24   23   . . .   0

| S | 2^6 ... 2^0 | 2^{-1} ... 2^{-24} |

- Sign ⟨   Biased exponent   ⟩⟨   Mantissa   ⟩

The **IEE standard**:

Bit   31 30 29 28 27 26 25   24   23 . . .   0

| 2^6 ... 2^0 | S | 2^{-1} ... 2^{-24} |

⟨   Biased exponent   ⟩ Sign ⟨   Mantissa   ⟩

If numbers of a higher precision are required, then it is possible to store each number as four words of 16 bits instead of two words of 16 bits like those illustrated above. The numbers are then said to be stored in **double precision** in contrast to the numbers stored in **single precision** above.

Example 6.8   How the IEE standard works

How would a number be represented, for example 10.50_{10} in single precision floating point?

The base used in this standard is 16 so first of all we must convert 10.50_{10} to base 16, i.e. $A.8_{16}$.

Next we must normalise it (i.e. we must move the point to the left until the number is normalised); we obtain $.A8\ E_{16} + 1$.

In the IEE standard the exponent is biased by 64 (we say it is represented in excess 64_{10}): so

	Bias	+	Exponent	=	Biased exponent
and we have	64_{10}	+	1_{10}	=	65_{10}

that is 1000001_2.

The sign being positive, the bit representing the sign will be zero. We therefore have the result:

1000 001	0	1010 1000 0000 0000 0000 0000

Exponent	Sign			Mantissa			
8	2	A	8	0	0	0	0_{16}

Example 6.9   Determining the decimal value of a number in floating point form

If we find the hexadecimal values 84, 16, 38, 52 in a memory dump we first of all have to find the binary forms:

8	4		1	6	3	8	5	2
1000	010	0	0001	0110	0011	1000	1010	0010
⟨Exponent⟩	Sign	⟨			Mantissa			⟩

Sign: the sign bit is zero so that means the number is positive.

Exponent: $1000010_2 = 66_{10}$ therefore as the bias is 64, the true exponent is $E_{16} + 2$.

Mantissa: 163852_{16}.

Since the exponent we have just determined is $+2$ we know that we can denormalise by moving the point two places to the right to give 16.3852_{16}.

Converting now to base 10 we have:

$$(1 \times 16^1) + (6 \times 16^0) . (3 \times 16^{-1}) + (8 \times 16^{-2}) + (5 \times 16^{-3}) + (2 \times 16^{-4})$$

and finally 22.22_{10}.

This type of representation in floating point form enables large numbers to be coded; in the format described above we can represent numbers in the range of approximately $10^{-76.8}$ to approximately $10^{+75.6}$. Try to imagine how much space such numbers would occupy in condensed BCD, let alone extended BCD!

The choice of representation, single or double precision, in floating point form, is made with the help of instructions appropriate to the language being used. (COMP clauses in COBOL or use of CVS, CVD, MKS or others in BASIC, declarations in PASCAL, etc.).

It is the programmer's responsibility to choose the representation which is best suited to the problem being solved but bearing in mind that the main purpose of using floating point is to reduce the amount of storage space required.

SAQs

6.4 Using IEE format, code the number 27.75_{10} in floating point form.

6.5 Decode the number represented in IEE floating point single precision format by 86 79 F8 00_{16}.

EXERCISES

6.1 Code -407_{10} as a 16-bit integer.

6.2 Code -3.645_{10}, 31.0151_{10} and -0.45_{10} in extended BCD.

6.3 Code 3101511_{10}, 151.17_{10}, and -0.299_{10} in condensed BCD.

6.4 Code the number 12.0957_{10} in floating point form using IEE format.

6.5 Decode the following number coded in single precision IEE floating point form: 85 E4 B0 00_{16}.

The following figure shows data formats used in IBM 360 computers:

character	character	character

Alphanumeric data.

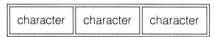

Data in extended BCD.

Data in condensed
BCD.

Positive integer (or negative in 2's complement) in one word or in two words.

S Exponent		Mantissa	

Floating point binary – single precision (one word).

S Expo			Mantissa				

Floating point binary – double precision (two words).

Solutions to SAQs

6.1 Code the number -357_{10} as a 16-bit binary integer.

The number being a negative number must be converted to 2's complement form. Recall that this can conveniently be achieved by converting to 1's complement then adding 1:

$$
\begin{array}{rll}
357 & = \ 0000000101100101 & \text{in 16-bit pure binary} \\
-357 & = \ 1111111010011010 & \text{in 1's complement} \\
+ & \underline{\qquad\qquad\qquad 1} & \\
-357 & \ \ 1111111010011011 & \text{in 2's complement}
\end{array}
$$

Notice that had we only worked with the 9 bits (101100101) from the right of the 16-bit word, we would have risked forgetting to pad the final result with sign bits (1's in this case because it is a negative number).

6.2 Code the following in extended BCD:

(a) 3867_{10}

Remember that in the case of extended BCD, each figure of the number is stored in its BCD (or 8421) form in the right half of each byte (the right nibble), the left part (or zone) of the byte usually being filled with 1's. As for the sign, it can take several forms; here we have decided arbitrarily to represent it by its shortened ASCII value:

$$
\begin{array}{cccccc}
1111 \ 0011 & 1111 \ 1000 & 1111 \ 0110 & \textbf{1011} \ 0111 \\
3 & 8 & 6 \quad + & 7
\end{array}
$$

(b) 34.675_{10}

$$
\begin{array}{ccccc}
1111 \ 0011 & 1111 \ 0100 & 1111 \ 0110 & 1111 \ 0111 \\
3 & 4 & 6 & 7 \\
\textbf{1011} \ 0101 & & & \\
+ \quad 5 & & &
\end{array}
$$

It should be remembered that the point does not exist as such but that it is a 'virtual' point which must not appear in the stored number.

(c) -34.45_{10}

$$1111\ 0011\ 1111\ 0100\ 1111\ 0100\ \textbf{1101}\ 0101$$
$$\qquad\quad 3\qquad\quad 4\qquad\quad 4\quad -\quad 5$$

6.3 Code the following in condensed BCD:

(a) 387_{10}
In condensed BCD, each figure of the number to be coded is represented in a nibble by its equivalent 8421, the sign (that we will represent in abbreviated ASCII) occupying the least significant nibble (the rightmost nibble):

$$0011\ 1000\ 0111\ \textbf{1011}$$
$$\quad 3\qquad 8\qquad 7\qquad +$$

(b) 35.47_{10}

$$0011\ 0101\ 0100\ 0111\ \textbf{1011}$$
$$\quad 3\qquad 5\qquad 4\qquad 7\qquad +$$

Again the point does not exist as such but is a 'virtual' point which must not appear in the stored number.

(c) -35.99_{10}

$$0011\ 0101\ 1001\ 1001\ \textbf{1101}$$
$$\quad 3\qquad 5\qquad 9\qquad 9\qquad -$$

6.4 Using IEE format, code the number 27.75_{10} in floating point form.
First we represent the number in base 16, i.e. $1B.C_{16}$. Next we have to normalise the number by shifting the point to the left, i.e. $.1BC\ E_{16}+2$. Recall that in this standard, the exponent is coded in excess 64 and the biased exponent will be:

$$64_{10}\ +\ 2_{10}\ =\ 66_{10}\text{ that is }1000010_2$$

The sign being positive, the bit representing it will be zero. We will then have as our final result:

$$1000\ 010\ 0\ 0001\ 1011\ 1100\ 0000\ 0000\ 0000\text{ in binary}$$

Exponent S   Mantissa

$$\quad 8\qquad 4\qquad\ \ 1\quad B\quad C\quad 0\quad\ \ 0\quad\ \ 0\quad\text{ in hexadecimal}$$

6.5 Decode the number represented in IEE floating point single-precision format by: $86\ 79\ F8\ 00_{16}$.

First we find its binary form:

```
8    6       7    9    F    8    0    0
1000 011  0  0111 1001 1111 1000 0000 0000
Exponent Sign            Mantissa
```

Sign: the sign bit is zero, saying that the number is positive.

Exponent: $1000011 = 67_{10}$ which by subtracting the bias of 64 gives true exponent of $E_{16} + 3$.

Mantisa: $.79F800_{16}$.

As the exponent that we have determined is $+3$, we can 'denormalise' the number by shifting the point three places to the right giving $79F.800_{16}$ which gives us in base 10:

$$(7 \times 16^2) + (9 \times 16^1) + (F \times 16^0) . (8 \times 16^{-1}) = 1951.5_{10}$$

Chapter 7

Boolean algebra: introduction

Computer operations are based entirely on logic functions. Let us first consider what this term logic involves.

7.1 Analog and digital logic

Before digital computers, there were analog computers which simulated mathematical functions and could be used, for example, to determine tide tables or the trajectories of shells shot from a gun. Early analog computers used mechanical devices for performing mathematical operations such as addition and multiplication and even integration and differentiation. Later analog computers replaced the mechanical devices with electrical circuits.

Voltages in an analog computer follow the continuous variations in the value being represented. A mercury thermometer is an analog device and temperatures measured with a mercury thermometer can register an infinity of values between two points on the scale. **Analog representation** allows an **infinity of states**. Figure 7.1 illustrates analog measurement.

In contrast to the continuity of analog representation there is **digital representation** in which values do not vary continuously but take a **finite number of states** and change directly from one state to another. Traffic lights have four different states, whereas a single lamp has only two states, on or off, and a door has two states, locked or unlocked. Figure 7.2 illustrates two-state logic values.

Digital computers, which is what we are concerned with, use two logic states: current flowing, or not flowing, in the computer's electronic components. Conventionally we associate the values 0 and 1 with these two logic states. Thus a lamp might indicate a logic state 1 when it is on and a logic state 0 when it is off; a transistor might indicate a logic state 1 when it allows current to pass (when it is said to be saturated) and a logic state 0 when it will not allow it to pass (when it is said to be blocked).

These logic states are used in a particular algebra which is attributed to **George Boole** (1815–1864), known as **Boolean algebra**. The propositions formulated in this algebra can only take the two logic values: **true** and **false.**

Boolean algebra can be applied equally well to logic problems as it can to the design of circuits for hydraulic, pneumatic, electrical or electronic applications. It

Figure 7.1　Analog values

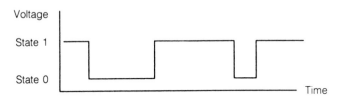

Figure 7.2　Two-state logic values

allows a rational approach rather than an empirical approach to the solution of problems.

7.2　**Boolean variables**

Any quantity which can take only two values is called a **boolean variable.** The values can be represented by the symbols 0 and 1.

　　With reference to electronic circuits, we will associate the logic value 1 with a voltage V (depending on the technology, V is generally about 5 volts) and the logic value 0 with a potential in the region of 0 volts.

7.3　**A study of basic logic operations**

Combinations of different logic values at the inputs to a logic circuit cause different logic values to appear at the output. If the state of the output depends **only** on the state of the inputs, and the output is always the same when the same inputs are applied, then we speak of **combinatory logic.** If the state of the output also depends on the **previous state** of the circuit we speak of **sequential logic.**

　　Circuits which accept logic values at their inputs and produce corresponding logic values at their outputs are called **logic gates.**

　　These are the components (chips) that we see on the circuit boards inside computers. The chips may contain either collections of logic gates or more elaborate components such as microprocessors, memories, input–output controllers, etc.

The logic gates (or functions) that we will be considering in the following sections are:

NOT
AND
OR
NAND
NOR
XOR

Figure 7.3 summarises some logic gates.
First we will consider a very simple logic circuit.

7.3.1 *The amplifier or delay*

The delay circuit or amplifier is the simplest logic gate, consisting of one input and one output. If we apply a 1 to the input we obtain a 1 at the output; conversely a 0 applied to the input results in a 0 at the output.

You may wonder why we should be interested in such a component. One reason is that there is always a time difference (**a gate delay**) of about 20 nanoseconds (ns) between the moment when the input is applied to a gate and the moment when the output signal appears. The amplifier provides an easy way of delaying the transmission of a logic signal. Another reason is that the amplified signal can be distributed to more components than the original signal could supply; it can be used to increase **fan-out**.

Logic operations are represented symbolically using several different standards some of which are met only rarely. A widely used standard and the one we will adopt here is the ANSI (American National Standards Institute) standard (ANSI-Y-32-14), shown below:

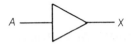

Delay or Amplifier

The function of the delay can be described by a truth table and by a logic equation.

Truth table		Logic equation
Input	Output	
A	*X*	
1	1	$X = A$
0	0	

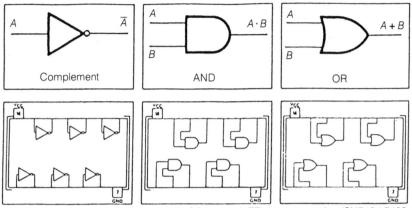

Graphical representation of the functions, AND, OR and their TTL implementation (SN7404,7408, 7432).

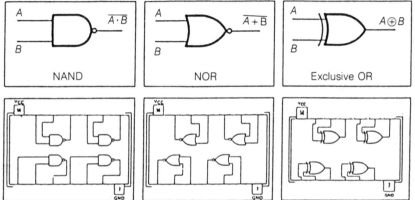

Graphical representation of the functions, NAND, NOR, Exclusive OR and their TTL implementation (SN7400,7402, 7486).

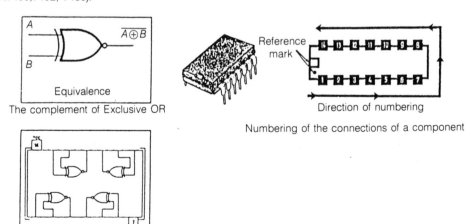

The complement of Exclusive OR

Numbering of the connections of a component

SN74LS266: 4 equivalence gates

Figure 7.3 Some logic gates

7.3.2 *The NOT function*

The **NOT** function is performed by a NOT gate or inverter. When we apply a logic 1 level at the input we obtain a logic 0 at the output and, conversely, if the input is at the logic 0 level, the output will be at logic 1. This is illustrated in the diagram and truth table below:

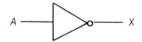

NOT gate or Inverter

Truth table   Logic equation

Input	Output
A	X
0	1
1	0

$X = \bar{A}$

Mathematically, to indicate that the value of the output is the complement of the input we write $X = \bar{A}$ (we say **not** A).

The role of this type of circuit is to produce at the output the opposite value to that at the input (we also call it a complementer).

A tiny circle shown at the output of any logic gate indicates that the output is complemented, that is, it is of the opposite state to that which would normally be output. A tiny circle at the input indicates that the signal arriving at the gate will be complemented before it is applied to the gate (see the following diagrams):

The circle indicates inversion

7.3.3 *The AND function*

This logic function provides an output at logic level 1 only when both its inputs are **simultaneously** at logic level 1:

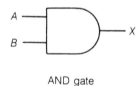

AND gate

Truth table		Logic equation
Input	**Output**	
A **B**	**X**	
0 0	0	Mathematically the
0 1	0	function AND is
1 0	0	written as (.)
1 1	1	$X = A . B$

The point is very often omitted and we write $X = AB$

It is possible to find AND gates with more than two inputs but the principle remains the same: all the inputs must be at logic level 1 to produce an output of 1.

7.3.4 *The OR function*

The logic circuit OR provides an output at logic level 1 when **one or the other or both** inputs have a logic level of 1. This is illustrated in the diagram below:

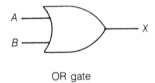

OR gate

Truth table		Logic equation
Input	**Output**	
A **B**	**X**	
0 0	0	Mathematically the
0 1	1	function OR is
1 0	1	written as (+)
1 1	1	$X = A + B$

It is possible to find OR gates with more than two inputs but the principle remains the same, if one or more of the inputs is at logic level 1, the output will be at logic level 1.

7.3.5 *The NAND function*

The NAND function, very often used in the design of electronic circuits, is formed by bringing together two of the logic circuits already studied, the NOT and the AND.

It produces an output state of logic 1 when **at least one** of its inputs is at logic level 0. The diagram below shows the principle (above) and the standard representation (below):

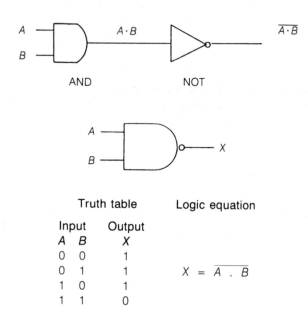

Truth table   Logic equation

Input		Output
A	B	X
0	0	1
0	1	1
1	0	1
1	1	0

$$X = \overline{A \cdot B}$$

This function is very useful because it can be used to perform any of the other logic operations. What is more, it is very cheap to manufacture on integrated circuits and so it is very frequently used.

As with previous circuits, NAND gates having more than two inputs are often used in practical applications. Figure 7.4 is an example.

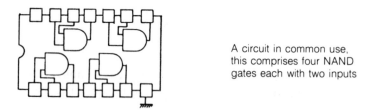

A circuit in common use, this comprises four NAND gates each with two inputs

Figure 7.4   A 7400 integrated circuit

7.3.6   *The NOR function*

This function is formed from a combination of an OR gate and a NOT gate. The combination produces a logic level 0 at its output when **at least one** input is at logic level 1.

Like the NAND, this function can also be used to perform any of the other logic operations.

The diagram below shows the principle (above) and the standard representation (below):

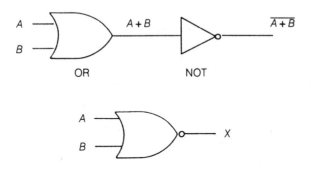

OR	NOT

Truth table   Logic equation

Input		Output
A	B	X
0	0	1
0	1	0
1	0	0
1	1	0

$$X = \overline{A + B}$$

7.3.7   *The EXCLUSIVE OR (XOR) function*

The XOR gate is a circuit with two inputs which produces a logic level 1 at its output when **one and only one** of its inputs is at logic level 1:

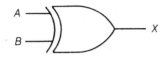

Truth table   Logic equation

Input		Output
A	B	X
0	0	0
0	1	1
1	0	1
1	1	0

The XOR is written with the symbol ⊕
$$X = A \oplus B$$

SAQs

7.1 Name each of the logic symbols given in the logic diagram below.

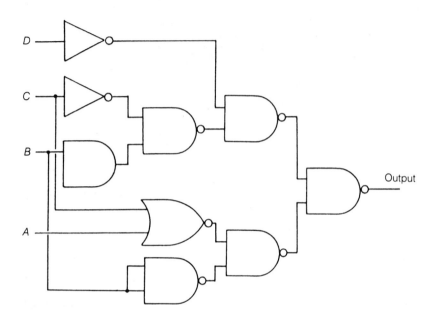

7.2 Taking the input values from the accompanying table, and with the aid of the truth tables given earlier, determine the output of the circuit for each combination of inputs.

D	C	B	A	Output
0	0	0	0	
0	0	0	1	
0	0	1	0	
0	0	1	1	
0	1	0	0	
0	1	0	1	
0	1	1	0	
0	1	1	1	
1	0	0	0	
1	0	0	1	
1	0	1	0	
1	0	1	1	
1	1	0	0	
1	1	0	1	
1	1	1	1	

EXERCISE

7.1 Complete the truth tables for the circuits illustrated below:

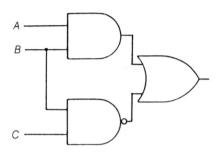

A	B	C	Output
0	0	0	
0	0	1	
0	1	0	
0	1	1	
1	0	0	
1	0	1	
1	1	0	
1	1	1	

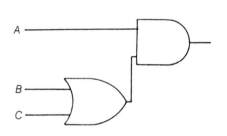

A	B	C	Output
0	0	0	
0	0	1	
0	1	0	
0	1	1	
1	0	0	
1	0	1	
1	1	0	
1	1	1	

Solutions to SAQs

7.1 Name each of the logic symbols in the logic diagram.

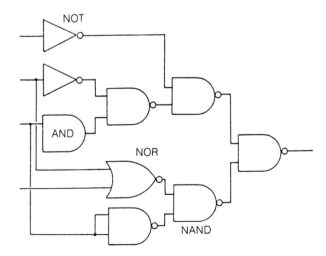

7.2 With the aid of the truth tables given earlier, determine the output of the circuit for each combination of inputs.

D	C	B	A	Output
0	0	0	0	1
0	0	0	1	1
0	0	1	0	1
0	0	1	1	0
0	1	0	0	1
0	1	0	1	1
0	1	1	0	1
0	1	1	1	1
1	0	0	0	1
1	0	0	1	0
1	0	1	0	0
1	0	1	1	0
1	1	0	0	0
1	1	0	1	0
1	1	1	1	0

Chapter 8

Combinatory logic

In combinatory logic, in contrast to sequential logic, the state of the output depends **only** on the combination of logic values currently present on the inputs.

Before studying the various circuits that we may encounter in combinatory logic, it will be helpful to gain a good understanding of some elementary properties of logic gates and of how to determine and to simplify the logic equations which link their outputs to their inputs.

8.1 Properties of elementary functions

As an aid to understanding, we have illustrated in Figure 8.1 some of the properties of elementary functions in the form of simple electrical circuits which cause a lamp to light. It goes without saying that the functions remain valid for pneumatic, electronic and other implementations of the logic. Note that in the figures, by convention, an open switch takes the value 0 while a closed switch takes the value 1.

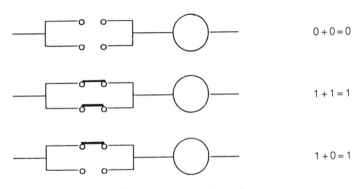

Figure 8.1 (continued)

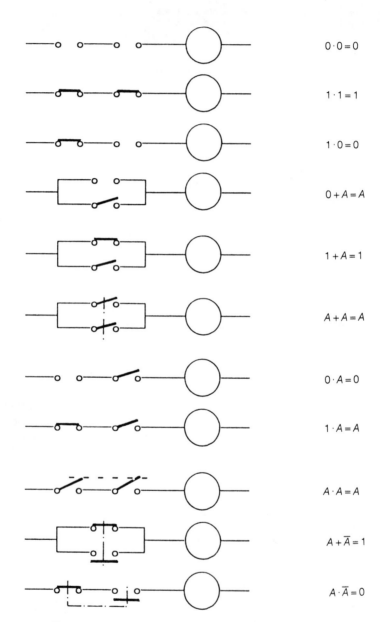

Figure 8.1   Some properties of elementary functions

8.2 **Use of NAND gates in functions**

We stated previously that because of their low cost of integration, NAND gates were very frequently used to construct other logic circuits. We are therefore going to see how to combine NAND gates so as to obtain the different types of basic gates that we studied in Chapter 7.

8.2.1   *Realisation of the delay function*

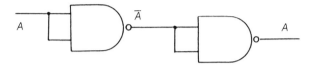

8.2.2   *Realisation of the NOT function*

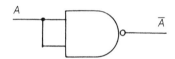

8.2.3   *Realisation of the AND function*

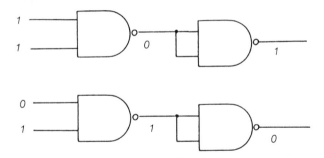

8.2.4   *Realisation of the OR function*

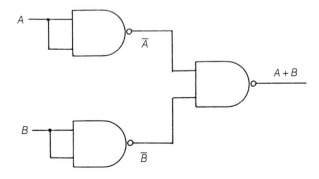

8.2.5 *Realisation of the NOR function*

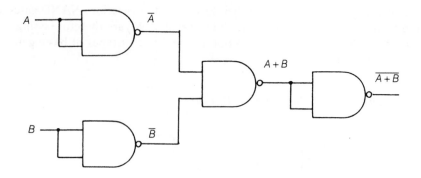

8.3 **Simplification of logic equations**

8.3.1 *De Morgan's theorems*

De Morgan was an English mathematician (1806–1871) who worked with George Boole in the study of combinational logic and formulated the following two theorems.

 Theorem 1. The complement of a logical sum is equal to the logical product of the complements.

$$\overline{A + B} = \overline{A} \cdot \overline{B}$$

Truth table

A	B	$\overline{A}$	$\overline{B}$	A + B	$\overline{A + B}$	$\overline{A} \cdot \overline{B}$
0	0	1	1	0	1	1
0	1	1	0	1	0	0
1	0	0	1	1	0	0
1	1	0	0	1	0	0

 Theorem 2. The complement of a logical product is equal to the logical sum of the complements.

$$\overline{A \cdot B} = \overline{A} + \overline{B}$$

Truth table

A	B	$\overline{A}$	$\overline{B}$	A . B	$\overline{A . B}$	$\overline{A} + \overline{B}$
0	0	1	1	0	1	1
0	1	1	0	0	1	1
1	0	0	1	0	1	1
1	1	0	0	1	0	0

8.3.2. *Karnaugh maps*

Karnaugh maps are one way of representing and simplifying logic expressions. They enable the representation of the logic states resulting from different combinations of the input variables.

8.3.2.1   Representation according to the number of variables

The diagram below shows a one-variable Karnaugh map

A

0	1

In two-variable maps each variable can take the values 0 or 1. Therefore, if the Karnaugh map is to show the result for every possible combination of the input variables, it must possess as many cells as there are possible combinations of two variables, that is $2^2 = 4$ cells. Each cell will correspond to one particular combination of values of the inputs and in each cell we will write the value of the output variable corresponding to that particular combination of inputs. In a Karnaugh map, just as in a truth table, we use 0's and 1's, whereas in a **Veitch** diagram we shade in the cells.

Example 8.1   A two-variable Karnaugh map

Let the output function be $M = A.B + \overline{A}.\overline{B}$, that is let M take the value 1 when $A.B$ is true or when $\overline{A}.\overline{B}$ is true. We will then obtain the Karnaugh map

In a normal three-variable truth table, the values of the independent variables (A, B, C) are listed in the order of the binary sequence 000, 001, 010, 011. In a Karnaugh map it is imperative that the variables are only separated by a Hamming distance of 1, and therefore for a three-variable map we must follow a sequence such as 000, 001, 011, 010, 110, 111, 101, 100 ... **Only one value changes at a time.** Such a code is called a **reflected binary** code or a **Gray** code.

AB

	00	01	11	10
C 0				
1				

Notice that the extreme cells (00 and 10) are separated by a Hamming distance of one and are therefore 'adjacent'. We can represent the adjacencies if we draw the map on the surface of a cylinder:

As we will see, these adjacencies are important in the simplification of equations.

The principle behind the map for four variables is the same as that described for two or three variables. A four-variable map is shown below:

AB

	00	01	11	10
CD 00				
01				
11				
10				

The cylinder that we demonstrated previously for the three-variable case can be applied in this case in two ways; the top and bottom edges are adjacent and the left and right edges are adjacent since they have a Hamming distance of 1 in accordance with the reflected binary code:

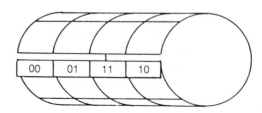

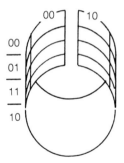

8.3.2.2 Axes of symmetry

A study of Karnaugh maps reveals a number of axes of symmetry, as in the table with four variables, shown below:

		00	01	11	10
	00				
	01				
	11				
	10				

AB

I is an axis of symmetry of order 1 (or principal axis of symmetry). **L** is also an axis of symmetry of order 1 according to the principle of adjacencies mentioned earlier. A principal axis divides the map into two half-tables. **J** and **K** are axes of symmetry of order 2 (or secondary axes of symmetry).

Vertical axes of symmetry are formed in the same way. In every case whatever the number of variables to be represented on the map, the axes of symmetry must always take into account possible adjacencies at the edges.

8.3.3 *Use of Karnaugh maps*

Now that we have seen how Karnaugh maps are made let us see how to use them by considering a concrete example.

Consider the Karnaugh map representing the output state of a drive motor for the paper in a printer. The state depends on the logical combination of four input variables (presence of paper, etc.). By convention we will write a 0 in the cell corresponding to a combination of input variables which causes the motor to be switched off and a 1 when the motor is activated, as shown below:

AB

		00	01	11	10
	00	0	1	1	1
	01	0	1	1	1
CD	11	0	1	1	1
	10	0	1	1	0

The question is to find the logic equation contained in this table describing the state of the motor and to simplify it.

Procedure: we group the cells all having the same logic state (generally we only consider logic 1), seeking to group them around the maximum number of axes of symmetry and around at least one axis. In grouping the cells, we must remember the end-around adjacencies.

We must always ensure that a group comprises a number of cells equal to an integral power of 2 (2 cells, 4 cells, 8 cells, etc.).

8.3.3.1   1st grouping

AB

		00	01	11	10
	00	0	1	1	1
	01	0	1	1	1
CD	11	0	1	1	1
	10	0	1	1	0

As a result of this first grouping we can state that within this group the state of the motor (we will call it M) is a logic 1 for the following combinations:

$$M = \overline{A}B\overline{C}\overline{D} + AB\overline{C}\overline{D} + \overline{A}B\overline{C}D + AB\overline{C}D + ABCD + \overline{A}BC\overline{D} + \overline{A}BCD + ABC\overline{D}$$

Applying the distribution rules of Boolean algebra, this simplifies to:

$$M = \overline{A}B(\overline{C}\overline{D} + \overline{C}D + CD + C\overline{D}) + AB(\overline{C}\overline{D} + \overline{C}D + CD + C\overline{D})$$

We then notice that the terms in the parentheses have the logic value 1 since they may be written $(\overline{C}(D + \overline{D}) + C(D + \overline{D}))$ and $D + \overline{D}$ is equivalent to 1, as we indicated in Section 8.1.

After simplification we have $C + \overline{C}$ which is also equal to 1. Thus from this first grouping we can deduce that the state of the motor is independent of the state of the variable C or of the state of the variable D and the expression reduces to:

$$M = \overline{A}B + AB$$

This simplifies still further to $M = B(\overline{A} + A)$ and then once again since $(\overline{A} + A)$ is equal to 1. Our final equation for this first grouping thus becomes $M = B$.

We still have not used all the 1-states of M, so we have to continue our solution with a further grouping. This grouping can include cells already used in the first grouping (we talk of them being re-covered) and this is often desirable indeed necessary, but each regrouping should include at least one cell that has not previously been included in a group.

8.3.3.2 2nd grouping

AB

		00	01	11	10
	00	0	1	1	1
CD	01	0	1	1	1
	11	0	1	1	1
	10	0	1	1	0

We proceed as above, which leads to an equation for the grouping of the form:

$$
\begin{aligned}
M &= AB\overline{C}\overline{D} + A\overline{B}\overline{C}\overline{D} + AB\overline{C}D + A\overline{B}\overline{C}D \\
\text{i.e. } M &= \overline{C}\overline{D}(AB + A\overline{B}) + \overline{C}D(AB + A\overline{B}) \\
\text{i.e. } M &= (\overline{C}\overline{D} + \overline{C}D) \cdot (AB + A\overline{B}) \\
\text{i.e. } M &= \overline{C}(\overline{D} + D) \cdot A(\overline{B} + B) \\
\text{i.e. } M &= \overline{C}A
\end{aligned}
$$

There are still some 1's in the map which have not yet been used so we must proceed to a third grouping.

8.3.3.3 3rd grouping

AB

	00	01	11	10
00	0	1	1	1
01	0	1	1	1
11	0	1	1	1
10	0	1	1	0

CD

We proceed as above, which leads to an equation for the grouping of the form:

$$M = AB\overline{C}D + ABCD + A\overline{B}\overline{C}D + A\overline{B}CD$$
$$\text{i.e. } M = AB(\overline{C}D + CD) + A\overline{B}(\overline{C}D + CD)$$
$$\text{i.e. } M = (AB + A\overline{B}) \cdot (\overline{C}D + CD)$$
$$\text{i.e. } M = AD$$

Let us note at present that the 1-states of our motor M can be represented by the association of the three equations we have just found:

$$M = B + A\overline{C} + AD$$

which can be simplified further to:

$$M = B + A(\overline{C} + D)$$

You have seen how we have progressed to reach this result via three separate groupings of cells around their axes of symmetry. We could have arrived at this answer more directly by writing a single equation which included appropriate groupings for all the cells corresponding to inputs giving an output of 1. We used this indirect approach deliberately because it gives a glimpse of a second method which allows us to eliminate variables in a straightforward way right from the start. In fact if we note that the same input variable takes successively, and for **equal numbers of times** the states 0 and 1 in successive cells of the table, we can think of the variable cancelling itself and therefore having no effect on the final state of the system being studied.

Example 8.2   Another look at the 3rd grouping

Let us look again at the third grouping that we made in the example above. Inspection shows that within the group the input variable A maintains a state of 1 in the two columns concerned. By contrast, variable B takes the value 1 or the value 0 in successive columns; its role is therefore ineffective within the grouping. The same argument can be applied to variable C which can also take states 1 or 0. As a result of this inspection we can deduce that only the combination AD of the variables is effective in producing an output of 1.

AB

CD	00	01	11	10
00	0	1	1	1
01	0	1	1	1
11	0	1	1	1
10	0	1	1	0

It is equally possible, and sometimes easier, to group the 0-states of M and so to find an equation for $\overline{M}$. To find the equation for M we would simply consider the complement of the equation for $\overline{M}$.

Now that our logic equation has been simplified it only remains to build a logic circuit for it from the elementary logic gates studied earlier. The diagram below gives the circuit for $M = B + A(\overline{C} + D)$:

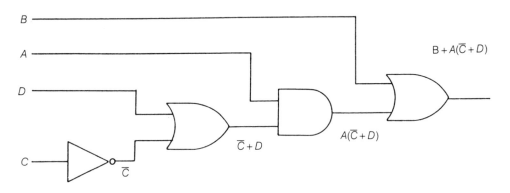

$B + A(\overline{C} + D)$

$A(\overline{C} + D)$

$\overline{C} + D$

$\overline{C}$

Example 8.3 Another Karnaugh map

AB

CD	00	01	11	10
00	1	1	0	0
01	0	0	1	1
11	0	0	1	1
10	1	1	0	0

By using two groupings and employing end-over adjacencies we obtain the following equation for M:

$$(\overline{ABCD} + \overline{ABC}D + \overline{AB}C\overline{D} + \overline{A}BC\overline{D}) + (A\overline{BC}D + ABCD + A\overline{B}CD + A\overline{BC}D)$$

    1st grouping   2nd grouping

that is $M = \overline{A}\overline{D} + AD$

Such groupings are said to be of order 4 because they group four variables. In a group of order 4 such as this, two of the variables will cancel themselves. Thus in the first group, B takes successively the values 0 and 1 and therefore has no effect; it is the same for C. In this way we can make an initial simplification of the equations of the groups.

Important: remember that only groups of 2, 4, 8, 16, ... are useful and that groups of, say, 6 cells must not be used even though they have an axis of symmetry.

SAQs

8.1 Write the logic equations for the following maps:

(a)

AB

C \ AB	00	01	11	10
0	1	1	0	0
1	0	1	1	0

(b)

AB

CD \ AB	00	01	11	10
00	1	1	0	0
01	1	1	0	1
11	0	1	1	1
10	1	0	0	1

(c)

	AB 00	01	11	10
00	0	0	1	1
01	0	0	0	0
CD 11	1	1	1	1
10	1	1	0	0

(d)

	AB 00	01	11	10
00	1	0	0	1
01	0	0	0	0
CD 11	0	0	0	0
10	1	0	0	1

(e)

	AB 00	01	11	10
00	1	1	0	0
01	1	1	0	0
CD 11	1	1	1	1
10	1	1	1	1

(f)

	AB 00	01	11	10
00	1	1	0	1
01	1	1	0	1
CD 11	0	1	0	0
10	0	1	0	0

8.2 Given the following logic equations, construct the corresponding four-variable Karnaugh maps:

(a) $S1 = \overline{A}\overline{B}C + \overline{A}BC + A\overline{B}C + ABC$
(b) $S2 = C\overline{D} + AB$
(c) $S3 = C + D$

EXERCISES

8.1 Given the following maps, write the corresponding logic equations.

(a)   AB

		00	01	11	10
	00	1	0	0	1
	01	1	0	0	1
CD	11	0	1	1	0
	10	0	1	1	0

(b)   AB

		00	01	11	10
	00	1	1	0	1
	01	0	1	0	0
CD	11	1	1	1	1
	10	1	0	0	1

(c)   AB

		00	01	11	10
	00	1	1	1	1
	01	1	1	1	1
CD	11	1	1	1	1
	10	1	1	0	0

8.2   Given the following logic equations, construct the corresponding Karnaugh maps and thus simplify the equations if possible:

$$M1 = A\bar{B}D + \bar{A}CD + A\bar{B}\bar{D} + ACD$$
$$M2 = \bar{A}B + \bar{C}D$$

Solutions to SAQs

8.1   Write logic equations for the maps on pages 82–3.

(a)

		AB		
C		00	01	11	10

	00	01	11	10
0	1	1	0	0
1	0	1	1	0

$S = \overline{AC} + BC$ or, with the extra group,
$S = \overline{AC} + BC + \overline{A}B$.

(b)

AB

CD	00	01	11	10
00	1	1	0	0
01	1	1	0	1
11	0	1	1	1
10	1	0	0	1

$S = \overline{AC} + BCD + A\overline{B}D + \overline{B}C\overline{D}$

(c)

AB

CD	00	01	11	10
00	0	0	1	1
01	0	0	0	0
11	1	1	1	1
10	1	1	0	0

$S = A\overline{CD} + CD + \overline{A}C$

(d)

AB

CD	00	01	11	10
00	1	0	0	1
01	0	0	0	0
11	0	0	0	0
10	1	0	0	1

$S = \overline{BCD} + \overline{B}C\overline{D}$, that is $S = \overline{BD}(C + \overline{C})$
and hence $S = \overline{BD}$.

(e)

AB

CD	00	01	11	10
00	1	1	0	0
01	1	1	0	0
11	1	1	1	1
10	1	1	1	1

$S = \overline{A} + C$

(f)

AB

CD	00	01	11	10
00	1	1	0	1
01	1	1	0	1
11	0	1	0	0
10	0	1	0	0

$S = \overline{A}B + \overline{B}C$

8.2 Give the four-variable Karnaugh maps for the following:

(a) $S1 = \overline{A}\overline{B}C + \overline{A}BC + A\overline{B}C + ABC$

AB

	00	01	11	10
00	0	0	0	0
01	0	0	0	0
11	1	1	1	1
10	1	1	1	1

CD

(b) $S2 = C\overline{D} + AB$

AB

	00	01	11	10
00	0	0	1	0
01	0	0	1	0
11	0	0	1	0
10	1	1	1	1

CD

(c) $S3 = C + D$

AB

	00	01	11	10
00	0	0	0	0
01	1	1	1	1
11	1	1	1	1
10	1	1	1	1

CD

Chapter 9

Combinatory logic circuits

With the aid of the various elementary logic circuits studied earlier, it will be possible to construct the main elements of a computer. We have now studied binary numbers, and the number systems used by computers, and we have studied the addition of binary numbers, let us now see how, with the aid of logic circuits, it is possible to build a binary adder.

9.1 Designing a binary adder

To construct a binary adder we will first show how to add two bits then we will go on to show how to take into account any carries that might arise from the addition of the preceding bits. In the first phase we will show how to construct a **half adder** and in the second how to build a **full adder**.

9.1.1 *The half adder*

The half adder is a circuit, composed of logic gates, that adds two binary digits (bits). The addition will generate two bits, one for the result, properly called the sum, and one for the carry.

Truth table

1st bit	+ 2nd bit	= Sum	Carry
0	0	0	0
0	1	1	0
1	0	1	0
1	1	0	1

We can deduce, by studying the truth table, that the equation for the sum corresponds to an XOR while the equation for the carry corresponds to an AND.

The diagram below shows a half adder using the elements in the truth table:

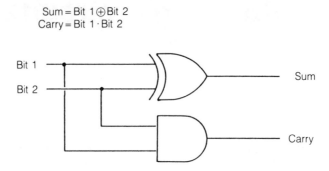

$$Sum = Bit\ 1 \oplus Bit\ 2$$
$$Carry = Bit\ 1 \cdot Bit\ 2$$

We have said that it is always possible and, for reasons of economy, usually desirable to build circuits using NAND gates. This is so in the case for the half adder:

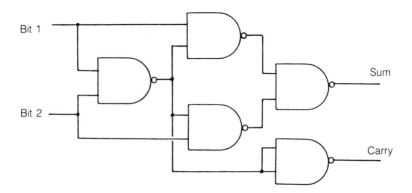

From now on, for simplicity, we will represent the half adder as a 'black box' with two inputs and two outputs, as shown below:

9.1.2 *The full adder*

To design a full adder we have to take into account the fact that a carry from the preceding stage may enter into our addition. The operation can be demonstrated as follows:

```
      1st bit
  +   2nd bit
  =   Intermediate sum (IS)

      Intermediate sum (IS)
  +   Carry in           (CI)
  =   Final sum          (FS)
```

Each of these two additions can generate a new carry which we will denote as $C1$ in the first case and $C2$ in the second:

Truth table

1st bit	+ 2nd bit	+ Carry in	= Sum	Carry out
A	B	CI	FS	CO
0	0	0	0	0
0	1	0	1	0
1	0	0	1	0
1	1	0	0	1
0	0	1	1	0
0	1	1	0	1
1	0	1	0	1
1	1	1	1	1

In effect we perform two simple additions in a full adder.

First we add two of the bits (here A and B) of the numbers to be added giving us an intermediate sum (IS) and a carry out ($C1$).

Then we add to this intermediate sum, the carry in (CI) from the previous stage. This second add gives us the final sum FS and generates a carry out ($C2$).

One or other of these carries will be the final carry out (CO). It is not possible to have both $C1$ and $C2$ and therefore we need not consider this case.

```
      A + B      will give us IS and C1
      S1 + CI    will give us FS and C2
      CO         comes from C1 or from C2
```

It is now a simple matter, thanks to our half adders, to draw a full adder:

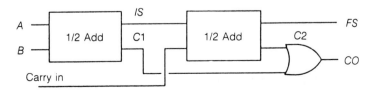

From now on, for simplicity, we will only show the full adder as a black box with three inputs and two outputs:

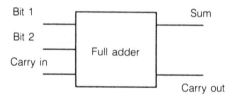

Using this basic full adder it is now possible to build circuits for the addition of *n* bits. A diagram of the principle is shown below:

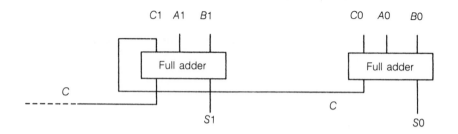

Example 9.1   An adder for two four-bit numbers

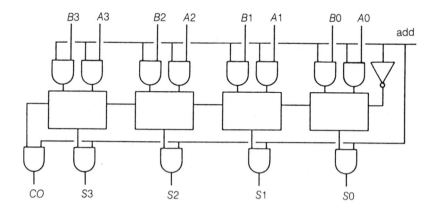

If add $= 0$ the addition is blocked ($0 \cdot B^n = 0$ and $0 \cdot A^n = 0$).
If add $= 1$ the addition is enabled and the values $A0, B0, A1, B1, \ldots$ enter the adder.

We have seen in our study of binary arithmetic, that subtraction can be performed by adding the complement of the number. This is the principle used in the adder–subtracter shown below:

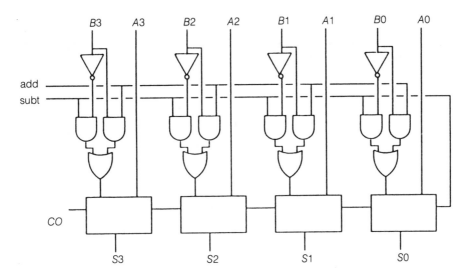

When sub = 1 and add = 0 the circuit functions as a subtracter.
When sub = 0 and add = 1 the circuit functions as an adder.

SAQs

9.1 Imagine a circuit which adds four binary digits. What is its minimum number of inputs and outputs and what is their purpose?

9.2 Using black boxes to represent adders that can add two 4-bit numbers, design an adder for two 16-bit numbers.

9.2 Designing decoders and multiplexers

Decoders and multiplexers are combinatory circuits which are widely used and which play important roles in computer design. Here we will use 8-bit circuits (although they might equally be 4- or 16-bit circuits) to present four important functions.

9.2.1 Decoding

A decoder is a collection of logic circuits which can convert, for example, a binary number to a decimal number. Each separate binary pattern applied to the inputs activates its own corresponding output line.

Example 9.2   A decoder

If for instance the inputs were $C = 1$, $B = 1$, $A = 0$ the output activated would be the line corresponding to a 6 (110_2 corresponding to 6_{10}). The diagram below shows a 1 out of 8 decoder:

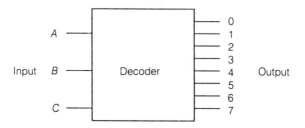

9.2.2 *Encoding*

An encoder is a collection of logic circuits which produces at its outputs a binary pattern corresponding to the input which has been activated.

Example 9.3   An encoder

If the input 4 is activated (that is to say if it is the only input at logic level 1 while the others are at level 0), the outputs will have the following values: $C = 1$, $B = 0$, $A = 0$ ($4_{10} = 100_2$).

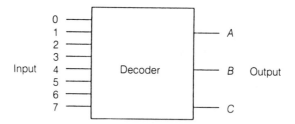

9.2.3 *Multiplexing*

The multiplexer is a collection of logic circuits which has several inputs and a single output. The inputs are of two types: data inputs and address inputs. The level of the output is the same as the level of the input whose number has been coded on the address inputs.

Example 9.4   A multiplexer

If we have the values $C = 1$, $B = 0$ and $A = 1$, on the address inputs, we will find at the output the same logic level as that which is present on input line number 5 ($101_2 = 5_{10}$).

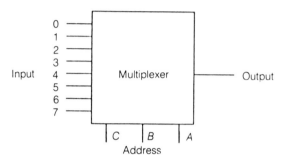

9.2.4   *Demultiplexing*

The demultiplexer is a collection of logic circuits which sends the logic level present on the input to the output whose number has been coded on the address inputs.

Example 9.5   A demultiplexer

If we have the values $C = 0$, $B = 1$ and $A = 0$, the logic level on the output line number 2 will be the same as that of the input line.

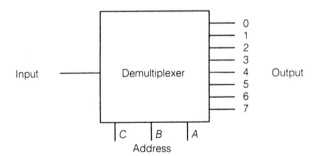

9.3   **Decoders**

In practice it is convenient to distinguish between two types of decoders: **binary decoders** which correspond to those described above where a single output is activated at a time, and **display decoders** which activate several outputs simultaneously, for instance so as to be able to drive the segments of a seven-segment display like that used in pocket calculators; in this case it is the binary code of the number to be displayed which serves as input.

9.3.1 *Binary decoder*

The binary decoder is a circuit with n binary inputs called an address and with p outputs where $p \leqslant 2^n$. A single output will be activated at a time; it is used mainly for selecting one element out of n.

Example 9.6   A binary decoder

The 74LS139 is a double decoder of type 1 out of 4, with negative outputs (that means the outputs are active when they are low or active low). It has a gating input G:

    if $G = 0$ the decoder is activated
    if $G = 1$ the decoder is inhibited (no output can be activated).

Truth table

Input			Output			
Gating	Address					
G	A	B	Y0	Y1	Y2	Y3
1	X	X	1	1	1	1
0	0	0	0	1	1	1
0	0	1	1	0	1	1
0	1	0	1	1	0	1
0	1	1	1	1	1	0

X indicates that the level (0 or 1) is not important.

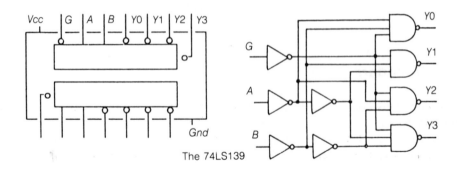

The 74LS139

9.3.2 *Display decoder*

These decoders, like the previous ones, decode a binary input combination but in this case they are used to drive **segment displays**. Seven-segment displays allow, depending on the segments activated, all the figures used for base-10 or base-16 numbers to be displayed. Each segment is made from an **LED** (**L**ight **E**mitting **D**iode), and there are two techniques employed in their manufacture, common cathode or common anode, according to whether it is their cathodes or their anodes that are joined together.

The problem with LED displays lies in the amount of power they consume and there is a tendency to replace them with liquid crystal displays which are much more economic. The illumination of the segments (called segments **a** to **g**), is governed by the output of the decoder which converts the binary value of the figure to be displayed:

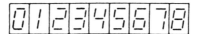

The diagram below shows the components of a seven-segment display:

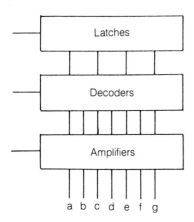

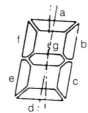

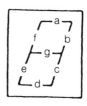

9.4 **Multiplexer**

9.4.1 *Definition of a multiplexer*

A multiplexer is a circuit with 2^n data inputs and n address inputs. The output copies the input data from the input line specified on the address inputs.

Example 9.7 A multiplexer

The 74 LS 153 is a four-bit multiplexer provided with a gating input which is active low. The truth table is as follows:

Truth table

| Gating | Addresses | | Input | | | | Output |
G	B	A	C0	C1	C2	C3	Y
1	X	X	X	X	X	X	0
0	0	0	0	X	X	X	0
0	0	1	X	0	X	X	0
0	1	0	X	X	0	X	0
0	1	1	X	X	X	0	0
0	0	0	1	X	X	X	1
0	0	1	X	1	X	X	1
0	1	0	X	X	1	X	1
0	1	1	X	X	X	1	1

X indicates that the level (0 or 1) is not important. The logic diagram of the 74 LS 153 is given below:

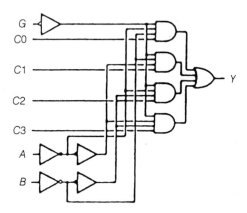

Logic diagram of the 74LS153 multiplexer

Note: an output shown with a little circle on it indicates a complemented output; similarly, a little circle shown on an input indicates a complemented input.

It is worth noting the difference between the following two circuits which, it must be emphasised, do not produce the same output:

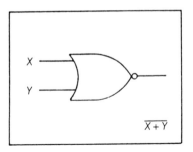

$$\overline{X+Y}$$

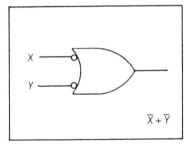

$$\overline{X}+\overline{Y}$$

9.4.2 *Applications of multiplexers*

Multiplexers are used for switching data, for generating combinatory functions, and for converting parallel data to serial data.

9.5 **Encoders**

9.5.1 *The priority encoder*

The priority encoder is a circuit with 2^n data inputs and n address outputs. The inputs have an order of priority and the outputs give, in binary, the rank of the currently active input with the highest priority.

Example 9.8   The eight-bit 4532 encoder

This encoder is provided with: a strobe input $E1$ which determines the moment when the inputs are to be read; it is active high, an output GS which is high if any of the inputs are active; an output $E0$ which is high if none of the inputs is active. This is illustrated in the truth table and logic diagram of the 4532 encoder given below.

Truth table

	Input									Output				
EI	D7	D6	D5	D4	D3	D2	D1	D0		GS	C	B	A	E0
0	X	X	X	X	X	X	X	X		0	0	0	0	0
1	0	0	0	0	0	0	0	0		0	0	0	0	1
1	1	X	X	X	X	X	X	X		1	1	1	1	0
1	0	1	X	X	X	X	X	X		1	1	1	0	0
1	0	0	1	X	X	X	X	X		1	1	0	1	0
1	0	0	0	1	X	X	X	X		1	1	0	0	0
1	0	0	0	0	1	X	X	X		1	0	1	1	0
1	0	0	0	0	0	1	X	X		1	0	1	0	0
1	0	0	0	0	0	0	1	X		1	0	0	1	0
1	0	0	0	0	0	0	0	1		1	0	0	0	0

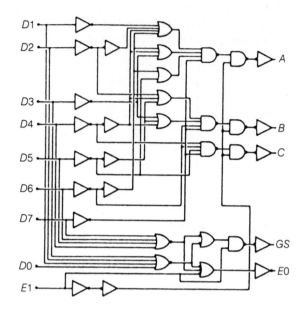

SAQ

9.3 Draw the logic diagram of a two-bit demultiplexer, whose role is to transmit the signal from its single data input to one of four outputs according to the binary value present on its address inputs.

EXERCISE

9.1 Draw the logic diagram of a two-bit encoder having four inputs and two outputs. The values at the outputs are to indicate in binary which of the inputs is in the 1 state.

Solutions to SAQs

9.1 Imagine a circuit which adds four binary digits. What is its minimum number of inputs and outputs and what is their purpose?.

The largest possible answer that can be obtained when adding four binary, digits is $1 + 1 + 1 + 1 = 100_2$. Therefore we need a box with four inputs and three outputs:

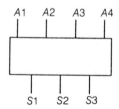

9.2 Using black boxes to represent adders that can add two 4-bit numbers, design an adder for two 16-bit numbers.

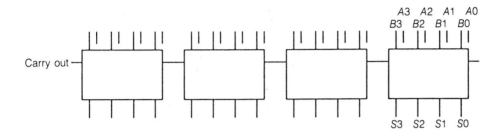

9.3 Draw the logic diagram of a 2-bit demultiplexer, whose role is to transmit the signal from its single data input to one of four outputs according to the binary value present on its address inputs.

Before drawing the logic diagram it is useful to construct a truth table. For this, look at the following diagram:

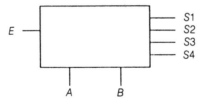

Truth table

A	B	S1	S2	S3	S4
0	0	1	0	0	0
0	1	0	1	0	0
1	0	0	0	1	0
1	1	0	0	0	1

We can then deduce the equations of the various outputs and draw the corresponding logic diagram:

$$S1 = (\overline{A + B}) \cdot E$$
$$S2 = (\overline{A} \cdot B) \cdot E$$
$$S3 = (A \cdot \overline{B}) \cdot E$$
$$S4 = (A \cdot B) \cdot E$$

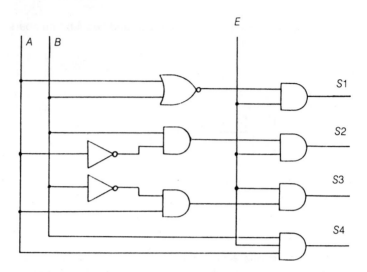

Chapter *10*

Sequential logic circuits: flip-flops

The circuits we have studied so far have been combinatory circuits; it was sufficient to know the logic state of their inputs; to know, without ambiguity, the logic state of their outputs. Circuits operating with sequential logic also depend on time, which is involved in two distinct ways: the **order** in which the operations occur, and the **duration** of each operation.

Thus, unlike combinatory logic, it will not be sufficient to know the state of the inputs in order to know the state of the outputs. The state could depend either on an earlier event or on the time which has elapsed since the input variables were applied and before the output is read.

To regulate the time we must use a specialised circuit which supplies regular pulses at a fixed frequency. The circuit (called a clock) is usually based on a quartz crystal and the regular pulses are called **clock pulses**. To measure the passage of time we now have to count the pulses generated by the clock and for this we use a **counter**.

10.1 General remarks

Flip-flops are circuits built from logic gates; they generally have 1 or 2 inputs where logic signals (1 or 0) are applied. 1 output is written Q and 1 output written $\bar{Q}$; its state is always the complement of that of Q. They sometimes also have a clock input. A diagram of a flip-flop is shown below.

By convention we often use so-called 'positive' logic where it is considered that the flip-flop is in the 1 state when output Q is in the 1 state.

Note: when we speak of the output, without specifying which of the two outputs we mean, it is the Q output which is being referred to.

There are four main types of flip-flop: RS, D, T and JK. We will consider RS, D and JK.

10.2 RS flip-flops

The name RS comes from the letters used to indicate the two inputs to the flip-flop: R indicates the **R**eset input and S indicates the **S**et input. These flip-flops are also called bistables because they have two stable states. To summarise (in positive logic):

$$\text{if } S = 1 \text{ and } R = 0 \text{ then } Q = 1$$
$$\text{if } S = 0 \text{ and } R = 1 \text{ then } Q = 0$$

Example 10.1   An RS flip-flop changing states

An RS flip-flop can be constructed from two NOR gates and represented in 'black box' form.

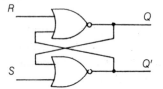

Let us look at the operation of such a flip-flop and see what happens in the case when we apply inputs $R = 1$ and $S = 0$.

There are two possibilities.

1st possibility: suppose that in the **previous** state **before** the new inputs are applied, $Q = 0$ and thus $\bar{Q} = 1$, and that $S = 0$ and $R = 0$.

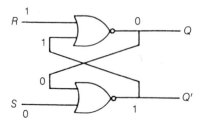

NOR

A B	X
0 0	1
0 1	0
1 0	0
1 1	0

When an input of 1 is applied to R, and an input 0 is applied to S, the gate with $R = 1$ has at least one input at logic level 1 and its output will therefore be 0; this output 0 is applied as an input to the other gate which now has both its inputs $= 0$ and so its output will be 1; the initial state of the flip-flop thus remains unchanged and we have $Q = 0$ and $\bar{Q} = 1$.

2nd possibility: suppose that the previous state was the opposite of the initial state considered above, i.e. suppose $Q = 1$ and $\bar{Q} = 0$, as in the diagram below:

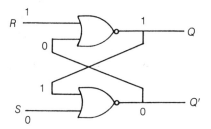

The fact that we apply an input $R = 1$ means that, whatever the other input to this gate, it will give an output of 0 which will be applied as an input to the other gate causing its output to be 1. Thus in the second case the output Q has changed from a 1 to a 0 while the output $\bar{Q}$ has changed from 0 to 1. The flip-flop has thus changed its state.

To distinguish the logic states before and after the new inputs were applied on R and S, we can use the subscripts n before and $n + 1$ after. So for the preceding example we can write:

R	S	Q_n	Q_{n+1}
1	0	0	0
1	0	1	0

Truth table

R	S	Q_n	Q_{n+1}	$\bar{Q}_{n+1}$			R	S	Q_{n+1}
0	0	0	0	1	$Q_{n+1} = Q_n$		0	0	Q_n
0	0	1	1	0					
0	1	0	1	0	$Q_{n+1} = 1 \lor Q_n$		0	1	1
0	1	1	1	0					
1	0	0	0	1	$Q_{n+1} = 0 \lor Q_n$		1	0	0
1	0	1	0	1					
1	1	0	0	0			1	1	invalid combination
1	1	1	0	0					

In the last case, Q and $\bar{Q}$ are both 0 and are no longer complements; this state is not defined and is therefore invalid. In the first case, the original state has been preserved and we can say that the flip-flop has 'remembered' its original state. RS flip-flops can therefore be used as **memories** to remember the state of a single bit and they are used in circuits called registers which we will be studying later.

10.2.1 *Clocked RS flip-flops*

In an ordinary RS flip-flop, changes in the input state are immediately followed by changes in the output state (such flip-flops are said to be **asynchronous**).

A flip-flop is said to be **synchronous** (or **clocked**) when, in addition to the normal *RS* inputs which receive logic signals, it also has an entry labelled *C* (the clock input), which receives its signals from a synchronising clock; these signals alternate between a high level and a low level. The diagram below shows a clocked RS flip-flop:

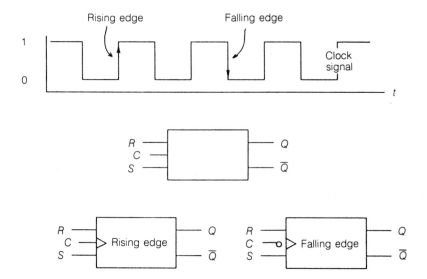

In such a flip-flop, either the output *Q* responds to inputs entered at *R* and *S* **only when the clock input is changing from a low level to a high level** (in which case we say the clock is active on the rising edge) or *Q* responds only when the clock is changing from a high level to a low level (falling edge). Different manufacturers use different names for these clock inputs: **C** or **CLK** clock, **T** timer, **S** strobe.

Certain flip-flops are equipped with special inputs to allow the output to be forced into a chosen state (low or high), irrespective of the current states of the *R* and *S* inputs:

The input PRESET or SET DIRECT forces the state $Q = 1$.
The input CLEAR or RESET DIRECT forces the state $Q = 0$.

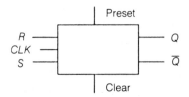

Truth table

PRESET	CLEAR	Q_{n+1}
0	0	Q_n
0	1	0
1	0	1
1	1	forbidden

When they are not being used the control inputs are kept at a low level.

10.2.2   *An application of RS flip-flops*

RS flip-flops are used in registers and numerous other applications where a bit has to be memorised (stored). As an example of a different kind of use we can describe its application as an anti-bounce device for switch contacts. The graph below shows how *VE2* changes when the switch is pressed:

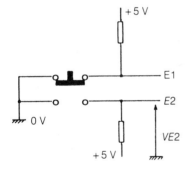 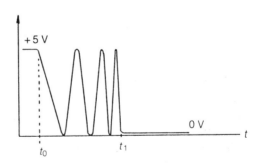

When a switch is opened or closed the contacts rebound causing a series of openings and closings in rapid succession before the contacts finally come to rest in their correct state. In the diagram on the next page, suppose that at time t_0 we have the initial situation where the switch contact is at position A, i.e. $S = 1$ and $R = 0$ and thus $Q = 1$. At the instant t_1 the switch is opened and at time t_2 the contact reaches B. During the interval $t_1 - t_2$, $S = 0$, $R = 0$ and therefore $Q_{n+1} = Q_n$, $Q = 1$.
   At time t_2, $S = 0$, $R = 1$ therefore $Q = 0$.
   At time t_3, the contact bounces off B but does not reach A again.
   During the interval $t_2 - t_3$, $S = 0$, $R = 1$ and therefore $Q = 0$. Hence Q changes state only once even though the switch contact continues to bounce for a while at B.

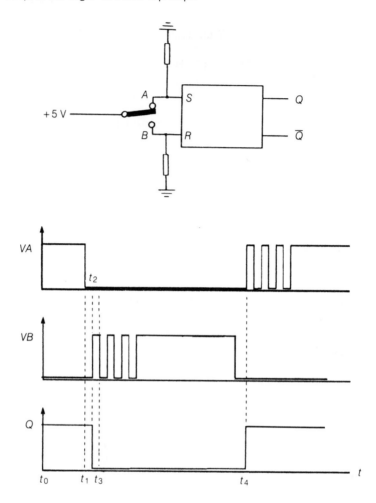

Similarly at the instant t_4 the switch is closed and this time it bounces on contact A but again this does not affect the state of the flip-flop.

10.3 D-type flip-flops

D-type flip-flops are synchronous flip-flops with a single input D. The output Q copies the input after a short delay.

10.3.1 D-type latch

This flip-flop, also called a latch, is a clocked RS flip-flop with which an inverter is used to ensure that R and S are always complements, as shown in the following diagram:

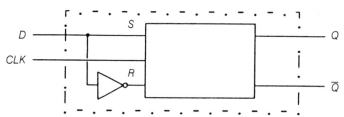

The invalid condition $S = 1$, $R = 1$ cannot occur with this type of flip-flop and so a condition which could cause indeterminate results has been eliminated. While the clock is at a high level the output copies the state of the input D. While the clock is at a low level the output does not change but remains in its previous state.

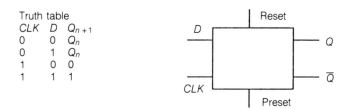

Truth table

CLK	D	Q_{n+1}
0	0	Q_n
0	1	Q_n
1	0	0
1	1	1

To summarise: the D-type flip-flop delays changing its output value to match that of a new input until a moment determined by the user (clock); it transfers the value of D to the output Q when the clock presents a rising edge and it remains **transparent** while the clock is maintained at a high level; when the clock presents a falling edge and returns to a low level, the flip-flop **latches** the output and isolates it from further changes at the input (the flip-flop becomes **opaque**).

10.3.2   *An application of D-type flip-flops*

Take, for example, the use of D-type flip-flops for the transfer of data from a counter to a display system, as in the diagram below:

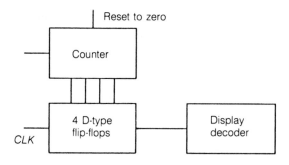

It is pointless and frustrating to watch the counter changing as it counts from zero before it stabilises at its final value. The solution is to isolate the counter from the display by placing as many D-type flip-flops between them as there are outputs from the counter; thus a BCD counter with four outputs would require four D-type flip-flops.

While the counter is changing, the display is blocked by the *CLK* input being held at level 0. When the count is finished the *CLK* input goes to level 1 and the flip-flops are unlatched; they become transparent and indicate the result of the count on their outputs. When the transfer is complete, *CLK* returns to 0; the counter can then be reset back to zero and begin a new measurement; the latched flip-flops continue to indicate the value of the previous count until the *CLK* input becomes high again. The display then changes instantly and remains stable throughout the next count cycle.

10.3.3   *Edge-triggered D-type flip-flops*

The preceding D-type flip-flops were transparent during the whole time that the clock signal was at a high level; but it can sometimes be necessary to latch a single value at a precise instant and then even the briefest of high levels would be too long. Only the rising edge (or the falling edge) of a signal is brief enough to specify a precise instant. This is the principle of edge-triggered D-type flip-flops; they are transparent only during the short interval while the clock pulse is rising (or falling) from one level to the other. Edge-triggered flip-flops are indicated in diagrams by a little triangle on their clock input.

10.4   **JK flip-flops**

We have seen that with RS flip-flops one of the four possible combinations of the two inputs is forbidden. For example in the RS flip-flop made from two NOR gates, the forbidden combination is $R = 1$, $S = 1$. It would be useful if the RS flip-flop could be modified so that these combinations were no longer forbidden. The question then arises as to what would be the effect on the output of such a combination. It is clear that if we wish to keep the rule that $\bar{Q}$ is always the complement of Q, there can only be four possible output states to correspond to the four input combinations. But we have already determined three of the four outputs:

$$R = 0 \text{ and } S = 0 \text{ gives us } Q_{n+1} = Q_n$$
$$R = 0 \text{ and } S = 1 \text{ gives us } Q_{n+1} = 1$$
$$R = 1 \text{ and } S = 0 \text{ gives us } Q_{n+1} = 0$$

There is only one other possibility: $R = 1$ and $S = 1$ giving Q_{n+1} to be the complement of Q_n ($\bar{Q}_n$). To emphasise that it behaves in a different way, we change the name of the inputs: S becomes J and R becomes K:

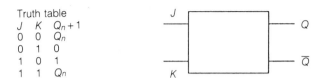

Truth table		
J	K	Q_{n+1}
0	0	Q_n
0	1	0
1	0	1
1	1	Q_n

SAQ

10.1 Show how to transform an RS flip-flop into a JK flip-flop. (Start by writing down the truth tables for the two types of flip-flop.)

RS flip-flop				JK flip-flop			
Q_n	R	S	Q_{n+1}	Q_n	J	K	Q_{n+1}
0	0	0	0	0	0	0	0
0	0	1	1	0	0	1	0
0	1	0	0	0	1	0	1
0	1	1	forbidden	0	1	1	1
1	0	0	1	1	0	0	1
1	0	1	1	1	0	1	0
1	1	0	0	1	1	0	1
1	1	1	forbidden	1	1	1	0

The problem then consists of determining a circuit (C), having inputs Q_n, J and K, and outputs S and R, to connect to the RS flip-flop so that the whole circuit forms a JK flip-flop.

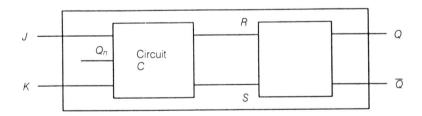

The incomplete truth table shown below is for the circuit C that has to be designed. It is obtained by starting with the tables given above and continuing as follows.

The columns Q_n, J and Q_{n+1} are those of the truth table for the JK flip-flop we have to obtain. The columns R and S are to be completed with the aid of the truth table for the RS flip-flop to cause the transitions from Q_n to Q_{n+1} required by the new circuit.

Hint: What values must we give to R and S so that starting with $Q_n = 0$ we will obtain $Q_{n+1} = 0$?

Looking at the truth table for an RS flip-flop we notice that there are two possible output combinations for which $Q_{n+1} = 0$ if $Q_n = 0$. Either $R = 0$ and $S = 0$ or $R = 1$ and $S = 0$. We can deduce that the value of R is not important in this case (the state of R is said to be **don't care**) and we note it with an X in the truth table.

Complete the truth table and then use the Karnaugh maps to deduce the equations for R and S; next determine the logic diagram of the circuit C.

Note: where there is an X in the truth table, put a corresponding X in the Karnaugh map. When simplifying the map the X's can be replaced by 0's or by 1's according to which gives the better results.

Q_n	J	K	R	S	Q_{n+1}
0	0	0	X	0	0
0	0	1	X	0	0
0	1	0			1
0	1	1			1
1	0	0			1
1	0	1			0
1	1	0			1
1	1	1			0

Karnaugh maps for R and S are given below, followed by a diagram of an incomplete JK flip-flop:

JK

R	00	01	11	10
Q_n 0				
1				

JK

S	00	01	11	10
Q_n 0				
1				

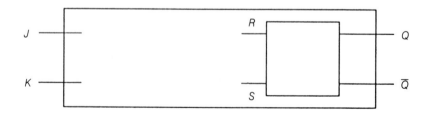

EXERCISE

10.1   Suppose that the outputs $A\,B\,C\,D$ of the circuit below are initially in the state 1011, that the inputs JK of the flip-flops are all at 1, and that there are clock pulses at regular intervals. What states will appear successively on the outputs A, B, C and D of the circuit after 1, 2, 3, 4 and 5 clock pulses respectively?

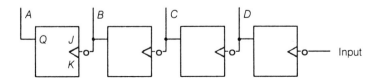

Solution to SAQ

10.1   Show how to transform an RS flip-flop into a JK flip-flop.
First we have to complete the truth table.

Q_n	J	K	R	S	Q_{n+1}
0	0	0	X	0	0
0	0	1	X	0	0
0	1	0	0	1	1
0	1	1	0	1	1
1	0	0	0	X	1
1	0	1	1	**0**	0
1	1	0	0	X	1
1	1	1	1	**0**	0

Starting with this truth table we can construct the Karnaugh maps for R and S.

$$JK$$

R	00	01	11	10
0	X	X	0	0
1	0	1	1	0

Q_n $R = Q_n \cdot K$

$$JK$$

S	00	01	11	10
0	0	0	1	1
1	X	0	0	X

Q_n $S = \overline{Q}_n \cdot J$

Now we can construct the circuit, which we give below:

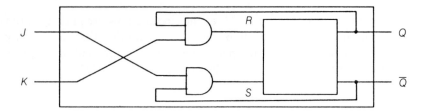

Chapter 11

Sequential logic circuits: counters

In numerous applications we need to perform counting operations. We could be counting the number of pulses in a given time to determine their frequency, for example, or quite simply counting the number of times that a certain instruction is repeated. In some cases we have to increment the counter, in others we have to decrement it, starting from zero or from some other specified value. A counter, in the widest sense, is a device capable of working as an **incrementer** (up counter) or as a **decrementer** (down counter) into which we can introduce a starting value, that is, we can **initialise** it or **load** it or **preset** it.

Counters can be classified according to whether they are: synchronous incrementers–decrementers or asynchronous incrementers–decrementers.

The basic component of counters is the clocked flip-flop; either D-type or JK. The clock input can be triggered by a rising edge or by a falling edge. The flip-flops may have inputs S (for entering a 1) and R (for entering a 0) which are independent of the clock and can be used to preset the counter at any time. The number of flip-flops required for the counter depends on the greatest number it has to count. With two flip-flops there are $2^2 = 4$ combinations and it is possible to count up to 3 (from 0 to 3). Such a counter has four states and is called a **modulo 4** counter. With four flip-flops there are $2^4 = 16$ combinations and it would be able to count from 0 to 15 (**modulo 16** counter).

11.1 Synchronous counters

A counter is said to be **synchronous** when the inputs to be counted are applied simultaneously to the clock inputs of all its flip-flops.

11.1.1 *Basic element*

Let us consider a clocked JK flip-flop which is triggered by the falling edge of the clock signal. Its truth table is as follows:

Q_n	J	K	Q_{n+1}
0	0	0	0
0	0	1	0
0	1	0	1
0	1	1	1
1	0	0	1
1	0	1	0
1	1	0	1
1	1	1	0

The question to be answered is this: 'What must the logic levels at the inputs to the flip-flops be so that when the clock changes from high to low, the counter will count to its next value?' (Should a particular flip-flop change state or should it keep its previous state?)

Example 11.1   Changing a counter

If the clock has to change the counter from the value 4 (0100) to the value 5 (0101), only the flip-flop for the least significant bit needs to change. If the clock has to change the counter from 7 (0111) to 8 (1000), all the bits, and therefore all the flip-flops have to change.

If the output has to change from $Q_n = 0$ to $Q_n = 1$, what values must be applied to J and K before the clock changes? An examination of the truth table reveals that there are two possibilities:

$$J = 1 \quad \text{and} \quad K = 0 \quad \text{or}$$
$$J = 1 \quad \text{and} \quad K = 1$$

or in other words, J must always be 1 but K is a 'don't care' condition. Now a **state transition table** can be established for the basic component of the counter (X denotes a don't care):

Q_n	Q_{n+1}	J	K
0	0	0	X
0	1	1	X
1	0	X	1
1	1	X	0

From lines 2 and 3 of the state transition table, we can see that if the inputs J and K are permanently at 1, the output of the flip flop will change from 0 to 1 and then from 1 to 0 with each falling edge of the clock, and therefore the output will change at a rate which is half that of the clock input. We say that it functions as a **divide-by-two**.

11.1.2 *Timing diagram*

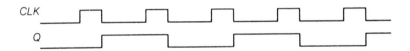

With each falling edge of the clock, the output Q of the JK flip-flop changes value. Therefore we have a division by 2.

11.1.1.3 A synchronous scale-of-4 counter

The modulo 4 synchronous counter allows counting from 0 to 3. Since the number of states attainable with n flip-flops is 2^n. This counter will require 2 $(2^2 = 4)$ flip-flops which we will call A and B. We will assume that A represents the least significant bit (**LSB**) and B the most significant bit (**MSB**). The sequence of values registered on the counter will be: 00 01 10 11 which after decoding will give 0 1 2 3_{10}.

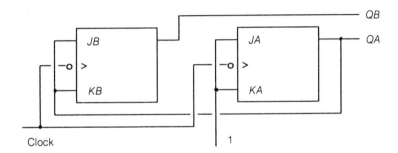

The diagram below gives the state of the output QA and QB as a function of time:

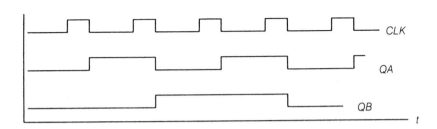

Note: if it is fed by a periodic signal, the counter can be thought of as a frequency divider; thus on applying a frequency of 200 hertz to the clock input we obtain an output of 100 Hz at the output of A and 50 Hz at the output of B. By using the $\bar{Q}$ outputs instead of the Q outputs this count up counter (incrementer) becomes a count down counter (decrementer).

An incrementer (or decrementer) with ten states is called a **decade** counter (or decrementer). The logic diagram below shows a synchronous up/down decade counter such as can be found in the integrated circuit 74LS90:

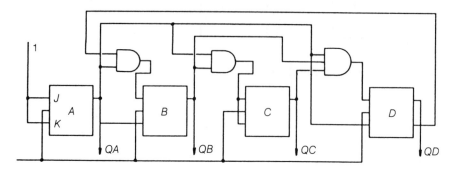

SAQ

11.1 Derive the logic diagram of a synchronous natural binary modulo 5 counter using JK flip-flops. (*Hints:* How many flip-flops are needed? What must the outputs of QA, QB, QC be? What states therefore must the inputs JA KA, JB KB and JC KC have at the **next** clock signal for the flip-flops to have the correct outputs?) Now produce the Karnaugh maps for JA KA, JB KB, and JC KC as functions of the variables QA, QB, QC. Simplify these equations and then draw the diagram.

11.2 **Asynchronous counters**

In asynchronous counters (or ripple-counters), the first flip-flop is triggered periodically and its output triggers the following flip-flop whose output triggers the next and so on as a ripple of activity gradually propagates through the counter; the output of flip-flop n being applied to the input to flip-flop $n + 1$. This type of counter is simple to construct but it can give rise to false values due to timing problems (hazards and races).

11.2.1 *Example of a 16-state asynchronous counter*

Suppose we want to design a counter having one input, E (functioning on the falling edge of the clock) and four outputs A, B, C and D counting in natural binary (or 8421):

The logic diagram above shows such a counter made from four JK flip-flops mounted in **cascade**. Each flip-flop, as we explained above, functions as a divide-by-two and thus the timing diagram of its operation will be as follows:

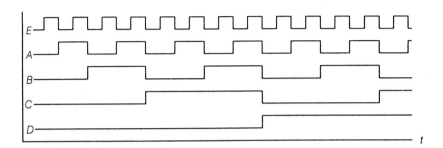

Depending on how the flip-flops are joined in cascade and depending on whether positive or negative logic is being used, we can build either incrementers or decrementers. In the following diagrams the J and K inputs, which have been omitted to aid clarity, are all at 1.

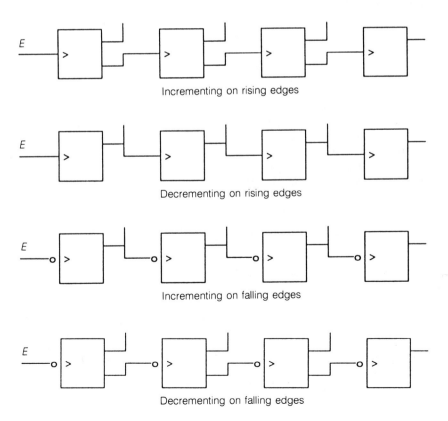

Incrementing on rising edges

Decrementing on rising edges

Incrementing on falling edges

Decrementing on falling edges

11.2.2 *Asynchronous restart – interruption of counting*

When control inputs, whose purpose we explained in Chapter 10, are connected in parallel they enable the counter to be preset independently of the current value held on the flip-flops. This can be done by external signals such as R01 and R02 in the 74LS93 shown below.

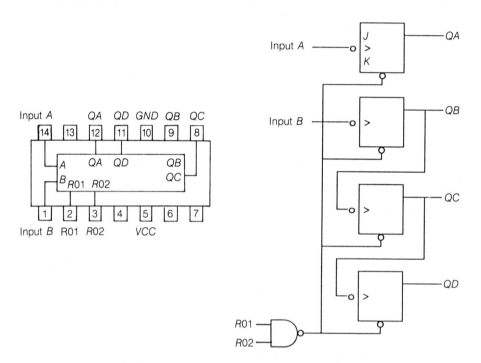

It can also be done by internal signals from the counter which will have the effect of interrupting the count (or countdown). As an example we will use the 74LS93 counter to create a decade counter:

Table of output combinations

Decimal value	D	C	B	A	
0	0	0	0	0	←
1	0	0	0	1	
2	0	0	1	0	
3	0	0	1	1	
4	0	1	0	0	
5	0	1	0	1	
6	0	1	1	0	
7	0	1	1	1	
8	1	0	0	0	
9	1	0	0	1	
10	1	0	1	0	activation of RTZ

Only the first ten combinations (from 0000 to 1001) must appear on the outputs. In fact the combination 1010 must be replaced by the combination 0000, that is the counter must be **restarted**. To achieve this restart, the reset to zero (RTZ) is activated when $B = 1$ AND $D = 1$. If the inputs of reset to zero are active low as on the 74LS93 a NAND would be used.

EXERCISE

11.1 Determine the purpose of the following circuit by studying its truth table.

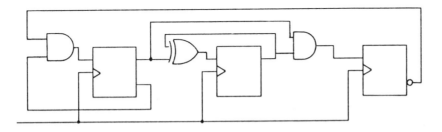

Solution to SAQ

11.1 Logic diagram of the synchronous modulo 5 counter.

Since we have to represent five states at the output of the counter, we will need three flip-flops ($2^3 = 8$; 2^2 is insufficient). The truth table can be deduced from the state transition table studied earlier.

Truth table

	Outputs				Inputs				
	QC	QB	QA	JC	KC	JB	KB	JA	KA
0	0	0	0	0	X	0	X	1	X
1	0	0	1	0	X	1	X	X	1
2	0	1	0	0	X	X	0	1	X
3	0	1	1	1	X	X	1	X	1
4	1	0	0	X	1	0	X	0	X

Note: It should be understood that the states of the inputs JA, KA, ... KC are those that have to be applied to the flip-flops at the next clock signal to obtain the next value of the counter on the outputs.

Timing diagram

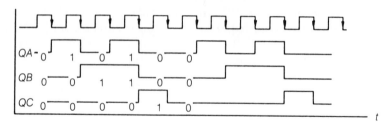

It is now possible to determine the Karnaugh map and the corresponding equations of the *JK* inputs:

		JC	KC	JB	KB	JA	KA
	QA	0 1	0 1	0 1	0 1	0 1	0 1
QC QB	00	0 0	X X	0 1	X X	1 X	X 1
	01	0 1	X X	X X	0 1	1 X	X 1
	11	· ·	· ·	· ·	· ·	· ·	· ·
	10	X ·	1 ·	0 ·	X ·	0 ·	X ·

The states not shown are unknowns which can be treated as don't cares (0 or 1 according to needs). Finally, after taking the largest groupings and eliminating all the superfluous variables, we have:

$$JC = QA.QB$$
$$KC = 1$$
$$JB = QA$$
$$KB = QA$$
$$JA = \bar{Q}C$$
$$KA = 1$$

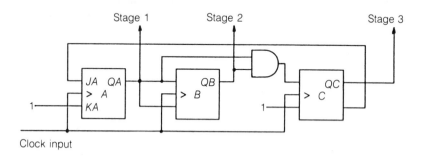

Clock input

Chapter 12

Sequential logic circuits: registers

A register is a collection of basic memory cells each of which can store 1 bit (0 or 1) of data. The number n of cells corresponds to the number of bits to be stored in the register. Thus there are 4-bit, 16-bit, 32-bit ... registers.

Registers play a major part in the design of computers and we will have an opportunity in the following chapters to study various forms of register such as the accumulator, the instruction register, the status register, and memory registers. Registers may be either **static** or **dynamic** depending on their method of construction.

In **static** registers, information is stored for as long as the power supply to the register is maintained. In this case the basic cells are generally made from RS flip-flops.

In **dynamic** registers, constructed using MOS transistors, information is only **preserved** for a certain length of time (several milliseconds), even if the power supply is maintained. This means that either there must be a sufficiently rapid supply of new data to be stored or the data stored in the register is re-stored periodically for as long as the data needs to be kept. This last operation is known as **refreshing** the data. The popularity of dynamic memories is due to the fact that they are less complex and therefore allow a greater density of integration (that is, there can be more flip-flops for a given area).

Finally, if we consider the internal organisation of registers, we can distinguish two more categories: **registers of separate cells** which are not interconnected, and **shift registers**, in which the output of one cell is connected to the input of the next cell so that data can be shifted from one cell to the next.

12.1 Registers of non-interconnected flip-flops

Let us take for example a register of four clocked D-type flip-flops.

If data is present on the inputs it will be transferred to the outputs at the next clock signal. We say that the data has been **written** to the flip-flops. The data will only reach the outputs S if the enable signal E is at logic level 1. The contents of the register are then said to have been **read**. The clock signal is therefore a write signal while the enable signal E is a read signal.

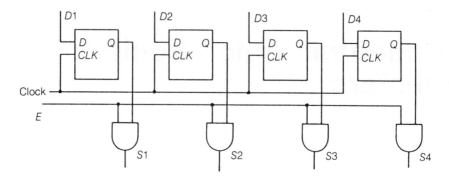

12.2 **Shift registers**

In these registers data appearing at the output of one cell is transferred (**shifted**) to the output of the following cell, at each clock signal. This is achieved by connecting the output of the cell to the input of the next cell either directly or via some other logic circuit.

The circuit below is an example of such a shift register built from four JK flip-flops:

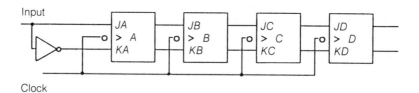

SAQs

12.1 (a) In considering the preceding circuit, what are the possible inputs to flip-flop *A*? Using the truth table for the JK flip-flop to help you, check that the register contents are shifted at each clock pulse.

(b) How many lines of the truth table did you use? Can these lines be found in the truth tables of other types of flip-flop? What can you deduce from this?

12.2 The output signal *E* in the following diagram is obtained from the signals *S1*, *S3* and *S4* shown in the timing diagram below. The signal *E* is then fed as input to the flip-flop *A* in the diagram of a shift register above and *CLK* is the clock signal (falling edge) for the shift register.

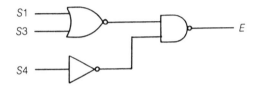

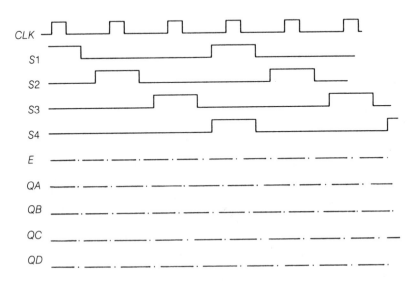

(a) Express *E* as a function of the input signals.

(b) Then complete the timing diagram by showing the signals obtained for *E*, *QA*, *QB*, *QC* and *QD*, assuming that the outputs of the flip-flops are initially zero.

(c) What will be the state of the flip-flops after the fourth falling edge of the clock?

12.3 Different modes of data input/output

In the previous example, the data bits enter the first flip-flop one after the other and leave the last flip-flop one after the other. Such a register is called **serial input** and **serial output**.

If *n* items of data are applied simultaneously to the *n* inputs of the cells and if *n* items appear simultaneously on the *n* outputs, the register is called **parallel input** and **parallel output**.

In summary there are four modes of input/output for registers:

- serial input/serial output
- serial input/parallel output
- parallel input/serial output
- parallel input/parallel output

These are shown below:

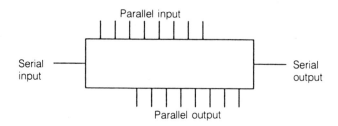

Example 12.1   A shift register

The diagram below shows a shift register with serial and parallel inputs.

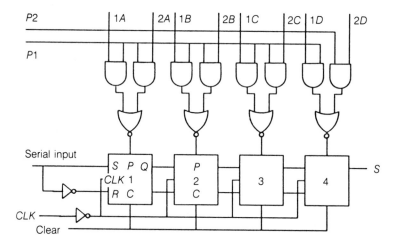

Writing in parallel: logic level 1 applied to input P1 (Preset 1), enables the states on inputs $1A$, $1B$, $1C$ and $1D$ to be stored in the register. A logic level 1 applied on input $P2$ (preset 2) allows the states on inputs $2A$, $2B$, $2C$, $2D$ to be stored.

Writing in serial: inputs $P1$, $P2$ and Clear must be at level 0. The logic state applied to the serial input will appear at the output S four clock pulses later.

Shifting to right and left: in the example above, data is shifted from left to right. In certain cases it can be useful to have a shift to the left.

Consider, for example, a four-bit register in the initial state , $0010 = 2_{10}$. If the contents of the register are shifted right one place and a zero is introduced as the MSB, the state of the register becomes $0001 = 1_{10}$. If alternatively the contents had been shifted to the left and a zero introduced as the LSB, the state of the register would have become $0100 = 4_{10}$.

Shifting one bit to the right divides by 2, shifting one bit to the left multiplies by 2. These shifting operations are currently used in assembly language or 'assembler'. Left and right shifts can be obtained by the addition of a combinatory logic circuit like the one shown in the following diagram:

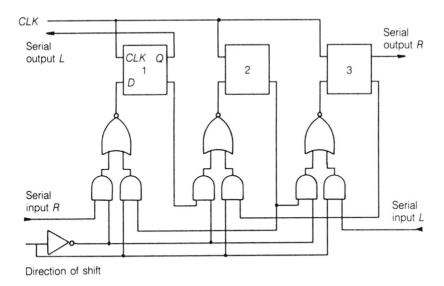

Direction of shift

Each flip-flop input is controlled by a circuit which governs left (L) and right (R) shifting. If the 'direction of shift' input is at level 1, the output from flip-flop 2 is fed to the input of flip-flop 1 and there is a shift to the left. If on the contrary the 'direction of shift' is at level 0, the output of flip-flop 2 is transferred to the input of flip-flop 3. This time there is a shift to the right.

12.4 **Variable length registers**

These registers, also called programmable registers, have a length that can be varied. They are made from several registers, each of which can either be in use or be 'short circuited' under the control of signals applied to their 'program inputs' – see diagram below:

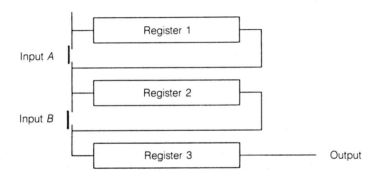

SAQ

12.3 Suppose that the registers in the example above were each of length one byte, what would be the lengths of the resulting registers for all possible combinations of logic states on the *A* and *B* inputs?

12.5 **Recirculation registers**

Recirculation registers are shift registers in which the serial output is connected back to the serial input. Data is written into the register via the serial input or via the parallel inputs (initialisation or loading of the register). The clock inputs then cause the data to recirculate in the register. This is how the rotations used in assembly languages are performed.

SAQ

12.4 Consider the recirculation register below. The inputs *JA*, *JB*, *JC*, *JD* have the values 1000 respectively. (a) What will be the successive states of the register after each clock pulse? (b) Compare the output S with the clock signal; what can you deduce?

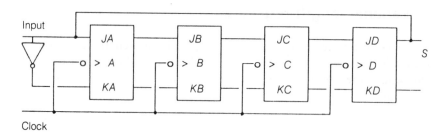

EXERCISE

12.1 You have been given the following circuit made from a 74LS93 chip. Determine its timing diagram.

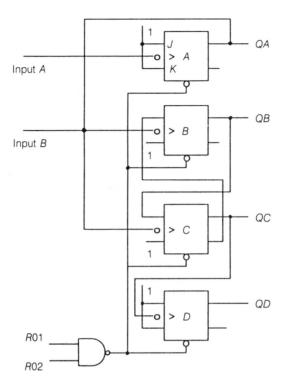

Solutions to SAQs

12.1 (a) What are the possible inputs to flip-flop A?

Because of the presence of the inverter, the only possible inputs are $J = 1$ and $K = 0$, or $J = 0$ and $K = 1$.

Using the truth table for the JK flip-flop, check that the register contents are shifted at each clock pulse.

According to the truth table, at the falling edge of the clock, $QA = 1$ in the first case and $QA = 0$ in the second and therefore due to the direct connection $JB = 1$ or $JB = 0$. The data is therefore passed from the input of flip-flop A to the input of flip-flop B. At the following clock signal it will pass to the input of flip-flop C. Thus the data is shifted at each clock signal.

(b) How many lines of the truth table did you use? Can these lines be found in the truth tables of other types of flip-flop? What can you deduce from this?

Two lines of the truth table were used. They could be found in the truth table of an RS flip-flop or of a D-type flip-flop. Hence either RS or D-type flip-flops could be used in place of the JK.

12.2 (a) Express E as a function of the input signals.

$$E = \overline{(\overline{S1 + S3}) \cdot \overline{S4}}$$

$$E = \overline{\overline{S1 + S3}} + \overline{\overline{S4}}$$

$$E = S1 + S3 + S4$$

(b) Complete the timing diagram by showing the signals obtained for E, QA, QB, QC and QD, the outputs of the flip-flops being initially zero.

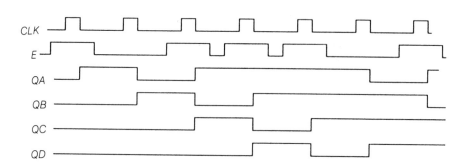

(c) What will be the state of the flip-flops after the fourth falling edge of the clock?
        When the clock signal changes from 1 to 0, the outputs of the flip-flops take the state that was previously on their inputs. The signals obtained on the outputs of the four flip-flops A, B, C and D are identical, but shifted in time by one clock cycle. After the fourth clock pulse the data input at A on the first falling edge of the clock will have reached the output of flip-flop D. Thus the input will have been shifted.

12.3 What would be the lengths of the resulting registers for all possible combinations of logic states on the A and B inputs?
        Assuming that the inputs A and B are at logic value 0 if they are open and do not allow current to pass, and at logic 1 if they are closed and do allow current to pass, short-circuiting one or other of the registers.

A	B	Registers	Length of 'final' register
0	0	1 + 2 + 3	3 bytes (24 bits)
0	1	1 + 3	2 bytes (16 bits)
1	0	2 + 3	2 bytes (16 bits)
1	1	3	1 byte (8 bits)

12.4 What will be the successive states of the register after each clock pulse?

The register will take the following states:

1000
0100
0010
0001
1000

. . .

(b) Compare the output S with the clock signal; what can you deduce?

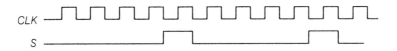

CLK

S

The logic level at the output changes from 0 to 1 on the fourth clock pulse, then from 1 to 0 on the fifth and the cycle starts again. The period of the output signal is five times that of the clock signal. Hence it is a divide-by-five circuit.

Chapter 13

Integrated circuits

An integrated circuit is an electronic component containing various elements of logic circuits (such as gates, flip-flops, registers, counters, memories, microprocessors, etc.) made in the same material. The circuits are built from elementary electronic components such as diodes, transistors, capacitors, resistors ...

13.1 A little history

The transistor first appeared in the 1950s and replaced the thermionic valve which was bulky and unreliable.

The first transistors were made as separate components. The 1960s saw the introduction of integrated circuits. An integrated circuit (IC) is a complete electronic circuit, concentrated on a wafer of semiconductor material generally of silicon or of gallium arsenide, and called a 'chip'. This progression is shown in Figure 13.1.

The number of components on a chip has been increasing ever since the first chips appeared. In 1965 approximately 30 components could be built on a chip 3 mm^2; fifteen years later this had increased to 100 000. Depending on the number of components on a single chip we speak of

- **SSI** (small-scale integration) for a few components.
- **MSI** (medium-scale integration) up to 500 components.
- **LSI** (large-scale integration) up to several thousand components (for example the 8080 microprocessor has 5000 transistors).
- **VLSI** (very large-scale integration) up to 10 000 components.
- **SLSI** (super large-scale integration); there can now be 1 200 000 components on one chip (INTEL i486 microprocessor).

The terms VLSI and SLSI are not yet recognised by all writers; some class them together as VLSI.

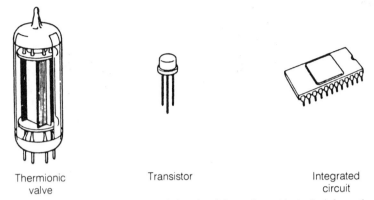

Thermionic
valve

Transistor

Integrated
circuit

Source: Peter Lafferty, *Introduction à la micro-informatique*, Hachette informatique.

Figure 13.1   Components from three generations

13.2   **Construction techniques for integrated circuits**

In order to make an integrated circuit, the electronic circuit is first drawn with the help of a computer specially built for computer assisted design (CAD). The circuit is drawn about 500 times bigger than the final circuit. The drawing is called a **mask** and it is used under computer control, to guide a luminous beam which exposes a photographic plate, and in the process, reduces the diagram of the circuit approximately 20 times.

The plate is examined carefully and corrected before being reduced photographically (photogravure) to its final size on a thin slice of silicon cut from a cylinder of 7.5 cm diameter and about 50 cm long. The slice, which is about 0.3 mm thick, is called a **wafer** and it can contain up to 500 circuits each about 5 mm^2. Another technique, called electron beam lithography, gives a finer resolution by 'engraving' the wafer directly with an electron beam resulting in a resolution about 20 times better than that obtained with photogravure

The wafer is heated to a temperature in the region of 1000 $^\circ$C in a diffusion oven, and it is then exposed to some chemical elements (e.g. boron, phosphorous) called dopants, which modify the semiconductor properties of the silicon. These dopants penetrate the silicon in areas precisely defined by the preceding photographic process and enable the creation of transistors, diodes, flip-flops, etc. In another doping technique, ion implantation, impurities are introduced at ambient temperature, the dopant atoms being ionised and implanted in the required place by means of ionic bombardment.

All the circuits thus constructed are tested before the wafers are cut into individual chips.

Each chip is then inserted in a plastic case and connected to the contact pins by tiny gold threads. This technique is currently being replaced by the use of film which allows the connections to be made about ten times faster.

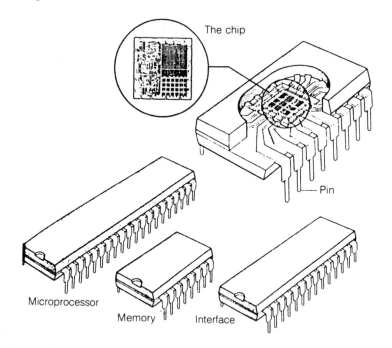

Source: Peter Lafferty, *Introduction à la micro-informatique*, Hachette informatique.

Figure 13.2 Some integrated circuit packages

The chip is then covered by a layer of black plastic (the operation is called packaging). The purpose of the packaging is to protect the circuit from the ravages of the environment, to aid the dissipation of heat from the components when they are working, and to enable the chip to be more easily handled. Figure 13.2 shows some integrated circuit packages.

Chapter 14

Microprocessors – a first glance

Let us briefly recall with the help of a block diagram, the composition of a computer system such as the one we presented in the introduction.

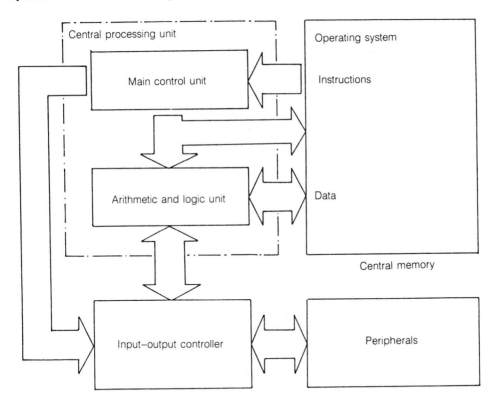

14.1 Description of the functional blocks

14.1.1 *The central processing unit (CPU)*

Before going any further we must make some distinctions between the different physical entities which are covered by the term **central processing unit** (CPU). This is the term used by salespeople and most microcomputer users when they refer to the main box of the system that usually contains the **microprocessor** and the **central memory**, and also possibly, one or two floppy-disk drives, hard disk, tape streamer (Figure 14.1 shows the parts usually defined as the CPU.)

In a more rigorous treatment we should distance ourselves from this false 'central processor' and think of the central processor as being the true central unit of the computer system (generally a single microprocessor chip). Some writers include the central memory in the central processing unit; and since these two units are not much use without each other it is difficult to argue with this definition.

For our purposes the central processing unit comprises two subassemblies:

- The arithmetic and logic unit.
- The control unit.

14.1.1.1   The arithmetic and logic unit (ALU)

Sometimes simply called the **arithmetic unit** (AU) this is at the heart of the processor and performs arithmetic operations (e.g. additions, multiplications) and logical operations (e.g. comparisons, AND, OR) on data being processed.

14.1.1.2   The main control unit (MCU)

Sometimes simply called the **control unit** it is responsible for the management of the execution of programs. Each instruction to be obeyed is brought in sequence to the control unit where it is analysed and orders are issued to various other parts of the

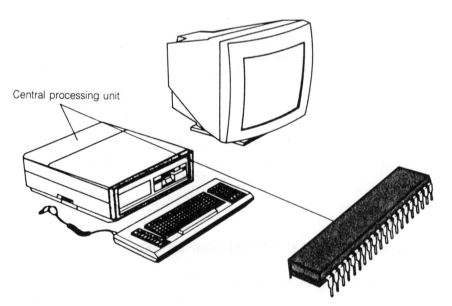

Central processing unit

Source: *Amstrad PC1512 User's Guide*

Figure 14.1   A personal computer

machine (e.g. read a data item from the disk, perform a calculation, write to the screen).

When one instruction has been executed, the control unit must fetch the following instruction, for this purpose it uses a special register to 'count instructions'. This register is generally called, somewhat misleadingly, **the program counter** but it is also known as the **instruction counter** or the **next instruction address register**.

14.1.2   *The central memory unit (CMU)*

The central memory, which is also known as the **main store**, can be represented as a collection of equal-sized locations (**memory words**). Memory words are used to store data and instructions from the operating system or user programs, and have a size dependent on the type of the machine (e.g. 8 bits, 16 bits, 32 bits).

In order to be able to find the memory location containing a required word, locations are each known by their own address (position) in memory. Addresses are usually written in hexadecimal from address 0 to, for example, address FFFF.

14.1.3   *The input–output controller (IOC)*

This unit controls the transfer of data between the central processor (or the main store) and the peripherals.

14.1.4   *The peripherals*

Peripherals are numerous and varied.

Some peripherals can only receive data (e.g. screens), others can only send data (e.g. keyboards), others serve as backing stores (auxiliary memory) to the main store (e.g. disks, diskettes), and some can be very specialised (e.g. temperature sensors, pressure sensors).

In the following chapters we will study these various components:

● Central processing unit.
● Main memory and auxiliary store.
● Input–output peripherals.

EXERCISES

14.1   Draw from memory a block diagram of a computer system and then check it.

14.2   Obtain permission to open the case of a microcomputer and try to identify the various components.

Chapter 15

The central processing unit (CPU)

In the preceding chapter we have seen that a program was composed of **instructions** which processed **data**, instructions and data being stored, at least at the time of execution, in the central memory.

First, therefore, we will study what form an instruction takes and then how it is brought to the central processing unit and processed.

15.1 Instruction formats

An instruction is an **elementary operation** in a programming language, that is, it is the smallest command that a programmer can give to a computer, e.g. in BASIC.

$$\text{LET C} = \text{A} + \text{B}$$

Each instruction corresponds to an order given to the computer, here it is to add the contents of memory location A to the contents of memory location B and place the result in memory location C. In fact instructions contain two types of information: **what has to be done** by the instruction (e.g. adding, subtracting, fetching data, storing data), and **with what data** to do it (e.g. A, B).

In the machine which, you will recall, only understands the binary logic states of electronic circuits, instructions and data are clearly not represented as strings of letters and symbols, but in the form of binary 0's and 1's.

The translation of an instruction from a high-level language (e.g. BASIC, COBOL, PASCAL) to a binary string is performed by a special systems program called either an **interpreter** or a **compiler** depending on the method of translation.

The translation from an **assembly** language, which is a low-level language, to a binary string is performed by an assembler specially written for the particular microprocessor (e.g. Z80, 8086, 68000, 80386) being used.

Just as instructions are 'coded', so, too, is data using, for example, ASCII or EBCDIC; or it may be represented in the form of BCD, floating point or fixed point, etc. Thus a person might write an instruction using assembly language in mnemonic form, as, say, ADD A,C which will cause the contents of register A to be added to the contents of register C and the result to be stored in register A. This instruction could translate to the binary string 10000001 but, to make it easier for people to read, it would often be shown in its hexadecimal form as 81H.

When the control unit receives such an instruction, it knows what has to be done and what data is to be used. At that moment it issues a stream of commands called **microinstructions** to all the units which will take part in the execution of the instruction (e.g. memory, arithmetic unit).

We can consider an instruction as being decomposed into two fields:

Operation code field	Data field

what has to be done ... with what data

But, as we stated above, data is stored in locations in central memory, and can be retrieved by giving its address. This leads us to a more precise description of the two fields in an instruction as:

Operation code field	Address field

Let us study these fields more precisely.

15.1.1 *The operation code (op-code)*

This field tells the machine what operation is to be performed and hence which parts of the computer will be involved in its execution.

The length of the operation code depends on the number of instructions that the machine can 'understand' or, more exactly that the microprocessor used by the machine can understand. An 8-bit op-code will allow an **instruction set** (or **instruction repertoire**) of 256 different instructions. In practice the op-code field comprises two subfields because we can usually distinguish groups of instructions which perform similar tasks.

Example 15.1 The op-code field

For addition, we can distinguish between
adding the contents of two central memory locations
adding the contents of two registers.
    Thus we can split the op-code field into:

Op-code field	
Group code	Subsidiary code

By consulting the instruction set of a microprocessor such as the 8086, you can see that most instructions of the same type begin with the same binary pattern, that is to say that they begin with the same group code and are differentiated by the subsidiary code.

15.1.2   *The address field*

Most of the time the **data field** does not contain the data to be used by an instruction but contains the **address** of the location in memory where the data is really stored (recall that the address is usually represented in hexadecimal e.g. FB80).

Depending on the machine an instruction may have zero, one, two or three addresses; but two-address and three-address machines tend to be slower.

For the most part, instructions usually work on two items of data and therefore might be expected to need **two addresses** (for example, the addition of A and B necessitates the knowledge of the addresses of both A and B). However the second address on a one-address machine is generally an **implicit address** and in most cases is that of the **accumulator** (we will return to these notions of addresses and addressing in a later chapter).

15.2   **The main control unit**

15.2.1   *Rôle*

We have already seen that the rôle of the control unit is to manage the execution of programs. It must take instructions one after the other; decode the current instruction and issue commands (**microinstructions**) to the other units of the system which participate in its execution. It must then fetch the next instruction and execute that. For this purpose it has a certain number of internal components with well-defined functions. A simplified block diagram of a main control unit is shown below:

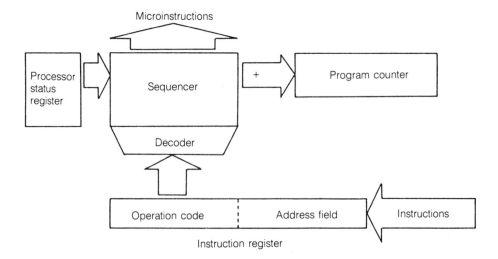

15.2.2 *Components*

15.2.2.1 The instruction register
The instruction that the control unit is to execute is loaded in advance into a special register called the **instruction register**.

15.2.2.2 The sequencer
To execute the instruction which has just been loaded into the instruction register, the control unit must issue a certain number of microinstructions to the other units of the system.

These microinstructions must clearly not be issued at random, nor to just any component, but must be issued at precise times according to the instruction being executed. The timing of microinstructions is determined by the system's internal clock; a quartz clock which in current microprocessors runs at between 4.7 and 50 MHz. Intuitively, the faster the clock, the quicker the central processor.

The component which sends out the appropriate microinstructions for the operation code (previously decoded) of the instruction currently in the instruction register is the sequencer. As its name suggests the sequencer sends a stream of microinstructions towards the components used in the execution of the instruction.

15.2.2.3 The processor status register
To do its work correctly, the sequencer has to know the state of certain other components and have available details concerning the operations which have already been executed (for example, it might need to know for the addition currently being executed whether a previous addition had generated a carry out). Such information can be obtained from another component called the **processor status register**, which using flip-flops (called flags), is able to remember certain information such as whether the previous instruction generated a carry out, whether the result was negative, zero, etc.

15.2.2.4 The program counter
When the sequencer has finished generating the microinstructions for the current instruction, it must cause the next instruction to be brought into the instruction register. For this it needs the **program counter** (instruction counter is a more accurate name, which is also used). This is a specialised register which is loaded automatically by the system at the start of the program's execution, with the memory address of the first instruction to execute. Following that, each time an instruction has been loaded into the instruction register and is ready to be executed, the program counter is **incremented** so that it acts as a pointer to the location containing **the next instruction** to be executed.

15.3 **The arithmetic and logic unit**

The **arithmetic and logic unit (ALU)** is composed of logic circuits like those we have

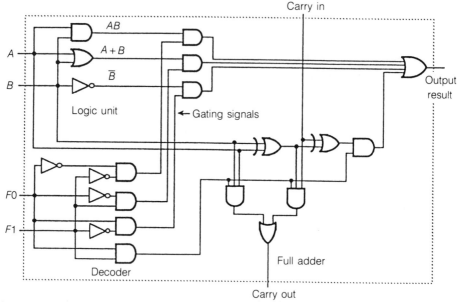

Source: Tanenbaum, *Architecture de l'ordinateur*, Inter-Editions.

Figure 15.1 Example of a one-bit ALU

already studied: adder, subtracter, comparator, etc., depending on what the manufacturer of the integrated circuit was able to include. The data to be processed arrives at the ALU, is processed, and the result appears at the output of the ALU where it is normally stored in an accumulator register.

These two components, the **main control unit** and the **arithmetic and logic unit** comprise the **central processor unit** (CPU).

The CPU thus:

- Manages the fetching and decoding of program instructions one after the other.
- Causes the processing by the ALU of the arithmetic and logic operations required by the instruction.
- Produces, with the help of the program counter, the correct sequence of instructions to be executed.
- Memorises the internal state of the machine in the form of flags set in the processor status register.
- Sends out command signals to control the operation of the other elements of the system.

15.4 **Buses**

The components of the central processing unit communicate with each other and

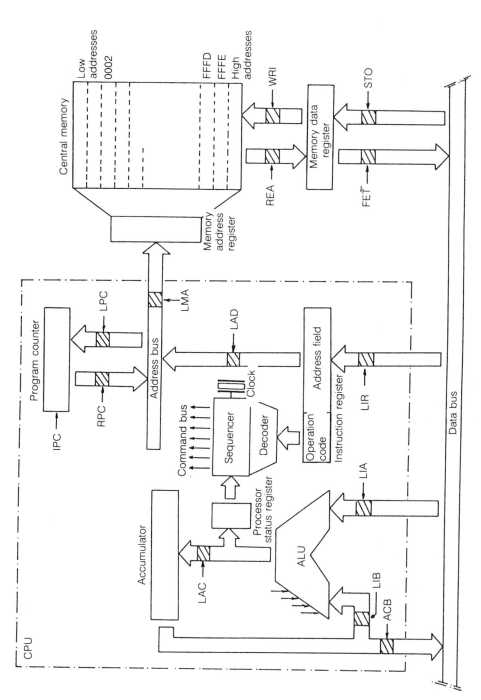

Figure 15.2 Block diagram of a CPU

with components from outside the CPU via electronic connections (wires, printed circuit tracks or connections within the integrated circuit), which allow the transfer of binary data. These 'wires' are collected together to form a bus.

There are three types of bus.

The **data bus** is, as its name suggests, used to transfer data (instructions or data to be processed) between the components of the system. Depending on the number of 'wires' forming the bus, words of 8, 16, 32 or 64 bits can be transferred in parallel. The number of bits that can be moved around the bus simultaneously (in parallel) determines what is known as the **bus width**. Data can circulate in both directions along such a bus (from the memory to the central processing unit or from the central processing unit to the memory for example); the data bus is said to be **bidirectional**.

The **address bus** is used to transfer addresses, such as the address of the next instruction to fetch into the instruction register, or the address of an item of data to be fetched to a particular register or to be sent to the ALU. In this type of bus, addresses are only sent in one direction, from the processing unit to the memory; this bus is said to be **unidirectional**. In systems having a narrow address bus, an address may be transferred in two successive halves; the most significant half followed by the least significant half. In other systems, the width of the address bus determines the size of the memory that can be addressed directly. For example, with a bus of width 16 bits, there can be 2^{16} different memory locations for storing instructions and data.

The **command bus** is for microinstructions generated by the sequencer to be passed to the various components of the system.

Figure 15.2 gives a block diagram of a complete CPU.

15.5 **Operation of the CPU**

From what has already been explained about the processing of instructions in the central processing unit, we can say that for each program instruction there is: a **fetch** phase, and an **execute** phase.

Let us look more closely at each of these two phases, starting with a very simplified example of how they function. As an aid to understanding we will use mnemonics to represent each of the microinstructions that the sequencer might generate (these mnemonics are **completely arbitrary** and do not exist as such in a real machine). In practice microinstructions are simple electrical pulses emitted by the sequencer.

You will see that in Figure 15.2 microinstructions are indicated as small arrows. The arrows are positioned wherever data is transferred between different parts of the CPU; the shaded areas to which the arrows point can be thought of as logic gates that the microinstruction is going to 'open' to allow data to pass between the components.

Example 15.2   Microinstruction

The microinstruction that we arbitrarily call RPC (Read Program Counter) points to the shaded area on the link between the program counter and the address bus. Hence it allows data to pass from the program counter to the address bus.

The microinstructions are described below (a term in parentheses means 'the contents of'):

RPC Read Program Counter
(Program counter) → Address bus

LPC Load Program Counter
(Address bus) → Program counter

LMA Load Memory Address register
(Address bus) → Memory address register

REA REAd from memory
(Memory) → Memory data register

WRI WRIte to memory
(Memory data register) → Memory

FET FETch memory data register
(Memory data register) → Data bus

STO STOre memory data register
(Data bus) → Memory data register

LAD Load ADdress from instruction register
(Instruction register address field) → Address bus

LAC Load ACcumulator
(ALU output) → Accumulator

LIR Load Instruction Register
(Data bus) → Instruction register

LIB Load Input B of arithmetic and logic unit
(Data bus) → Input B of ALU

LIA Load Input A of arithmetic and logic unit
(Data bus) → Input A of ALU

ACB ACcumulator to data Bus
(Accumulator) → Data bus

IPC Increment Program Counter
(Program counter) + 1

NOP No OPeration:
simply transfer data from input B to the output of ALU

ADD Addition, SUB Subtraction, AND, OR logic, etc.

15.5.1 *Fetching the instruction*

The machine code program to be executed is loaded into central memory where it occupies a certain number of memory locations, each location having a precise address.

The program counter is loaded before program execution starts with the address of the first instruction to be executed. This loading can be performed by the **loader** section of a program whose job is to supervise the operation of the whole system and which is called the **operating system**.

The sequencer, during the 'fetch next instruction' phase, then generates the microinstructions to bring the next instruction to be executed from the memory to the instruction register.

This 'fetch next instruction' sequence is as follows:

RPC (Program counter) $\rightarrow$ Address bus

LMA (Address bus) $\rightarrow$ Memory address register

REA (Memory) $\rightarrow$ Memory data register

FET (Memory data register) $\rightarrow$ Data bus

LIR (Data bus) $\rightarrow$ Instruction register

IPC (Program counter) + 1

This will cause (RPC) the transfer of the **contents** of the program counter, which is at the moment loaded with the address of the first instruction to be executed, on to the address bus. (Note, transfer does not mean that the contents of the program counter is now empty; in fact it would be better to say 'copied'.) The address of the first instruction is then transmitted (LMA) to the memory address register, which is a kind of pointer to indicate which memory location is about to be read.

The next microinstruction (REA) causes a copy of the data (here an instruction) contained in the memory location indicated by the memory address register, to be moved temporarily into the memory data register; because this register is used as a buffer for smoothing out any timing differences between the memory and the data bus it is called a buffer register.

The contents of the memory data register (which is our first instruction) is then transferred (FET) on to the data bus.

A microinstruction issued by the sequencer (LIR) now causes the contents of the data bus to be copied into the instruction register. At this point the instruction to be executed has reached the instruction register and is ready to be decoded and used by the sequencer which will generate the microinstructions necessary for its processing.

A last microinstruction from the sequencer (IPC) causes the program counter to be incremented so that it points to the **address of the next instruction** of the program. (In practice, as we will see later, the incrementing is not usually by 1 but for the time being it helps understanding to think of it this way.)

This sequence of microinstructions, generating the fetch next instruction phase, is almost always the same. It will be repeated automatically as soon as the processing of the current instruction has been completed.

15.5.2   *Processing the instruction*

Once the instruction has been loaded into the instruction register it will be decoded by a decoder associated with the sequencer, which will analyse the **op-code** (in the operation field), and then cause the appropriate series of microinstructions to be generated for that operation. In order to follow most easily the details of the process, we are going to take a very simple example of a program written in a microprocessor assembly language.

We will add together the two numbers 8H and 4H, which are stored in memory locations F800H and F810H, the result being stored at address F820H.

Note: to simplify the writing of bases, if a number is written with an H after it, the number is to be taken as a hexadecimal number, if it does not have an H after it, the number is to be taken as a decimal number.

This little program needs three successive operations:

- Load the first value (8H) from memory address F800H into the accumulator.
- Add the second data value (4H) in memory location F810H to contents of the accumulator, the result being put into the accumulator.
- Store the result (CH) at F820H, the required address.

The assembly language program for this sequence of instructions could be:

```
LD A,(F800H)    Load accumulator with the contents of address F800H
ADD A,(F810H)   Add the contents of address F810H to that of the accumulator
LD (F820H),A    Store what is in the accumulator at address F820H
```

These instructions are certainly not held in the memory in this form but in the form of machine codes generated by the assembler program. In practice they would look approximately like this:

```
3A   F8   00
C6   F8   10
32   F8   20
```

| | | CPU | | | | | | Central memory | | | | | | | | |
	Program counter	Accumulator	Instruction register	ALU Input A	ALU Input B	ALU Output	Address bus	Address register	Program 0001	Program 0002	Program 0003	Data F800	Data F810	Data F820	Data register	Data Bus
Starting values →	0001	×	×	×	×	×	×	×	3AF800	C6F810	32F820	8	4	×	×	×
1st INSTRUCTION — Fetch																
RPC	0001						0001									
LMA							0001	0001								
REA									3AF800						3AF800	3AF800
FET	0002		3AF800												3AF800	3AF800
LIR																
IPC																
Execute																
LAD			F800				F800									
LMA							F800	F800								
REA												8			8	8
FET																
LIB					8										8	8
NOP No operation					8	8										8
LAC		8				8										
2nd INSTRUCTION — Fetch																
RPC	0002						0002									
LMA							0002	0002								
REA										C6F810					C6F810	C6F810
FET	0003		C6F810												C6F810	C6F810
LIR																
IPC																
Execute																
LAD			F810				F810									
LMA							F810	F810								
REA													4		4	4
FET																
LIB					4										4	4
ADD Addition		8		8	4	C										
LAC		C		8 +		C										
3rd INSTRUCTION — Fetch																
RPC	0003						0003									
LMA							0003	0003								
REA											32F820				32F820	32F820
FET	0004		32F820												32F820	32F820
LIR																
IPC																
Execute																
LAD			F820				F820									
LMA		C					F820	F820								
ACB															C	C
STO														C	C	C
WRI																

These program instructions are arbitrarily stored in FB00H, FB01H and FB02H (this is a slight simplification). The diagram below gives the state of the memory before executing the program:

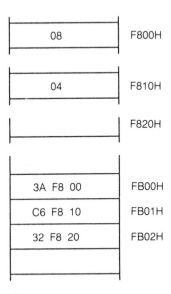

The state of the memory before executing the program

In Figure 15.3 you can find the microinstructions generated by such a program and the actions they involve.

SAQ

15.1 Produce a table to show how the CPU functions for the microsequence generated by the program that subtracts the number 3H, stored at the address F820H from the number 9H, stored at the address F810H and stores the result at address F820H. For the purpose of this exercise consider the instructions in a simple assembler and their equivalent in machine code to be as follows:

```
LD A,(F810H)      3A  F8  10
SUB A,(F820H)     D6  F8  20
LDA (F820H),A     32  F8  20
```

EXERCISES

15.1 Taking account of the fact that in most cases the size of a memory word is only a byte, think about how the system will go about the process of loading the instruction register. For a start think about how it can deduce the length of the instruction.

| | | CPU | | | ALU | | | | | Central memory | | | | | | | |
		Program counter	Accumulator	Instruction register	Input A	Input B	Output	Address bus	Address register	Program 0001	Program 0002	Program 0003	Data F800	Data F810	Data F820	Data register	Data Bus
Starting values →		0001	x	x	x	x	x	x	x	3AF810	D6F820	32F820	x	9	3	x	x
1' INSTRUCTION Fetch	RPC	0001						0001 → 0001	← 0001								
	LMA							0001	→ 0001								
	REA									3AF810						3AF810	3AF810
	FET															3AF810	3AF810
	LIR	0002		3AF810													
	IPC																
1' INSTRUCTION Execute	LAD			F810				F810 → F810	← F810								
	LMA							F810	→ F810								
	REA													9		9	9
	FET															9	9
	LIB					9											
	NOP		9			9	9										
	LAC						9										
2' INSTRUCTION Fetch	RPC	0002						0002 → 0002	← 0002								
	LMA							0002	→ 0002								
	REA										D6F820					D6F820	D6F820
	FET															D6F820	D6F820
	LIR	0003		D6F820													
	IPC																
2' INSTRUCTION Execute	LAD			F820				F820 → F820	← F820								
	LMA							F820	→ F820								
	REA														3	3	3
	FET															3	3
	LIB					3											
	LIA		9		9		6										
	SUB		6		–	3	6										
	LAC																
3' INSTRUCTION Fetch	RPC	0003						0003 → 0003	← 0003								
	LMA							0003	→ 0003								
	REA											32F820				32F820	32F820
	FET															32F820	32F820
	LIR	0004		32F820													
	IPC																
3' INSTRUCTION Execute	LAD			F820				F820 → F820	← F820								
	LMA																
	ACB		6														
	STO															6 →	6
	WRI														6	6	6

Figure 15.4   Solution to SAC

15.2   In the case when a program contains a branch to some distant address (label), think about the way in which this instruction might be executed in the central processing unit.

Solution to SAQ

15.1   Produce a table to show how the CPU functions for a given microsequence.
            The answer is given in Figure 15.4.

Chapter 16

Addressing modes

We have said in earlier chapters that the instructions of a program and the data they process are stored in central memory before execution. The storage locations occupied by the instructions and the storage locations occupied by the data are often known collectively as the **program segment** and the **data segment** respectively. A large program may have several program segments and several data segments. We have also described the memory as a collection of storage locations each containing a **memory word** of a particular size (at the moment stores are usually built with a physical word size of eight bits, but they can be grouped to form words of sixteen bits). Likewise we have described the **address bus** which carries the addresses of instructions and data in the memory.

In practice it is not so simple as that. The exercise at the end of the previous chapter will have led you to realise that instructions do not generally occupy just a single memory word. Nor are the addresses which pass along the address bus always the real addresses (or physical addresses) of the data in memory. There are several techniques for finding the physical addresses of information (instructions and data) in memory; techniques which are known as **addressing modes**.

These different modes of addressing, which are 'transparent' to all except assembly language programmers, are designed to make it easier to access data or groups of data items in central memory. The following basic addressing modes are found on most processors:

- Implied addressing.
- Immediate addressing.
- Absolute addressing.
- Relative addressing.
- Indexed addressing.
- Indirect addressing.

Examples taken from the Z80 (an eight-bit processor) assembly language will provide a sound basis for the explanations which follow. Later we will consider addressing techniques used on the 8086 and 68000 processors.

16.1 Implied addressing

We say that the addressing mode is **implicit** (or inherent) when the instruction concerned does not refer explicitly to the address of the operand on which it is working. Instructions which use implied addressing do not need an address field (also called an operand field) and thus only occupy eight bits. This is an advantage because eight-bit instructions can usually be processed more quickly than longer instructions.

Example 16.1   CPL

Complement the value in the accumulator ($A \leftarrow \bar{A}$) (machine-code 2F).

16.2   Immediate addressing

Strictly speaking no address is involved in this mode because the address field of the instruction does not contain the address of the operand; it contains the actual **operand itself**.

Example 16.2   ADD A,1BH

The immediate operand here has the hexadecimal value 1B (the H indicates that it is a hexadecimal value), which is added to the contents of the accumulator (machine code C6 1B).

16.3   Absolute addressing

The address is an absolute address when the operand field contains the real physical address (or absolute address) of the operand on which the instruction is to work.

Example 16.3   LD (F805H),A

This instruction stores the contents of the accumulator at absolute address F805 (machine code 32 05 F8).

16.4   Relative addressing

A relative address does not indicate the absolute value of the position of the data in memory, but its position (**displacement** or **offset**) relative to some reference point. This base address is normally the one held in the PC register (**program counter**). One advantage of this addressing mode is that it enables efficient branching, using only two words for an instruction (one word for the op-code and one for the address reference); in fact the operand field does not contain an address but a displacement relative to the reference address.

Thus an instruction with relative addressing can address a limited number of store locations in front of or beyond the address in the program counter. Remembering that this displacement is held in just eight bits of the instruction, it is clear that it can only address a limited number of locations. In fact with eight bits we can address a zone of only 255 locations situated on one side or the other of the address currently contained in the program counter.

Example 16.4   JR NC,025H

This instruction causes a forward jump of 37_{10} locations if the carry flag is not set (machine code 30 25).

This type of addressing has two advantages: an improvement in program performance (fewer bytes are used), and the possibility of placing the program anywhere in the memory if all jumps are relative to the current program counter value and are not specified absolutely (this type of program is called **relocatable**).

16.5 Indexed addressing

In the technique of indexed addressing, the value specified in the address field of the instruction is again a **displacement** but this time, not by reference to the program counter, but by reference to the contents of a special register, the **index register**.

Example 16.5   ADD A,(IX + 4H)

This instruction adds to the contents of the accumulator, the data found at the location whose address is given by adding 4 to the value in the IX register. Thus if the index register contains the value F800, the data would be taken from location F800 + 4, i.e. from F804 (machine code DD 86 04).

16.6 Indirect addressing

An address is called indirect if it allows access, not to the data required but to a **memory word containing the effective address** of the data.

Example 16.6   ADD A,(HL)

This instruction will add to the contents of the accumulator the data found at the address contained in the register HL. Thus if the register HL contained the value F800 the contents of the accumulator would have the value contained in store location F800 added to it (machine code 86).

It is interesting to note that, the indexed addressing mode described above serves the same purpose if a zero displacement were used: ADD A,(IX + 0); but notice the difference in the number of bytes of machine code generated in each case.

16.7 **8086 addressing**

The registers in the 8086 can be divided into three groups (not counting special registers such as the program counter or the processor status registers):

- The general registers.
- Index registers used for data transfer.
- Special addressing registers.

The 8086 microprocessor has 20 pins for addresses which allows the addressing of 1 Mbyte (16 times greater than an 8-bit microprocessor such as the Z80). Its data bus has a width of 16 bits allowing the reading or writing of 8 bits or 16 bits in a single operation.

The central memory of the 8086 is considered by the microprocessor to be a collection of 16-byte paragraphs rather than a series of single bytes. This division of the available space into packets of 16 allows 4 bits of the 20-bit address to be dropped so that an address of a paragraph, wherever it may be in memory, can be held in a 16-bit register; the four least significant bits of the absolute address being put at 0. Dedicated registers, addressing registers, are used for paragraph addressing.

Each time an instruction refers to an address register, a displacement (or offset), coded 8 or 16 bits, is added to the absolute address of the paragraph to determine the absolute address of the data. Thus a space of 64 kbytes is addressable from the base address of the paragraph; this space of 64 kbytes is called a **segment** and the addressing register which indicates where the segment begins is called the **segment register**.

The four segment registers are each dedicated to a specific purpose.

The first (**Code Segment CS**) is used to address program (code) segments. The second (**Stack Segment SS**) covers the space reserved for the stack, used to store the return address in the main program when executing subroutines. The two other registers (**Data Segment DS** and **Extra Segment ES**) allow references to two segments reserved for program variables and data.

This specialisation of the registers does not prevent a programmer, who wants to do so, from pointing to the same paragraph with two different segment registers. So, 256 kbytes of memory are directly addressable at the same time provided that the segments do not overlap.

A segment register is not, by itself, sufficient to specify an absolute address; its role is simply concerned with the rational use of memory space. In fact the segment register only points to the first absolute location of the given segment. As explained above, a displacement (**offset**) must be added to the value contained in the segment register to obtain the required absolute address. An example of memory addressing is shown in the diagram below:

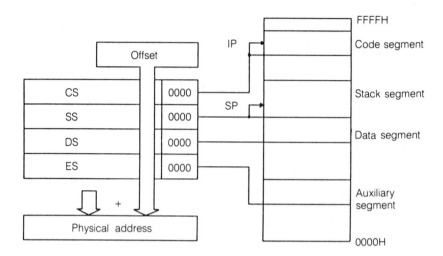

The offset (or displacement) can be given explicitly in the instruction in the form of an immediate value of 8 or 16 bits, or specified with reference to an address contained in some register, in which case the absolute address is obtained from the sum of:

- The value contained in the segment register (multiplied by 16, that is to say extended by four 0 bits).
- Plus the value contained in the designated register.
- Plus the offset specified in the instruction.

It is also possible to use three registers and one displacement.

16.8 **The MC68000**

The original 68000 from Motorola provides eight 32-bit data registers and eight 32-bit address registers, 14 addressing modes and a 16 Mbyte address space. Later versions are upwardly code-compatible with earlier versions but provide more powerful features such as a wider address bus and more addressing modes (the 68020 has 18 addressing modes).

The 68000 has seven general-purpose address registers A0–A6 which, depending on the addressing mode, may contain operand addresses, addresses of pointers to operands, base addresses or indexes. An eighth address register A7 is used as a stack pointer.

The 68000 has eight 32-bit data registers (D0–D7). Depending on the instructions using them they may contain 8-bit data (bytes), 16-bit data (words), or

32-bit data (long words). Byte operands occupy bits 0–7, word operands occupy bits 0–15, and long word operands occupy bits 0–31:

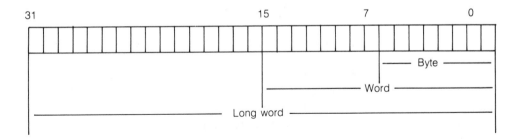

When an instruction uses a data register as a source register or as a destination register, only the specified bits are involved; the high-order bits are unchanged. For example, if data register D1 contained the value $12345678 then the result of applying the assembler instruction CLR.B D1 (clear) would be to make D1 contain $12345600. If we had applied the assembler instruction CLR.W D1 instead, the result would have been to make D1 contain $12340000.

16.8.1   *68000 addressing modes*

The MOVE instruction from 68000 assembler code is used in the following examples since it has the widest range of addressing modes of all the 68000 instructions.
      Data or address register direct: the operand is contained in a data register or an address register specified in the instruction. For example, in assembler code,

```
MOVE.L D3,D1
```

means copy into data register D1 the long word (32 bits) held in data register D3.
      Immediate addressing: the operand is a constant and is given as part of the instruction. For example,

```
MOVE #123,D2
```

means write the value 123 into data register D2.
      Absolute addressing: the actual physical address of the operand is given in the instruction. For example,

```
MOVE D3, 400400
```

means transfer the contents of data register D3 to main memory location 400400.

Address register indirect addressing: the address of the required operand is stored in an address register. For example

MOVE (A1),D2

means copy the contents of the memory location whose address is stored in A1, to data register D2.

Address register indirect with offset: this is a variant of address register indirect addressing. In this case the address of the required operand is obtained by adding a specified offset to the address in the address register before the operand is accessed. The actual contents of the address register remains unchanged. For example,

MOVE.B 3(A1),D2

means copy into D2 a byte from the location which is 3 bytes beyond the byte whose address is in A1. The offset is a 16-bit 2's complement integer.

Address register indirect with post-increment: this is another variant of address register indirect addressing. The contents of the address register specified in the instruction is incremented *after* it has been used to access the operand. For example,

MOVE.B (A1) + ,D2

means copy the contents of the memory location whose address is stored in A1, to data register D2 and then add 1 to the address in A1.

Address register indirect with pre-decrement: this is identical to address register indirect with post-increment except that the address register is *decremented before* the operand is accessed. For example,

MOVE − (A1),D2

means subtract 1 from the contents of the address register A1 *and then* copy the contents of the memory location whose address is now stored in A1, to data register D2.

Indexed addressing: the address of the operand is given by the sum of a constant offset and the contents of two registers at least one of which must be an address register. The offset is an 8-bit 2's complement number in the range − 128 to + 127. For example,

MOVE 123(A1,D0),D2

means copy into register D2 the memory location whose address is given by the sum of the contents of address register A1, data register D0 and the offset 123.

Relative addressing: in this mode the address is relative with respect to the current contents of the program counter. For example,

MOVE 123(PC,D0), D2

means copy into register D2 the memory location whose address is given by the sum of the contents of the program counter, the contents of the register D0, and the 16-bit 2's complement offset 123. In 68000 code, relative addressing cannot be used to specify a destination address.

Stack addressing: the processor has two stack pointers both referred to as A7; one is accessed in the user mode and the other in supervisor mode.

The processor builds a stack from high memory to low memory using pre-decrement and post-increment indirect addressing.

To push a word from data register D0 on to the system stack the following instruction could be used:

MOVE.W D0, –(A7)

Conversely the instruction,

MOVE.W (A7)+,D0

could be used to pull a word from the system stack into data register D0, as illustrated below:

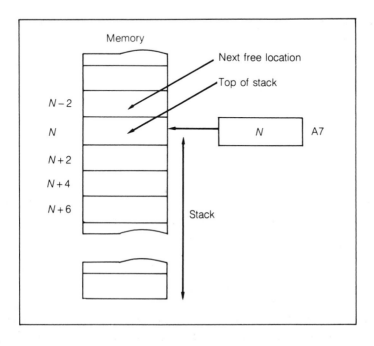

Chapter 17

Interrupts

17.1 The principle of interrupts

A program may be interrupted during its execution in order to service a different task considered to be more urgent. When this task is finished the interrupted process must be restored to the processor in the same state as that in which it had been temporarily abandoned. The principle of interrupts can be likened to a telephone which is only picked up when there is a call; it is useless, in the absence of a ring, to pick up the telephone to see if 'by chance' someone is at the other end of the line.

Interrupts allow peripherals ready to send or receive data, or allow events such as errors and power cuts, to attract the attention of the CPU. They enable peripheral controllers to force the microprocessor to suspend its current activity and enter a subroutine, called an interrupt service routine, to service the peripheral.

17.2 Types of interrupt

An interrupt can arise in several ways: from an input/output controller, in which case it is called an **external** interrupt; from the processor itself when certain exceptional events occur, it is then called an **internal** interrupt. These exceptional events are known as **traps**. The most common traps are division by zero, overflow and address violation.

Some interrupts can be more important than others and must therefore be given priorities; thus there is a certain **hierarchy of interrupts**.

Most systems are provided with instructions for inhibiting interrupts in certain circumstances, so that if the execution of a program must not be disturbed, interrupts can be suspended. There are, however, some types of interrupts which cannot be ignored either because it would be damaging to ignore them or because they have a high priority level. The most obvious example is the interrupt warning that the power supply has been cut off! Interrupts such as this which cannot be inhibited are called **non-maskable** interrupts.

In contrast, an interrupt is said to be **maskable** when the CPU can be asked to ignore it. Certain interrupts can be masked at a given time to prevent them from disturbing particular code sequences where an interrupt could result in errors.

17.3 **Recognition of interrupts**

There are several different methods for determining the sources of an interrupt so that an appropriate response can be made.

17.3.1 *Multilevel interrupts*

Each source that can issue an interrupt is connected to its own interrupt input to the CPU. This solution, although technically the simplest, is costly in CPU input pins and because of this it is rarely used. The diagram below shows how it works:

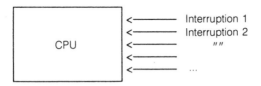

17.3.2 *Single interrupt line*

In this technique one input to the CPU is used to indicate when an interrupt has been requested. If several sources of interrupt are connected to this line, when the CPU receives a request it must investigate all the possible sources to determine which one issued the request; this technique is called **polling**, and is illustrated below:

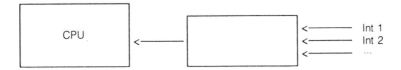

17.3.3 *Vectored interrupt*

In this type of interrupt, the interrupt request signal is accompanied by an identifier which enables a direct branch to be made to the appropriate interrupt service routine. This identifier is a number called a **vector**, identifying the source of the request. The vector can be placed on the data bus either by a component called the **interrupt controller** or directly by the peripheral itself; but then it is necessary to have some means of resolving priorities when several interrupt vectors are placed on the data bus at the same time.

The determination of priorities can be achieved automatically by connecting the interrupting components in series in order of their priority so that the interrupting device of highest priority is able to block the interrupts from lower priority devices. This technique is called **daisy chaining**.

17.4 **Interrupt processing**

The processing of an interrupt generally takes place as follows:

1. An interrupt request is received (internal or external).
2. The processing of the current instruction is completed.
3. The interrupt request is accepted (or rejected) by the CPU.
4. The present state of the system is saved, i.e. the contents of registers (e.g. program counter, processor status) is saved, so as to be able to continue the interrupted program from exactly the same point and in exactly the same state as when it was interrupted.
5. The program counter is forced to take the address of the first instruction of the service routine associated with this interrupt.

17.5 **Interrupts in the 8086-8088**

The 8086 microprocessor can receive up to 256 different interrupts, identified by a number called the **type** of interrupt.

17.5.1 *External interrupts*

The 8086 possesses two input pins for external interrupts: NMI and INTR.

NMI is for external non-maskable interrupts, used to signal catastrophic events or, for example, to extricate the processor from the execution of an infinite loop when no other interrupt is possible.

INTR is for signals generated by an interrupt controller (8259A), itself connected to the peripherals which may need to interrupt the processor. When INTR is active, the current state of one of the flags in the processor status register determines the processor's response. The interrupt will have no effect until the execution of the current instruction has been completed.

Figure 17.1 illustrates 8086 interrupts, while Figure 17.2 shows an 8086/8088 application.

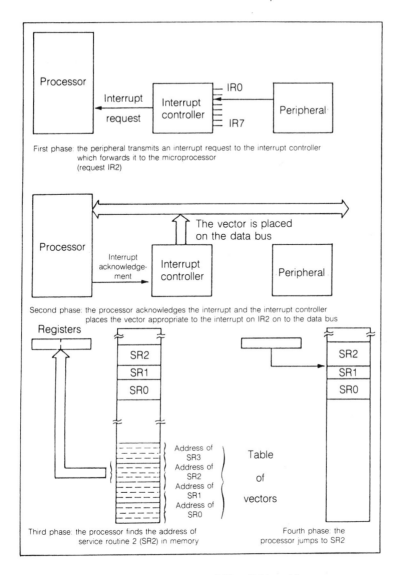

First phase: the peripheral transmits an interrupt request to the interrupt controller
which forwards it to the microprocessor
(request IR2)

Second phase: the processor acknowledges the interrupt and the interrupt controller
places the vector appropriate to the interrupt on IR2 on to the data bus

Third phase: the processor finds the address of
service routine 2 (SR2) in memory

Fourth phase: the
processor jumps to SR2

Source: M. Aumiaux, *Microprocesseurs 16 Bits*, Editions Masson.

Figure 17.1   8086 interrupts

17.5.2 *Internal interrupts*

An internal interrupt is called by the INT instruction. The type of interrupt required
is placed in the operand field of the instruction to indicate which procedure the
processor is to execute.

In the operating system MS-DOS, interrupts are called by an INT instruction

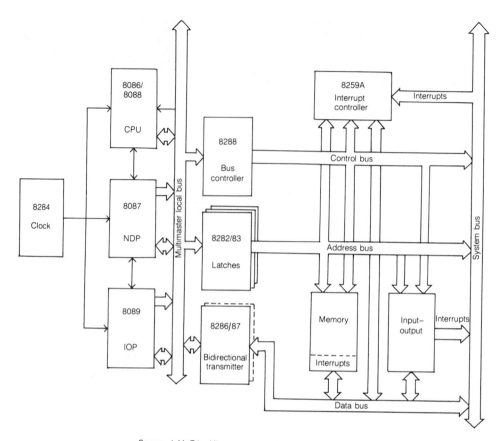

Source: J.-M. Trio, *Microprocesseurs 8086–8088*, Editions Eyrolles.

Figure 17.2 An 8086/8088 application

followed by the interrupt number. Amongst those in current use is interrupt 21 which calls DOS functions.

17.6 **Interrupts in the 68000**

The 68000 microprocessor recognises seven different levels of priority for external interrupt requests. It avoids the use of seven different acknowledge pins by placing the level number of the interrupt it is acknowledging on the three least significant bits of the address bus.

When a **device** controller issues an interrupt it waits for a signal on its IACK input and inspects the value on the three least significant bits of the address bus. If its interrupt is being acknowledged the controller places a vector number on the data bus. When the 68000 receives the vector number it multiplies the number by four to convert it into an address which it uses to access the interrupt vector table. The

Table 17.1 Interrupts for microcomputers under MS-DOS

Number	Address	Use	
0	0–3	Divide by zero	
1	4–7	Single step	
2	8–B	Non-maskable (NMI)	
3	C–F	Breakpoint (1 byte)	
4	10–13	Overflow	
5	14–17	Print Screen	
6–7	18–1F	Reserved	
8	20–23	Time of day (8259 IR0)	
9	24–27	Keyboard (8259 IR1)	
A	28–2B	Extensions (8259 IR2)	
B	2C–2F	Serial port 2 (8259 IR3)	
C	30–33	Serial port 1 (8259 IR4)	
D	34–37	Hard disk (8259 IR5)	
E	38–3B	Diskette (8259 IR6)	
F	3C–3F	Printer (8259 IR7)	
10	40–43	Video	
11–12	44–4B	Configuration	
13	4C–4F	Disk	
14	50–53	Serial port	
15	54–57	Cassette	
16	58–5B	Keyboard	
17	5C–5F	Printer	
18	60–63	Resident BASIC	
19	64–67	BOOT	
1A	68–6B	Time of day	
1B–1F	6C–7C	Hardware control	
20	80–83	Program terminate	DOS version 1
21	84–87	Function call	DOS
22	88–8B	Return address	DOS
23	8C–8F	Response to CTRL C	DOS
24	90–93	Fatal errors	DOS
25	94–97	Absolute disk read	DOS
26	98–9B	Absolute disk write	DOS
27	9C–9F	DOS terminate	DOS version 1
28–5F	A0–17F	Reserved	
60–67	180–19F	User	
68–7F	IAO–1FF	Not used	
80–85	200–217	Reserved for BASIC	
86–F0	218–3C3	BASIC interpreter (RUN)	
F1–FF	3CF–3FF	Not used	

Source: J.-M. Trio, *Microprocesseurs 8086-8088*, Editions Eyrolles.

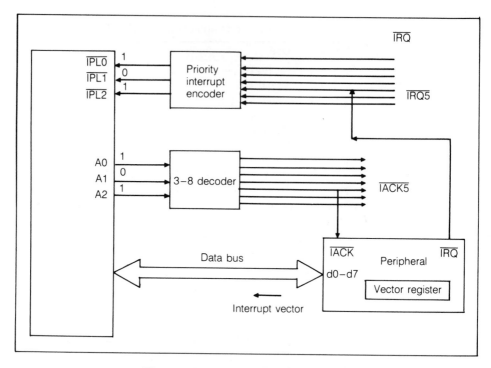

Figure 17.3 68000 vectored interrupt

interrupt vector obtained from the table points to the interrupt handling routine for the interrupt. This interrupt vector is loaded into the program counter. Figure 17.3 illustrates a 68000 vectored interrupt.

The interrupt table has space for 256 entries, each entry occupying four bytes. The first 64 entries in the table are reserved for internal interrupts and externally generated exceptions of highest priority (bus error or reset).

Chapter 18

A study of three processors

According to the complexity of the physical machine of which it forms a part, the processor can be made from a single component (microprocessor) or from several components each having responsibility for some of the functions of the whole, as we saw in the study of the CPU.

For the sake of simplicity, we will begin this study with a simple although now rather ancient microprocessor, the Z80 made by Zilog; we will then consider the Intel 8086 and the Motorola 68000 which are more recent microprocessors.

18.1 The Z80 microprocessor

First made available to the commercial market by Zilog in 1976, the Z80 is an integrated circuit with almost 8000 transistors.

This microprocessor, which at one time was one of the most widely used in numerous applications, provides a useful introduction to the study of a processor. It has 40 pins, and a repertoire of 158 instructions using 22 registers and 8 addressing modes.

18.1.1 Pin connections

18.1.1.1 Physical connections
The diagram below shows pin connections to the Z80 microprocessor:

A11	1	40	A10
A12	2	39	A9
A13	3	38	A8
A14	4	37	A7
A15	5	36	A6
Ø	6	35	A5
D4	7	34	A4
D3	8	33	A3
D5	9	32	A2
D6	10	31	A1
Vcc	11	30	A0
D2	12	29	Gnd
D7	13	28	RFSH
D0	14	27	M1
D1	15	26	RESET
INT	16	25	BUS RQ
NMI	17	24	WAIT
HALT	18	23	BUSACK
MREQ	19	22	WR
IORQ	20	21	RD

D0/D7	Data bus
A0/A15	Address bus
WR	Write select
RD	Read select
IORQ	Input/output request
MREQ	Memory request
M1	First machine cycle (instruction fetch)
RFSH	Refresh memory
HALT	CPU halt
WAIT	Wait request (for synchronisation with slow memory or peripherals)
INT	Interrupt request (maskable)
RESET	Initialise CPU
BUSREQ	Bus access request
BUSAK	Acknowledge bus access request
Ø	CPU clock
Vcc	Power supply + 5 V
Gnd	Power supply ground

165

18.1.1.2 Logical connections
To simplify our study of the pin connections, we can divide them into three logical groups of signals:

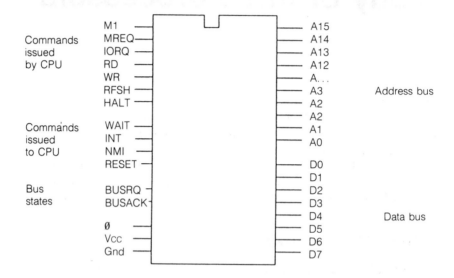

The first logical group (**address bus**) has 16 outputs A0–A15, the LSB or least significant bit being A0. Each output can deliver a current of 1.9 mA. If a stronger current is necessary, a 'driver' (or current amplifier) can be used. At this stage it can be deduced, by counting the pins, that the **addressing range** (the size of memory that can be directly addressed by the processor) is 2^{16}, i.e. 64 kbytes.

The second logical group (**data bus**) has 8 pins D0–D7. Data input from the peripherals which comprise the external environment of the microprocessor, or data output from the microprocessor to the peripherals, must therefore be in words of 8 bits. We say that the **external data bus** is an 8-bit bus or that it has a width of 8 bits.

The third logical group (**command bus**) has 13 pins and can be further divided into three subgroups of signals:

- Commands emitted by the microprocessor.
- Commands received by the microprocessor.
- The state of the command bus.

Pins 11 and 29 carry the power supply (+5 V, ground) to the processor. Pin 6 receives the clock signals.

18.1.2 *Pin assignments*

The command bus can, as we have seen, be divided into three subgroups of signals all of which are active low, i.e. they are active at a level of 0 V. A signal which is active low is indicated by a bar drawn above the signal name.

18.1.2.1   Signals output from the processor

M1: first machine cycle
The signal M1 indicates that the CPU is in the instruction fetch part of the fetch–execute cycle. An instruction can have a minimum length of 1 byte and a maximum of 5 bytes.

MREQ: Memory REQuest
The signal MREQ indicates that the address on the address bus is valid and that a read or a write operation is about to take place.

IORQ: Input/Output ReQuest
This IORQ signal indicates the microcomputer is addressing one of the peripherals (not to be confused with a memory address). In order to save pins, the Z80 uses the least significant 8 bits of the address bus (A0 to A7) to address peripherals. So the microprocessor can address up to 256 input–output controllers for either reading (input) or writing (output).

RD: ReaD
The signal RD indicates that the microprocessor is about to read data either from a previously specified memory location or from an input device controller.

WR: WRite
The signal WR indicates that the data placed on the data bus by the processor is valid and can be stored in a previously addressed memory location or in the output register of an input/output controller.

RFSH: ReFreSH
The signal RFSH is used for refreshing dynamic memories (a type of memory that we will consider later).

HALT
This pin indicates that the microprocessor is in a stop state (in practice it causes NOP 'no operation' instructions) and is waiting for an external command.

18.1.2.2   Signals input to the microprocessor

WAIT
This signal allows the suspension of the action of the central processing unit for as long as this input is activated. It is frequently used for synchronising the processor with slow peripherals or memories having relatively long access times.

INT: INTerrupt request
The INT pin is in general used by a peripheral unit to request an interrupt as explained in the preceding chapter.

When the request is accepted, the microprocessor finishes its current instruction, saves the machine state (the context) and transfers to the interrupt service routine. The interrupted program is resumed when the processing of the interrupt service is completed.

$\overline{NMI}$: Non-Maskable Interrupt
This input indicates to the microprocessor that it **must** accept this interrupt and service it as soon as the current instruction is completed.

$\overline{RST}$: ReSeT
This input resets the microprocessor to its initial state, resetting certain flip-flops. It forces the program counter to the value 0000H which is normally the start address of an initialising (or BOOT) program.

18.1.2.3   Command bus states
In certain particular cases it is necessary to isolate several pins electrically from the processor. This is sometimes called the 'third' logic state or high impedance state. Pins which can have this high impedance state are:

- The address bus.
- The data bus.
- The pins MREQ, IORQ, RD and WR.

This state is used in conjunction with the following two signals.

$\overline{BUSRQ}$: BUSReQuest
This input is to request the microprocessor to switch to its high impedance state. This the processor will only do at the end of its current cycle.

$\overline{BUSAK}$: BUS AcKnowledge
This output indicates that the 'three-state' pins are effectively isolated from the rest of the microprocessor and therefore the peripheral circuit requesting use of the address bus, the data bus, and the command bus is free to use them.

18.1.3   Z80 registers

As we stated at the beginning of this chapter, the Z80 has 22 registers which can be divided into two classes; general registers and special registers.

18.1.3.1   The general registers
The Z80 microprocessor has two 'symmetric' sets of general registers, a little like two panels of a blackboard. Only one set can be used at a time, the swapping from one set to the other is effected by an exchange instruction.

Each set of registers comprises a collection of six 8-bit registers, that can be used independently or in specific combinations, as 16-bit registers.

These registers are designated B, C, D, E, H and L. The symmetric registers are B′, C′, D′, E′, H′ and L′. The permitted register pairs are BC, DE, HL and from the symmetric set B′C′, D′E′, I′L′.

Words manipulated internally by the Z80 are in most cases 8-bit words, and so the **internal data bus** of the Z80 is 8 bits wide. When a microprocessor has an external data bus of *n* bits and an internal data bus which is also *n* bits it is said to be a **true *n*-bit** processor. The Z80 microprocessor is therefore a true 8-bit processor.

18.1.3.2   The special registers
The Z80 microprocessor has six special 8-bit registers and four special 16-bit registers.

The accumulator register
This 8-bit register referred to as A (and its symmetric register A′) is used to hold the first operand and the result of arithmetic and logical operations.

The processor status register
This 8-bit register denoted by F (F′ is its symmetric register), plays an important role because its six indicator bits (flags) can be tested to give information about the present state of the system. The roles of the indicators are as follows:

```
7 6 5 4 3  2  1 0  Bit
S Z * H *  P/V N C  Indicator
```

- The C bit or bit 0 is the carry bit; it is set when an arithmetic operation causes a carry out from the most significant bit position.
- The N bit or bit 1 is used by the 'decimal adjust' instruction to allow the manipulation of numbers coded in BCD.
- The P/V bit or bit 2 acts both as a parity indicator and as an indicator of overflow in 2's complement arithmetic.
- The H bit or bit 4 is a **half carry** bit indicating a carry from the 4th bit and is used by decimal adjust instructions.
- The Z bit or bit 6 signals that the result of the last operation was zero.
- The S bit or bit 7 indicates the sign of the 8-bit number currently in the accumulator. It assumes that the accumulator holds a signed 8-bit integer.

The interrupt vector register
This 8-bit register I, is used when the processor operates in the vector interrupt mode. It contains the 8 upper bits of the starting address of the interrupt service routine. The device supplies the lower 8 bits of the 16-bit address.

The memory refresh register
This 8-bit register R, is used during dynamic memory refreshing which we will examine in more detail in the chapter on memories.

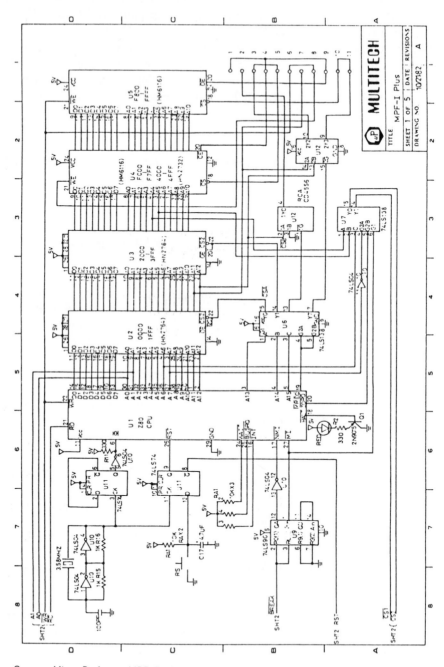

Source: *Micro Professor MPF-IP*, Editions Multitech Industrial Corporation.

Figure 18.1 Circuit of the MPF1 Plus

The program counter
This 16-bit register PC, contains the address of the next instruction to be executed by the processor.

The stack pointer register
This 16-bit register SP contains the address of the top of the stack which is used during subroutine calls to store the return address to the correct instruction in the calling program.

The index registers
These two 16-bit registers IX and IY, contain the addresses used in indexed addressing.

EXERCISES

18.1   Locate the different buses in the diagram of the MPF1 Plus (Figure 18.1), and thus identify the various pins mentioned above.

18.2   Knowing that the 74LS138 is a decoder whose truth table is the one shown below, explain the role of the MREQ pin in the logic diagram of the MPF1 Plus shown in Figure 18.1.

Inputs					Outputs							
Validate		Select										
G1	G2	C	B	A	Y0	Y1	Y2	Y3	Y4	Y5	Y6	Y7
X	1	X	X	X	1	1	1	1	1	1	1	1
0	X	X	X	X	1	1	1	1	1	1	1	1
1	0	0	0	0	0	1	1	1	1	1	1	1
1	0	0	0	1	1	0	1	1	1	1	1	1
1	0	0	1	0	1	1	0	1	1	1	1	1
1	0	0	1	1	1	1	1	0	1	1	1	1
1	0	1	0	0	1	1	1	1	0	1	1	1
1	0	1	0	1	1	1	1	1	1	0	1	1
1	0	1	1	0	1	1	1	1	1	1	0	1
1	0	1	1	1	1	1	1	1	1	1	1	0

18.2   The 8086 and 8088 microprocessors

The Z80 is one of the 'old generation' of microprocessors; the technology has evolved rapidly and other microprocessors employing more advanced integration techniques have appeared.

While not being truly state of the art, the 8086 and 8088 are widely used in PCs and compatibles. The 8086 introduced in 1978 is made by INTEL and has approximately 29 000 transistors and 40 pins. It is the first of a series of microprocessors known under the general name of iAPX of which the latest listed to date is the 80486 which has approximately 1 200 000 transistors.

18.2.1 *Physical connections*

The 8086 and the 8088 are logically completely compatible, a program written for one can be executed on the other. The essential difference between the two microprocessors originates from the width of the external data bus which is 16 bits for the 8086 but only 8 bits for the 8088.

The 8086 is a true 16-bit microprocessor because it has internal and external data buses each of 16 bits: see Figure 18.2. The 8088 is not a true 16-bit processor because although its internal data bus is 16 bits its external data bus is only 8 bits. Hence it must access memory twice in order to fetch or store 16 bits.

Two operating modes are possible for these microprocessors, the minimum mode and the maximum mode, depending on whether pin 33 is at logic level 1 or 0.

18.2.1.1 The minimum mode
In the minimum mode, which allows the number of external circuits required to be reduced to a minimum, the CPU is able to use the full range of addresses and exercise full control of the command bus. However, if the number of circuits connected to the bus is considerable, amplifiers (drivers or buffers) such as the 8286 or 8287 can be used. Figure 18.3 shows the minimum mode of the 8086.

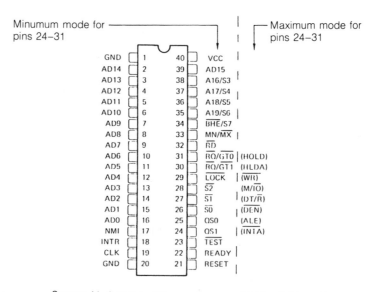

Source: M. Aumiaux, *Microprocesseurs 16 bits*, Editions Masson.

Figure 18.2 Pin connections for the 8086

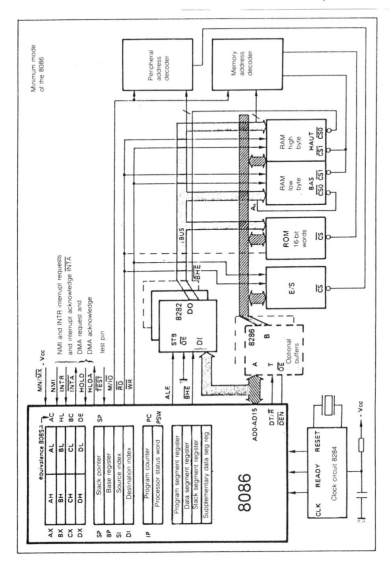

Source: M. Aumiaux, *Microprocesseurs 16 bits*, Editions Masson.

Figure 18.3 The minimum mode of the 8086

18.2.1.2 The maximum mode

The maximum mode allows the architecture to be extended to multiprocessor configurations. This mode enables, by the addition of an 8087 numeric coprocessor, the extension of the instruction set to include that of the 8087. An 8089 input–output processor may also be added to control input and output operations. Figure 18.4 shows the maximum mode of the 8086.

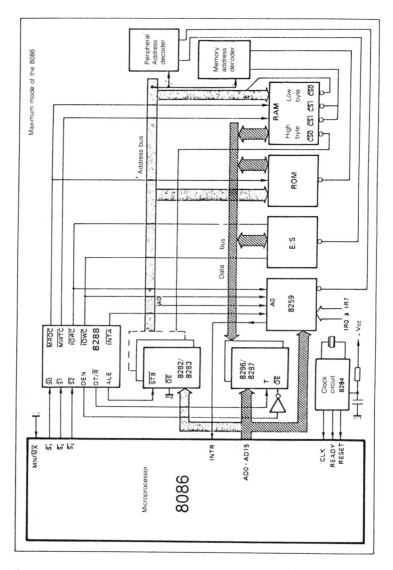

Source: M. Aumiaux, *Microprocesseurs 16 bits*, Editions Masson.

Figure 18.4   The maximum mode of the 8086

18.2.2   *Pin assignment*

18.2.2.1   Pins common to the two modes

Power supply
The chip is supplied with +5 V and ground.

CLK (clock)
This input receives clock signals from the system clock, usually provided by the 8284 circuit.

INTR (INterrupt Request)
Provided for an Interrupt request from the input—output processor 8259A.

NMI (Non-Maskable Interrupt)
It is used for interrupts arising from power supply failure or an alarm. It also allows an interrupt out of an infinite loop when other interrupts may be ineffective.

RESET
This input initialises the microprocessor, i.e. it resets to 0 the various segment registers (with the exception of segment register CS) and the processor status, and passes control to the operating system.

READY
When a slow peripheral (a printer for example) is addressed, not having the capability of executing the requested transfer at the speed of the processor it informs the clock generator (8284) which, in synchronism with the clock signal, puts the READY input to zero. The CPU must then wait for the signal to rise again before it can continue executing the program.

$\overline{TEST}$
This input also enables the CPU to be synchronised to data from an external source. For example, consider what happens when the microprocessor needs the result of a calculation currently being performed in the 8087 coprocessor before it can continue its own processing. The BUSY signal from the 8087 is fed into the $\overline{TEST}$ input of the microprocessor which is then forced to wait until the BUSY signal is no longer active. It can equally serve to check for the completion of a slow operation such as the starting up of the disk drive motor or reading and writing a disk.

$\overline{RD}$ (Read Data)
This signal, when it is low (active low), indicates to the system that the processor is performing a read cycle.

AD0—AD7
These pins can have one of three logic states, high, low or high impedance. They are multiplexed and correspond to the low part of the address bus or to the data bus. In fact on the 8088 and the 8086, to limit the number of pins to 40, the data bus and the address bus are multiplexed, i.e. the same pins serve sometimes to send addresses and sometimes to send or receive data.

The high impedance state allows the CPU to be isolated from the bus when the bus is being used by a peripheral.

AD8–AD15 for the 8086 or A8–A15 for the 8088
They have similar roles to those of AD0–AD7 except that for the 8088 the pins are only used to output addresses.

A16 (S3)–A19 (S6)
These pins are also multiplexed and used either for the output of the four most significant bits of the address, or pins S3 and S4 are used to indicate the segment register (described later) used to generate a physical address.

$\overline{BHE}$ (S7) (Bus High Enable)
During the output of an address, $\overline{BHE}$ and A0 enable data on the high part and the low part respectively, of the data bus.

MN($\overline{MX}$) MiNimum/ MaXimum)
This input is either connected to earth to cause the processor to function in maximum mode or to +5 V to cause it to work in minimum mode.

18.2.2.2   Pins used in maximum mode

$\overline{S2}$, $\overline{S1}$, $\overline{S0}$
These pins are active at the beginning of a bus cycle, to indicate to the bus controller circuit (8288) the nature of the current cycle (e.g. reading or writing memory, reading or writing externally), thus enabling it to generate the appropriate signals.

$\overline{RQ(GT0)}$, $\overline{RQ(GT1)}$ (ReQuest/GranT)
Each of the two (bidirectional) pins is used to receive requests from the coprocessors to use the internal bus (REQUEST) and send permission (GRANT) to do so at the end of the current processor cycle. The coprocessor uses the same pin to inform the processor when it has finished so that the processor can resume its use of the bus.

$\overline{LOCK}$
This signal is generated under program control by writing the prefix LOCK at the start of an instruction. It prevents access to the bus by all other circuits until the instruction has been completely executed.

QS0, QS1 (Queue)
These pins enable the numeric coprocessor (8087) or other circuits to know what the processor is doing with its instruction queue.

18.2.2.3   Pins used in minimum mode

M($\overline{IO}$) (Memory or Input–Output)
This signal is used to distinguish between a memory access and an input–output peripheral access.

DT($\overline{R}$) (Direction of Transmission)
This pin controls the direction of the data bus buffers (8286/8287) (1 = transmit, 0 = receive).

$\overline{WR}$ (WRite)
This signal indicates that the processor is performing a write operation.

$\overline{INTA}$ (INTerrupt Acknowledge)
This signal is used during the recognition of an interrupt. The processor reads the interrupt number placed on the data bus by the interrupt controller.

ALE (Address Latch Enable)
This signal is used to 'capture' (latch) the address at the start of an operation cycle.

HOLD, HLDA (HOLD Acknowledge)
HOLD indicates to the processor that another circuit wishes to use the bus. The processor responds at the end of the current cycle by putting HLDA to high and putting its own access to the bus into the high impedance state.

$\overline{DEN}$ (Data ENable)
This signal enables all data transfers in both directions.

18.2.3   *The registers*

18.2.3.1   The data registers
The data registers AX, BX, CX and DX serve both as accumulators and as 16-bit operand registers. Each of these registers can be separated into two 8-bit registers. The letter X is then replaced by H for the high part and by L for the low part. Hence AH and AL together make AX.

Although these are general registers they do have certain specialised uses:

- AX is used for input–output operations, multiplications, and divisions.
- BX serves as a base register during indirect addressing and base register addressing.
- CX is used as a counter in operations on character strings.
- DX is used with AX for multiplications and divisions, and is used in indirect addressing.

18.2.3.2   The segment registers
The segment registers CS, DS, SS and ES form part of the built-in memory management system of the 8086. Each of the registers contains the physical base address of a segment of 64 bytes. (See Chapter 16 on addressing modes.)

18.2.3.3 The pointer registers

These are the registers SP, BP, SI and DI. They are used during arithmetic or logic operations. The first two are also used to indicate a displacement in the stack segment while the last two indicate displacements in the data segment.

The program counter
This register called IP (instruction pointer) holds the displacement from the base of the relevant code segment.

18.2.3.4 The other registers

The processor status register (status word)
This register has 16 bits of which only 9 are used:

- AF (Auxiliary Flag) is the carry flag of weight used 2^4 during decimal arithmetic operations.
- PF (Parity Flag) is the parity indicator.
- SF (Sign Flag) indicates the sign.
- ZF (Zero Flag) indicates that the result of an arithmetic or logical operation is zero.
- OF (Overflow Flag) indicates that the capacity of the byte or word has been exceeded.
- DF (Direction Flag) is an indicator used during the manipulation of strings of characters.
- IF (Interrupt Flag) indicates whether or not maskable interrupts are enabled.
- TF (Trace Flag or Trap Flag) puts the CPU into single-step mode.

The diagram below shows a status word:

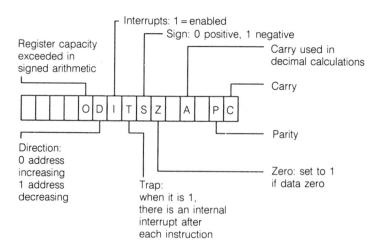

The instruction queue
The internal architecture of the 8086 comprises two parts: the execution unit (EU)

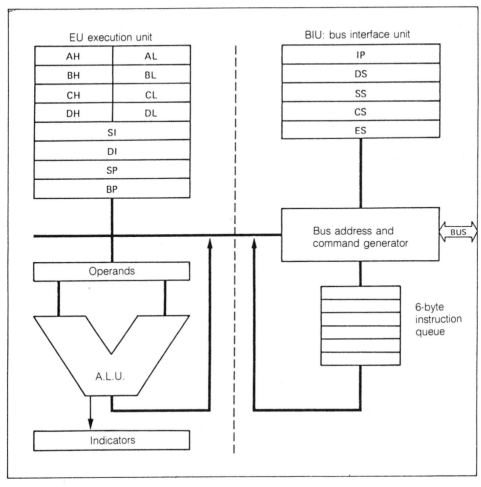

Source: M. Aumiaux, *Microprocesseurs 16 bits*, Editions Masson.

Figure 18.5   Internal architecture of the 8086

which executes arithmetic and logical instructions; and the Bus Interface Unit (BIU) which pre-fetches 6 bytes of instructions into an instruction queue.

Thus while the execution unit is executing an instruction, the BIU fetches the next instruction from the current program segment. This mode called **pipe-line** mode, enables faster processing rates to be achieved and is frequently used in computing. The 8086 was the first microprocessor to use this method of operation; its internal architecture is shown in Figure 18.5.

18.3 **The 68000 microprocessor**

The 68000 microprocessor is a member of the 68000 family comprising the 68008,

68010, 68012, 68020, 68030, 68040 processors. The 68000 is compatible with the other members of the family in the sense that assembly language programs written for the 68000 will run on the others. The converse is not true because programs written for say the 68020 will not necessarily run on the 68000.

The 68000 has 32-bit wide internal registers and can be regarded as a 32-bit microprocessor. However, its external data bus is only 16 bits wide and so 32-bit operands must be moved as two consecutive 16-bit words. For this reason it is also regarded as a 16-bit microprocessor. Motorola who produce the 68000 refer to it as a 16-/32-bit microprocessor.

18.3.1   *Physical connections*

The MC68000 chip is supplied in a variety of packages in either plastic or ceramic casing. The diagram shows a dual-in-line (DIL) package but it is also available in a pin grid array (PGA) package or on a leadless chip carrier (LCC):

64-Pin Dual-in-line 68000 package

Pin	Signal		Pin	Signal
1	D4		64	D5
2	D3		63	D6
3	D2		62	D7
4	D1		61	D8
5	D0		60	D9
6	$\overline{AS}$		59	D10
7	$\overline{UDS}$		58	D11
8	$\overline{LDS}$		57	D12
9	R/$\overline{W}$		56	D13
10	$\overline{DTACK}$		55	D14
11	$\overline{BG}$		54	D15
12	$\overline{BGACK}$		53	GND
13	$\overline{BR}$		52	A23
14	Vcc		51	A22
15	CLK		50	A21
16	GND		49	Vcc
17	$\overline{HALT}$		48	A20
18	$\overline{RESET}$		47	A19
19	$\overline{VMA}$		46	A18
20	E		45	A17
21	$\overline{VPA}$		44	A16
22	$\overline{BERR}$		43	A15
23	$\overline{IPL2}$		42	A14
24	$\overline{IPL1}$		41	A13
25	$\overline{IPL0}$		40	A12
26	FC2		39	A11
27	FC1		38	A10
28	FC0		37	A9
29	A1		36	A8
30	A2		35	A7
31	A3		34	A6
32	A4		33	A5

Top view

18.3.2 *Logical connections*

The input and output pin connections can be grouped into 8 groups of logic signals.

18.3.2.1 The address bus
The address bus has 23 lines A1−A23 allowing up to 8 megawords of data to be directly addressed. Address line A0 is not required because all words must begin on even addresses. During interrupt cycles, A1, A2 and A3 provide information about what level of interrupt is being serviced (see section 17.6).

18.3.2.2 The data bus
The data bus has lines D0−D15 and accepts data transfers of either words (16 bits) or bytes. During an interrupt acknowledge cycle, the external device places the vector number on lines D0−D7. The logical significance of the 68000 pin connections is shown in the diagram below:

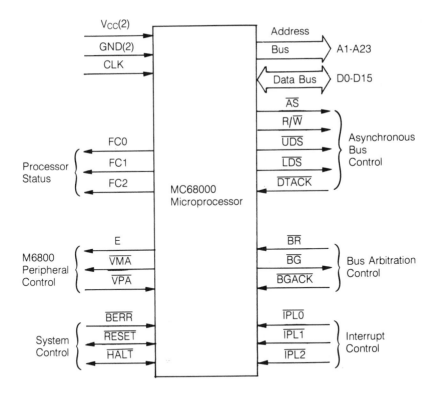

18.3.2.3 Asynchronous bus control
The asynchronous bus control signals are used to control the address and data buses.

$\overline{AS}$: *Address Strobe*
This signal indicates that there is a valid address on the address bus.

R/W̄: Read/Write
This signal indicates whether the transfer on the data bus is a read or a write.

ŪDS, L̄D̄S̄: Upper Data Strobe and Lower Data Strobe
When ŪDS is low the data on data bus bits 8–15 is valid; when L̄D̄S̄ is low the data on data bus bits 0–7 is valid.

D̄TACK: Data Transfer ACKnowledge
This signal indicates that the data transfer is complete and that the data can be safely removed from the bus.

18.3.2.4   Bus arbitration control
The group of signals concerned with bus arbitration control enables the CPU to grant temporary control of the bus to certain external devices.

B̄R̄: Bus Request
A device which wants to become bus master in order to effect a bus transfer issues this signal.

B̄Ḡ: Bus Grant
The processor issues this signal when it is ready to release bus control at the end of the current cycle.

B̄GACK: Bus Grant ACKnowledge
A device issues this signal when it becomes bus master. In order to avoid errors the signal should only be issued by a device when it has received a bus grant **and** the address and data buses are not currently in use **and** no other device is issuing a B̄GACK signal.

18.3.2.5   Interrupt control
The interrupt control signals indicate the priority level of the device requesting an interrupt. The use of these signals is illustrated in section 17.6.

18.3.2.6.   System control
The system control group of signals is used to reset or halt the system and to indicate that bus errors have occurred.

B̄ERR: Bus ERRor
This signal indicates to the processor that an error, such as a peripheral device not acknowledging a data transfer or an illegal access request to memory, has occurred during the current bus cycle. Depending on the nature of the error the processor might enter a bus error exception (interrupt) sequence or it may try to run the bus cycle again.

$\overline{RESET}$: RESET
This is a bidirectional signal. When it is generated externally it causes a system initialisation sequence to be entered by the processor. When it is generated internally (by a RESET instruction), it does not affect the internal state of the processor but it could be used to cause all external devices to be reset.

$\overline{HALT}$: HALT
This too is a bidirectional line. An external device can use this signal to halt the processor at the end of the current bus cycle; or the processor can use the signal to indicate to external devices that it has stopped.

18.3.2.7   Peripheral control
Whereas the 68000 microprocessor uses an asynchronous system for bus control, the earlier 6800 series of microprocessors used a synchronous bus interface. This group of three peripheral control signals was included in the 68000 so that system designers could make use of the widely available 6800 peripheral chips.

E: Enable
The enable signal provides the synchronising clock required for all 6800 transfers. Its period is equal to 10 68000 clock periods (E is low for six CLK cycles and high for four CLK cycles).

$\overline{VPA}$: Valid Peripheral Address
This signal is an input signal used by 6800 devices to inform the 68000 that they require a 6800-type data transfer. When the 68000 receives this signal it adjusts its data transfer timing to synchronise it with the E clock.

$\overline{VMA}$: Valid Memory Address
This signal is used to indicate to the 6800 devices that the address on the address bus is valid.

18.3.2.8   Processor status
The three function code outputs FC0, FC1, FC2 are used to indicate the current state of the processor and the type of bus cycle currently in progress. For example, when all the outputs are high (at logic level 1) it indicates an interrupt acknowledge, and when FC0 is high but FC1 and FC2 are low it indicates a user data cycle.

Chapter 19

The central memory

A memory is a device capable of recording data, keeping it as long as necessary (or as long as possible) and providing copies of it on request. As we have indicated in previous chapters, there are two main types of memory in computer systems:

- A fast memory, physically small but expensive, which is the working memory of the computer and which is called the **central memory** or **main memory** or **central store.**
- A less expensive memory of larger size but with a slower access, which is the **secondary memory** or **auxiliary memory** or **backing store.**

19.1 General considerations

Certain characteristics, common to most memories can be distinguished and used to compare one memory with another.

The capacity indicates the quantity of data that the memory can store. This capacity can be measured in bits, bytes or words. Measurements are usually expressed in multiples of the kilo (which in computing terms is worth 1024). Thus we talk of memories of 640 kbytes, 512 kwords ...

Example 19.1   512 kwords

A central memory of 512 kwords of 16 bits is equivalent to

$$512 \times 1024 \text{ words}$$
$$\text{or } 512 \times 1024 \times 2 \text{ bytes}$$
$$\text{or } 512 \times 1024 \times 2 \times 8 \text{ bits}$$

The volatility represents the length of time for which the memory is capable of retaining the data in a readable form, particularly after the electricity supply is cut off. A magnetic tape memory will be called non-volatile because the data will be preserved even if the current is cut off from the tape drive, whereas the working memory of a computer is very often volatile, i.e. it will be erased if the power supply is inadvertently cut off.

The access time is the time required to access in memory the data to be fetched. Thus a memory made from electronic components will generally be faster than one on tape which has a very large access time.

The type of access is the method used to access data. Can the data be accessed directly or can it only be accessed after passing over other data? Thus to reach a data item stored on tape memory requires that all the data preceding it on the tape has to be skipped over (such access is said to be serial access); whereas an electronic memory will give direct access.

The physical size: the development of smaller and smaller systems, and thus of smaller and smaller memories, has long been a goal of computer designers and largely accounts for the rapid growth of computing.

The cost of memory is usually measured as the cost per bit. As a general rule, electronic memories have a relatively high cost per bit compared with that of magnetic memories (tapes, disks, etc.). This explains why they normally have a smaller capacity.

The ideal would be to have a memory combining all the advantages but such a solution would still unfortunately be very costly. This leads designers to gain the most effective results by adopting compromise solutions using a mixture of store technologies.

Memories can be broadly classed in two types:

- **Central memories**, generally electronic.

Advantages	*Disadvantages*
Fast	Often volatile
Small	Expensive
Directly addressable	

- **Auxiliary memories**, generally magnetic.

Advantages	*Disadvantages*
Inexpensive	Bulky
Non volatile	Slow
Large capacity	

In this chapter we will consider central memories which can be further classified into three major groups:

- Read–write memories.
- Read only memories.
- Specialised memories.

Central memory is, in fact, a collection of memory cells capable of storing data. Depending on the type of memory, these cells are each capable of storing a bit, a nibble, a byte or several bytes.

We use the term **memory word** to distinguish the quantity of information contained in a 'logical' memory cell. We use this term 'logical memory cell' because, most of the time, physical memory cells are just a single bit and to store a memory word of eight bits requires eight cells.

To identify the correct cell for reading or writing, each logical cell (each memory word) has its own **address**:

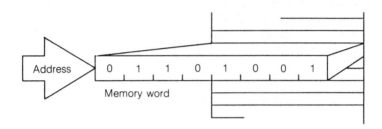

19.2 **Read–write memories (RWM)**

Read–write memories are volatile memories which can be written to or read from at will. They are generally known as **RAM** to signify that they are Random Access Memory because any location can be accessed directly in any order (and not because they are accessed 'by chance'!).

19.2.1 *Pin significance in read–write memories*

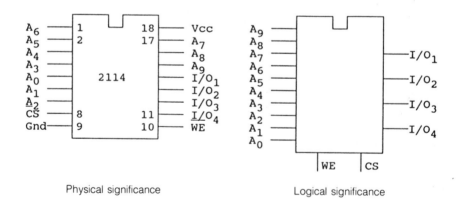

Physical significance   Logical significance

I/O1 to I/On (or D0 to Dn) input or output pins for data.

CS (Chip Select) to select this chip during addressing.

WE Write Enable (or Read/Write, R/W) causes the data at the input or output pins to be written or read.

Vcc Gnd are power supply inputs.

19.2.2 *Principles of operation*

19.2.2.1 Writing

- Select the correct memory address by placing the correct binary pattern on the address bus.
- Place the data on the data bus.
- Select the circuit by activating the Chip Select pin.
- Activate the writing command (Write or R/W).

19.2.2.2 Reading

- Select the correct memory address by placing the correct binary pattern on the address bus.
- Select the circuit by activating the Chip Select pin.
- Activate the reading command (Read or R/W).
- Read the data on the data bus.

These functions can be represented on a timing diagram such as the one shown in Figure 19.1 for reading data.

Within this general classification of read—write memories we can distinguish two types of memory according to their design:

- Read-write static memories.
- Read-write dynamic memories.

19.2.3 *Read—write static memories*

In the Static **RAM** or **SRAM**, the basic cell is a transistor flip-flop. If the power is maintained then, depending on the type of transistors used, data can be stored indefinitely without degradation.

19.2.4 *Read—write dynamic memories*

In a Dynamic **RAM** or **DRAM**, the basic cell is no longer made from a transistor flip-flop but from a charged 'capacitor' (in reality it is the base—emitter capacitance of a transistor). Leakage currents always exist, and little by little the capacitor discharges and could give rise to errors in the stored data. To avoid this the memory has to be reread at frequent intervals and the data rewritten after each read. The read and write-back cycle is called a **refresh** cycle. This type of memory is currently widely used because of its greater density of integration (i.e. more can be stored per mm^2).

The problem with read—write memories is their volatility; the slightest discontinuity in the power supply causes data to be lost, but they do have a very short access time, they only consume small amounts of power, and they can be read,

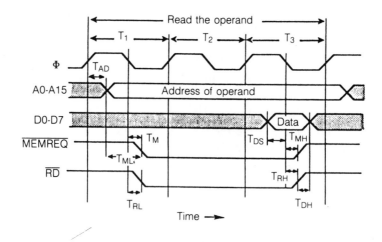

Source: Tanenbaum, *Architecture de l'ordinateur*, Inter-Editions.

Figure 19.1   Timing of several critical parameters for a read operation

SYMBOLS	MEANING	VALUES Min	VALUES Max	UNITS
T_{AD}	Putting the address on the bus		110	ns
T_{ML}	Stabilising the address	60		ns
T_M	Applying $\overline{\text{MEMREQ}}$		85	ns
T_{RL}	Applying $\overline{\text{RD}}$		85	ns
T_{DS}	Placing data on the bus before Z80 takes it	50		ns
T_{MH}	Maintaining $\overline{\text{MEMREQ}}$ after Z80 takes the data		85	ns
T_{RH}	Maintaining $\overline{\text{RD}}$ after Z80 takes the data		85	ns
T_{DH}	Maintaining the data after end of $\overline{\text{RD}}$	0		ns

erased and rewritten, whenever necessary. They are used mainly for working memory.

19.3 **Read only memories (ROM)**

In contrast to read–write memories, read only memories, generally known as **ROM**, are used only for reading and not for writing (under normal circumstances). Read only memories have evolved in several directions as a result of attempts to improve their performance, and a number of different types can be distinguished.

19.3.1   *ROM memories*

Data is written into the memory during manufacture and cannot be altered. The cost is relatively high for small production runs and thus its use is confined to volume production.

19.3.1.1   Operating principles
This type of memory is constructed as a diode matrix. The network of diodes is arranged to insert the required words at the various addresses.

Example 19.1   A ROM diode matrix

A ROM diode matrix

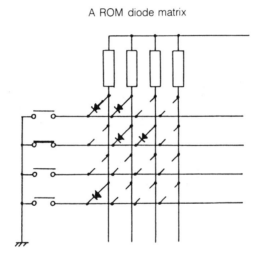

Here it is the word at address 2 which has been selected by closing the contact corresponding to this word (in practice a device similar to the decoder would be used).

In the leftmost column (the most significant bit of the word) there is no diode which means that no current flows to earth along the address line for word 2. A logic 1 can therefore be detected on this column.

At the next column a diode has been built in during manufacture permitting a current to flow towards earth, hence a zero will be detected in the second column.

A memory constructed in this way cannot be altered. This has led manufacturers to produce read only memories which can be easily written by the user.

19.3.2 *PROM memories*

The **PROM** or **Pr**ogrammable **ROM** is a ROM which is not written during manufacture but is written by the user with the aid of a machine called a PROM programmer.

The manufacturer provides a complete matrix of diodes. The method of programming such ROMs is usually to blow or not blow fuses (diodes). A PROM once blown cannot be rewritten or reprogrammed. The diagram below shows a PROM:

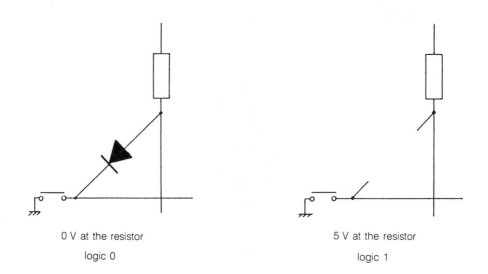

0 V at the resistor

logic 0

5 V at the resistor

logic 1

Such memories will therefore be used for small production runs.

19.3.3 *EPROM memories*

EPROM memories (or Erasable **PROM**), which are sometimes also called **REPROM** (**RE**programmable **PROM**) have the advantage of being erasable and re-writable. The erasing is done by an EPROM eraser, which is no more than a source of ultraviolet light. This is why EPROMs can be readily distinguished from other memories by the presence on their top surface of a little quartz window, often covered with adhesive tape so as not to expose the memory to natural rays of ultraviolet light – see the following diagram.

These memories are currently used for small production runs and during the development of ROM programs.

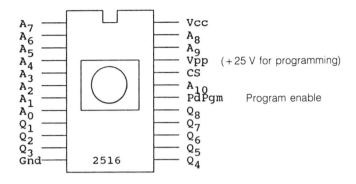

19.3.4 *EEPROM and EAROM memories*

EPROMs have the disadvantage of requiring a source of ultraviolet light for their erasure, a process which is also relatively slow taking several minutes to erase a memory. Manufacturers have produced the **EEPROM** (Electrically **EPROM**), which has to be completely reprogrammed after erasure, and the **EAROM** (or Electrically Alterable **ROM**), which allows individual locations to be rewritten. Both these memories have the advantage of being non-volatile and yet easily reusable; but their price inhibits their wide application.

SAQ

19.1 What is the memory word-size and how many words can be stored in a DIL pack like the one shown below? What type of memory is it?

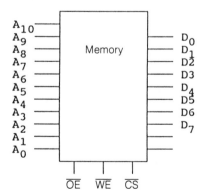

19.4 **Memory size/word length**

The static or dynamic memories we have considered, can store binary words of

1, 4 or 8 bits. How can we use such memories (8 bits for example) to obtain memories of 16-bit words? The answer is simple; just join two memories with their address selection and chip selection pins connected in parallel, as shown below:

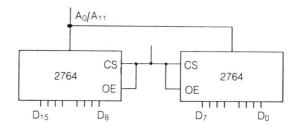

Another problem which arises is that of the memory size. If we have 8-bit memories of 4 or 8 kwords (therefore 4 or 8 kbytes) how can we construct a memory of 16 bytes? Again the answer is simple; just join memories with their outputs connected as shown in the following diagram:

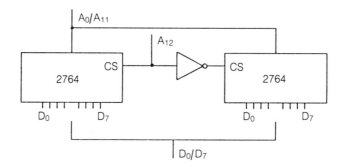

A single address bit (or several) is used for chip selection (either directly or through a decoder).

SAQ

19.2 With the aid of modules like those used in SAQ 19.1 show how to construct a memory block of 4k, 16-bit words. (A diagram showing the logical pin connections is required.)

19.5 **Specialised memories**

19.5.1 *Registers*

Registers are electronic devices made from transistor flip-flops which serve as temporary storage devices in the CPU and allow rapid access to data. Every computer system has a certain number of more or less specialised registers (program counter, accumulator, processor status, etc.).

Depending on the technology used for their construction, access to such registers can be extremely rapid. Although central memory is very fast, it cannot always match the speed of the CPU. For this reason some computer systems have a small very fast memory (**cache memory**) placed between the CPU and the central store which stores frequently used data and instructions. This memory, made of specialised fast registers, is managed entirely by the operating system and the user is unaware of it (hence its name cache − from the French *cacher*: to hide).

19.5.2 *CCD registers*

CCD (**C**harge **C**oupled **D**evice) registers are electronic memory devices which have been developed since 1970. The principle of binary data storage depends on the presence or not of electrostatic charges in a substrate where they can easily be moved from place to place. These CCDs have the advantage of offering very high densities of integration and a very short access time; however, nowadays they are only used in very specialised applications such as computer vision or scanning devices.

19.5.3 *Associative memories*

Associative memories, also known as Contents Addressable Memories (**CAM**), are designed to be searched for a particular item of data (called a descriptor) to determine whether or not it is present, and if it is, to fetch the associated data. In fact they comprise two parts: the first part contains the descriptors and the second part stores the data associated with the descriptors. Associative memories are used for cache memories and for some types of memory management systems but they are mostly confined to use in specialised computers for such applications as pattern recognition.

EXERCISES

19.1 Identify the type of memory, read−write or read only, in the following diagram:

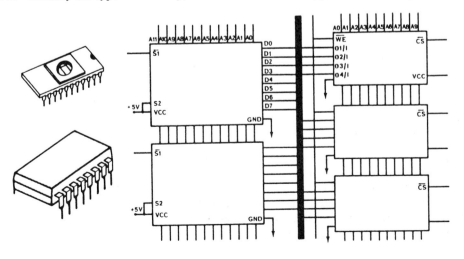

19.2 On a microcomputer originally possessing 512 kbytes of memory there are sockets, arranged as shown in the following diagram, for additional memory chips. Knowing that the maximum capacity that the operating system can support is 640 kbytes, suggest suitable memory chips for the 16 empty sockets (capacity of the chips, size of memory word on each chip, type of memory) to bring the system up to 640 kbytes.

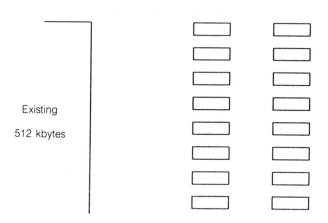

Existing

512 kbytes

Solutions to SAQs

19.1 What is the memory word-size and how many words can be stored in a DIL pack like the one shown below? What type of memory is it?

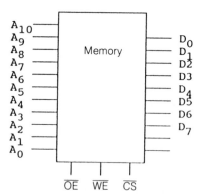

The size of the memory word can easily be determined by noting the number of data input–output pins. Here there are 8 pins (D_0 to D_7), hence the words must have 8 bits.

The memory capacity is easily calculated by noting the number of address inputs. Here the chip has 11 address pins (A_0 to A_{10}) which allows 2^{11} different addresses, i.e. 2 kbytes.

Finally, we know that it is a read–write memory from the presence of the WE (Write Enable) pin which would not be on a memory chip that could only be read.

19.2 With the aid of modules like those used in SAQ 19.1 show how to construct a memory block of 4k, 16-bit words. (A diagram showing the logical pin connections is required.)

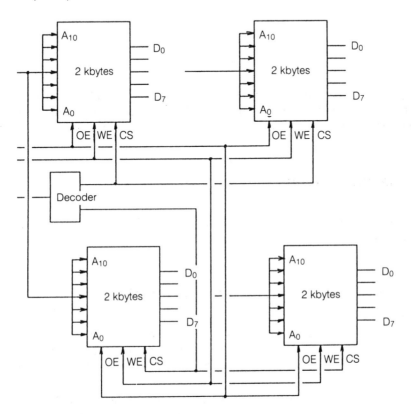

Chapter 20

Serial access backing stores

Backing stores or auxiliary memories have the advantage of a large capacity but the disadvantage of slow access times. Because of their large capacity and relatively low cost, backing stores play an important role in computer systems.

20.1 Magnetic tape

Due to its low cost, magnetic tape still remains one of the most common media for archiving data.

20.1.1 Principles of magnetic recording techniques

The magnetic tape used in computing is a polyester tape approximately 1.5 μm thick. It is generally 0.5 inches wide but its length may be 600, 1200 or 2400 feet. The polyester tape is coated on one side with particles of magnetic oxide acting like microscopic magnets.

If a ferromagnetic bar is subjected to a magnetic field created by passing a direct current through a coil surrounding the bar, then the bar will become magnetised with a north pole and a south pole at opposite ends. If the same bar is subjected to a magnetic field of the opposite sense by reversing the current in the coil, the magnetism in the bar will be reversed:

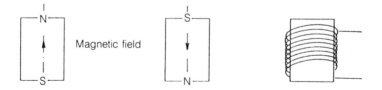

The oxide particles coating the blank tape, all oriented in the same sense, are subjected to a magnetic field in one sense or the other depending on whether 0's are to be written or 1's. The diagram below shows the principles of recording on a magnetic tape:

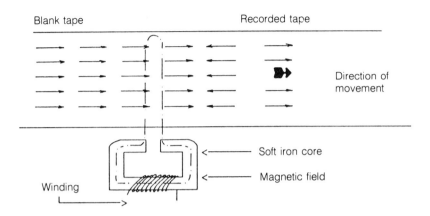

A magnetised particle will retain its magnetism for a length of time determined by the **magnetic remanence** of the oxide. As we stated above, a ferromagnetic bar submitted to a magnetic field created by an electromagnet becomes magnetised. Conversely, if a magnet is moved in the neighbourhood of a coil of wire, a current, called an induced current, will flow in the coil, in a direction depending on the direction of the field, as in the diagram below:

The reading of a magnetic tape is achieved by moving the tape at a constant speed under a reading head made of a core of ferromagnetic material surrounded by a winding. The direction of current induced in the winding depends on the direction of magnetisation of the particles on the tape and thus indicates whether a 1 or a 0 is being read.

To store binary data, a tape is divided into **7 or 9 tracks** (also called **channels**) allowing the recording of 7 or 9 bits simultaneously across the tape. The diagram below shows a 9-track tape:

20.1.2 *Methods of recording*

The bare principles we have presented above are clearly not used as such for recording data; in fact there are several methods for recording on tape. These methods evolved with the development of the technology with the aim of storing the maximum amount of data in the smallest possible space with the greatest possible reliability. The classic methods of recording (some people refer to methods of coding or encoding) are **NRZ1** and **PE**.

20.1.2.1   NRZ1 (Non-Return to Zero 1)

In this method of recording (also known as **NRZI** – **N**on **R**eturn to **Z**ero **I**nvert), the value of the bit being recorded is not associated with a particular direction of magnetisation of the oxide. The recording of a 1 causes a change in the direction of magnetisation; the recording of a 0 does not cause any change, it is ignored. Reading of the recorded data is achieved by sensing the direction of magnetisation at regular intervals and comparing it with the previously observed direction.

If a change of direction is detected, the bit read is a 1, if no change is detected the bit read is a 0.

This method of recording is gradually becoming less used because it does not allow more than 800 bytes per inch to be stored.

20.1.2.2   PE (Phase Encoding)

PE mode writes a 1 with one direction of magnetisation and a 0 with the other direction of magnetisation. Reading requires the direction of magnetisation of the tape to be tested at regular intervals.

This recording mode allows up to 1600 bytes per inch to be stored. For higher packing densities we use techniques which are identical to those described later for recording on magnetic disks.

The following diagram illustrates the various recording methods:

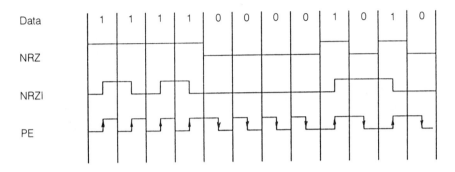

20.1.3   *Physical organisation of tapes*

Reading character by character is not possible on a magnetic tape where a character only occupies a few hundredths of a millimetre. A succession of characters (from several hundred to several thousand) must be read at a time. Reading and writing also depend on the tape being moved at a constant speed past the read–write heads and this too necessitates the reading and writing of groups of characters in succession. Such groups of characters are known as **physical blocks**.

To allow the tape to come to rest after reading a block or to accelerate to full speed before it starts to read the next block, successive blocks are separated from each other by blank spaces, called **interblock gaps**, of 1.5 to 2 cm.

To read from the tape, it is accelerated up to speed in the interblock gap and then the whole block **is read at once** and its contents transferred to a special part of the store called an input–output buffer; the tape is then stopped in the next interblock gap and will eventually be started again to read another block.

20.1.4   *Logical organisation of tapes*

A physical block can contain a single record, i.e. a collection of data all relating to a single entity, or depending on the size of a record, several records can be grouped together in the same physical block.

Example 20.1   A physical block

Suppose that a tape has blocks of 5000 characters and that each record of a file to be written to the tape has 800 characters; it is easy to see that rather than put a single record in each block it is better in this case to put the maximum of six records in each block.

There is therefore a distinction between the physical blocks and the **logical** records. The number of logical records held in a physical block is called the **blocking factor**. The diagram below shows the layout of data on a tape:

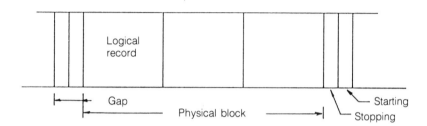

Large blocking factors have the advantage of using the tape more efficiently because the number of interblock gaps is reduced and therefore the space available for recording is increased. The choice of blocking factor is determined either by the programmer or by the system and once defined affects the length of time needed for reading or writing. This is the purpose of the **block contains** clause in COBOL.

20.1.5   *Error checking*

To avoid errors of coding, which are always possible during reading or writing, it is necessary to include error checking bits with the data stored on the tape. We have seen that for each character recorded, a corresponding parity bit could be written; this is called vertical parity or **VRC** (**V**ertical **R**edundancy **C**heck).

A simple vertical parity check is not always sufficient as we have shown in a previous chapter. We are thus led to use a 'horizontal' parity check or **LRC** (**L**ongitudinal **R**edundancy **C**heck) which can be a simple parity check, or more often nowadays a Hamming code. Other techniques beyond the scope of this book are also used such as CRC or a variation on CRC which enables errors not only to be detected but also to be corrected.

20.1.6   *Labels*

Labels are information written at the beginning of reels (or as we sometimes say at the beginning of volumes), and at the beginning of each file, and even at the end of files and reels. They provide a means of identifying each tape and each file to ensure that the correct tape is loaded on to the tape drive or that the requested file is present on the tape. Labels can be standard, i.e. fixed by the manufacturer or non-standard in which case they are defined by the user. That is the purpose of the **label records are** clause in COBOL.

Volume header labels (VH)
These labels are written at the beginning of the tape and generally contain the sequence number of the tape, and the names of the files stored on the tape.

File header labels (FH)
These generally state the name of the file, the creation date, the purge date (the date after which the file will no longer be required and can be overwritten).

File trailer labels (FT)
These detail in general the number of logical records, the number of blocks contained in the file, and the reel number if the file is contained on several tapes (called a multivolume file).

Volume trailer labels (VT)
These are written at the end of the tape and generally give the same information as that contained in a file trailer label.

Tape marks (TM)
Tape marks are special blocks that indicate the 'frontier' between label blocks and data blocks.

The diagram below illustrates tape labels:

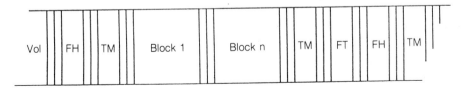

20.1.6.1 Beginning and end of tape

To use a tape it must first be mounted on a tape drive. The tape has a **leader** which cannot be written on but which serves to lead the tape through the drive mechanism. There is also some unusable tape at the end of the reel. To mark the transition between the ends of the tape on which data cannot be recorded and the useable part on which data can be recorded, a strip of metal foil is stuck on to the tape at the boundaries. As the foil passes photoelectric cells it is detected and indicates to the mechanism where recording is allowed.

20.1.7 *Storage capacities*

We have seen how the blocking factor can affect tape capacity. We also have to consider the effect of various items of data concerned with the management and control of tapes, data occupying space which might otherwise be occupied by records of the file. Clearly we must make a distinction between the **theoretical** capacity and the **practical** capacity of the tape.

20.1.7.1 Theoretical capacity
The theoretical capacity of a magnetic tape is the number of characters that could be stored one after the other on the same tape if there were no interblock gaps, i.e. the product of the length and the packing density:

$$Tc = L \times d$$

Example 20.2   Tape capacity

A magnetic tape has a length of 730 m and is used with a packing density of 1600 bytes per inch (bpi). To determine the theoretical capacity of the tape, we have:

$$730 \text{ m} = 73\,000 \text{ cm} \qquad \text{an inch} = 2.54 \text{ cm}$$
$$73\,000 \text{ cm} \times 1\,600 \text{ bpi}/2.54 = 45\,984\,252 \text{ bytes}$$

20.1.7.2 Practical capacity of a magnetic tape
To calculate the practical capacity of a tape, we must take into account the number of interblock gaps on the tape. This depends on the blocking factor used.

The length of a physical record is therefore, neglecting control characters and the various labels:

$$l = (f \times N)/d$$

where f is the blocking factor, N the number of characters per logical record, and d the packing density.

The practical capacity of a tape is therefore:

$$Pc = (L/(l + lg)) \times (f \times N)$$

where L is the length of the tape and lg is the length of an interblock gap.

SAQs

20.1 Calculate the theoretical capacity and the practical capacity of a magnetic tape 730 m long if recordings are made with a packing density of 1600 bpi, knowing that:

● The blocking factor is 5 records per block.
● The number of characters per record is 150.
● The length of an interblock gap is 1.5 cm.

20.2   Repeat the calculation using a blocking factor of 8.

20.2   **Magnetic streamers**

There are three types of streamer, cassettes or mini-cartridges of 0.15 inches which can store up to 10 Mbytes, cartridges of 0.25 inches going up to 60 Mbytes, and cartridges of 0.5 inches which can store more than 150 Mbytes.

Unlike magnetic tape on which blocks of data are separated from each other by interblock gaps, streamers are recorded as a continuous succession of blocks without interblock gaps. Instead of interblock gaps there are **IRG**s (Inter Record Gaps) of 13 bytes and recordings are made without stopping the tape. This technique enables a much higher percentage of the tape to store useful data, of the order of 95%, as against 40 to 60% for conventional methods.

Currently studies are in progress to bring the capacity of streamers up to 5 Gbytes or even more. For this the recording technique will be modified and the new method, inspired by **DAT** (**D**igital **A**udio **T**ape), will use VHS 8 mm video cassettes and a helical-scan recording technique with several recording heads. Combining helicoidal recording and efficient coding methods will result in packing densities of up to 43 200 bpi and ensure recordings of 5 Gbytes of data in about 20 minutes.

20.3   **Conclusions**

Magnetic tape has been and remains still a widely used medium for backing storage; this is due to various reasons such as:

- A low cost per character stored (0.00005 p/bit).
- A low physical volume compared to the amount of data stored (up to 10^{10} bits on a tape).
- The non-volatility of the stored data.

However, magnetic tape also has disadvantages such as:

- Reading being entirely serial.
- A long average access time (10 seconds).
- Relatively high sensitivity to environmental conditions (e.g. dust, humidity).

This is why at the present time magnetic tapes serve mostly as archive storage and will in the near future be usurped by other media such as optical disks which we will describe in a later chapter.

EXERCISES

20.1 Calculate the theoretical capacity and the practical capacity of a magnetic tape 730 m long if recordings are made with a packing density of 3200 bpi, knowing that:

- The blocking factor is 8 records per block.
- The number of characters per record is 340.
- The length of an interblock gap is 1. 5 cm.

20.2 Repeat the calculation using a blocking factor of 12.

Solutions to SAQs

20.1 Calculate the theoretical capacity and the practical capacity of a magnetic tape 730 m long if recordings are made with a packing density of 1600 bpi, knowing that: the blocking factor is 5 records per block, the number of characters per record is 150, the length of an interblock gap is 1.5 cm.

20.2 Repeat the calculation using a blocking factor of 8.
        Theoretical capacity: (73 000 cm /2.54) × 1600 bpi that is 45 984 252 bytes or 45 984 252/150 = 306 561 records.
        Practical capacity: knowing that a character occupies one byte, a record of 150 characters recorded with a density of 1600 bpi will have a length of 1 inch/1600 × 150, i.e. 0.09375 inch or 0.238125 cm.
        A block of 5 records will therefore have a length of 1.190625 cm.
        This block is followed by a gap of 1.5 cm, giving a total length for a physical block of 1.10625 + 1.5 = 2.690625 cm.
        In a length of 73 000 cm we will therefore have 73 000 cm/2.690625 cm = 27 131 physical blocks each containing 5 records, giving a total of 135 655 records.
        With a blocking factor of 8, we would have 171 512 records.

Chapter 21

Magnetic disks

Magnetic tapes, while having the advantage of low cost, have the major disadvantage of allowing only serial access. Since 1957 manufacturers, such as IBM, have therefore developed magnetic disk systems giving direct access to data.

21.1 General considerations

Data is recorded on magnetic disks or hard disks, according to the same principles that we described in our treatment of magnetic tapes.

The magnetic disk is a circular plate of aluminium (a light non-magnetic metal) 3.5 or 5.25 inches in diameter for the hard disks of microcomputers and up to 30 cm or more for mini- or mainframe systems. The disk is covered with a thin layer (0.5 to 0.75 μm) of ferromagnetic oxide for systems using standard methods. In a more recent technological development called **thin film** it is covered with a very thin layer (0.05 to 1 μm) of phosphor–nickel or phosphor–cobalt which gives a recording density of 8000 bits per centimetre, i.e. almost double that of standard recording methods.

Each face of the disk is divided into concentric circular **tracks** varying from 10 to 1000 tracks per surface depending on the model. Each track is divided into **sectors** (from 8 to 25), which are lengths of track between two radii. All the tracks have the same capacity and so the recording density increases towards the centre of the disk. This maximum density is the one usually quoted by the manufacturers.

These tracks and sectors are not visible to the naked eye. Beginning with a blank disk, the tracks and the sectors and all the data required for the management of the disk are written by a special operating system routine called the disk **formatter**.

Several disks (up to twenty) stacked one above the other on the same axis form a disk pack. These disks are separated from each other by a gap of 10 to 15 mm to allow read–write heads to pass freely between them. Thus several read–write heads one above the other give simultaneous access to a group of tracks one above the other forming a **cylinder**, as shown in the diagram:

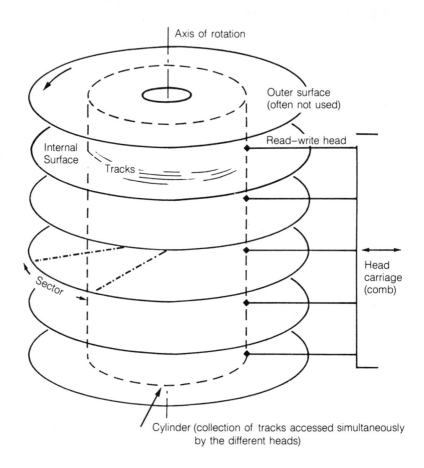

Cylinder (collection of tracks accessed simultaneously
by the different heads)

In order to increase the recording density of data and thus increase the storage capacity, the magnetised zone associated with each recorded bit has to be reduced to the minimum. Three methods are used for magnetising a zone:

- Longitudinal recording: this is the type most often used today. The oxide is magnetised parallel to the surface and tangentially to the track.
- Transverse recording: here the magnetisation is also parallel to the surface of the oxide but this time it is perpendicular to the track.
- Vertical recording: in this type of recording, which is currently being developed and which enables recording densities up to 40 000 bits per centimetre (i.e. ten times that obtained with standard methods), the magnetisation is perpendicular to the surface of the oxide.

The diagram below illustrates these three methods:

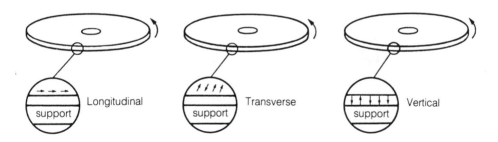

The disks in a disk drive turn at high speed (from 2400 to 3600 rpm). At this speed the read–write heads must not be in contact with the oxide because this would result in overheating and wear of the oxide layer. The heads (from two to ten per disk) must therefore be maintained at a certain distance, called the **flying height** (of the order of 0.2 to 0.8 μm) from the surface of the disk. This means that the surface of the disk must be absolutely clean to avoid a **head crash** which would seriously damage the thin layer of magnetic oxide.

The heads 'fly' in the fast moving layers of air very close to the surface of the disk caused by the disk's rotation. The heads have to be very light and very accurately positioned. The technology necessary for this has been developed by IBM at their laboratories in Winchester, UK. The distance is illustrated in the following diagram:

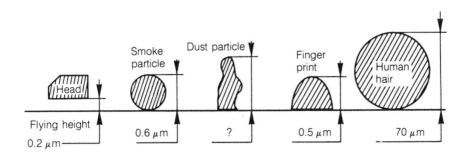

Since the flying height of the heads is maintained by the movement of the air caused by the disk's rotation, the heads must be retracted before the disks stop rotating. For this purpose special lubricated tracks are built into the disk where the heads can 'land' or be fully retracted away from the disks. This retraction can be accomplished by the PARK function of the operating system MS-DOS.

The necessity to keep the disk surfaces absolutely clean has led to the development of the **Winchester** disk where the heads are enclosed with the disks in an airtight case. Figure 21.1 shows a Winchester head, and Figure 21.2 illustrates the architecture of a hard disk.

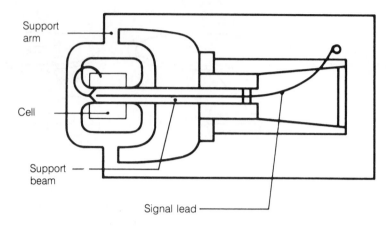

Support
arm

Cell

Support
beam

Signal lead

Source: *Soft et micro*, No. 28, March 1987.

Figure 21.1   View of a Winchester head

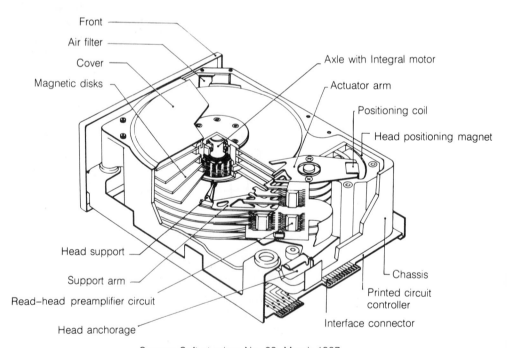

Front

Air filter

Cover

Magnetic disks

Axle with Integral motor

Actuator arm

Positioning coil

Head positioning magnet

Head support

Support arm

Read–head preamplifier circuit

Head anchorage

Chassis

Printed circuit
controller

Interface connector

Source: *Soft et micro* No. 28, March 1987.

Figure 21.2   Internal architecture of a hard disk

21.2 Interfaces

The role of the interface is to manage the transfer of data between the CPU and the disk drive. The three most common interfaces at the present time are the ST 506/412 with a transfer rate of 5 Mbytes/s, the SCSI used mostly by Apple which has a transfer rate of up to 32 Mbytes/s, and the EDSI used on the IBM PS/2 at up to 15 Mbytes/s.

21.3 Methods of recording

There are four main methods used for recording data on disks.

- **FM or frequency modulation:** this technique of recording is now more widely known as **single density** recording and it is the oldest. The principle of this method is simple; there is a flux change (north to south or south to north) at each cell boundary and an additional change at the midway point if a 1 is to be written. In reading, two signals during a cell interval signify a 1, one signal signifies a 0.
- **MFM or modified frequency modulation:** this technique is more recent and results in **double density** recording. There is a change of flux at the midway point of a cell to record a 1 and a change of flux at the cell boundary to separate two consecutive 0's.
- M2FM or **modified-modified frequency modulation:** this coding method reduces still further the number of transitions needed to record the data. It is similar to MFM but the flux direction only changes at the beginning of a cell if there has not been a flux change in the previous cell and the present cell does not contain a 1.
- **RLL or run length limited:** up to now this is the most efficient coding system. It allows 50% more data to be stored than MFM for the same number of flux transitions. The data to be recorded first has to be coded, the codes being chosen to limit the number of consecutive 1's or 0's. The details of the method are beyond the scope of this book.

At the current time MFM and RLL are the most widely used methods. FM, MFM and M2FM are shown in the following diagram:

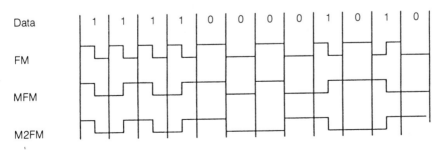

21.4 **Recording formats**

In addition to the recorded data, tracks and sectors also contain the information necessary for the correct interpretation of the data. Certain tracks are reserved for system use to indicate which sectors are available for recording data, which files are contained on the disk and what their parameters are.

Each sector stores certain information, as illustrated in the following diagram:

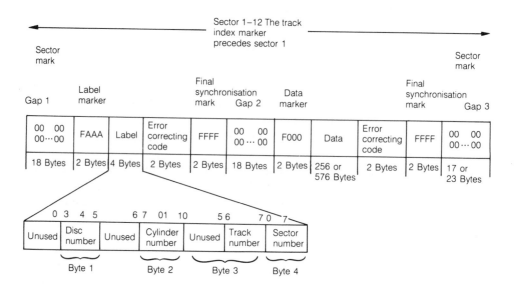

- Sector gap: serves to mark the beginning and end of a sector and comprises 18 zero bytes.
- Label marker: warns that a label is about to arrive under the read heads (equivalent to the tape mark on a magnetic tape).
- Sector label: the label holds the address of the data stored in the sector and contains: the number of the disk; number of the cylinder; the number of the track; and the number of the sector. The required sector can thus be distinguished from all the other sectors on the disk.
- The error correcting code: produced by a special algorithm which can detect and often also correct errors occurring in the labels or the data.
- Final synchronisation mark: this is a zone with a twofold purpose. It allows time for the controller to switch from recognising the address it has just read, to writing the data, and it also sends timing signals to the control electronics for synchronisation purposes to ensure the correct reading of data.
- Gap 2: normally consists of 0's but can be used as an overflow zone after an update.
- Data marker: equivalent to a tape mark.

- Data zone: consists of 256 to 512 bytes of data. It is normally cleared to zero during disk formatting but this is not always the case. For example, disks which are formatted under MS-DOS, only have the tracks which record the file allocation table (FAT) erased. It is possible, with the help of certain utility programs, to recover a disk which has been accidentally reformatted. It is better, though, to take precautions with tapes and disks to prevent accidental erasure.

21.5 Storage capacities

21.5.1 General considerations

As we have already seen, a certain amount of information in addition to the stored data is associated with each sector of the disk. So, as with magnetic tapes, we need to distinguish between the theoretical capacity and the practical capacity of the disk (sometimes referred to as the capacity before formatting and the capacity after formatting).

The theoretical capacity of a disk is the product of the theoretical capacity of a track, the number of tracks on each surface, and the number of surfaces used for recording.

The practical capacity is normally that given by the manufacturer or supplier. At the present time capacities of up to 1.6 Gbytes are quoted.

21.5.2 'Blocking' records on disks

In a computer application using files, the unit of data processed is the logical record. Records can be grouped into larger units for transfer between the disk and central memory. These would be **blocks** on magnetic tape but are **control intervals** (CIs) or **clusters** on disks.

Since a CI is transferred in a single read or write operation, its size is determined by that of the associated input–output buffers in central memory. Up to a certain limit, the larger the CI the faster the disk access will be but the greater the amount of central memory occupied by disk buffers. These choices are, in some systems, made when the files are created to ensure that space is reserved on the disk. For example, typical parameters might be the length of the CI, or the number of CIs in the initial file.

These parameters are therefore of some importance.

SAQ

21.1 Calculate the amount of space reserved for a file on a theoretical machine assuming the following creation parameters:

(a) CR FIC1 – LRSZ 90 – CISZ 256

(b) CR FIC2 – LRSZ 90 – CISZ 512

where FIC1 or FIC2 are the names of the files created; LRSZ gives the length of a file record, and CISZ gives the length of the CI in bytes.

Consider for this exercise that logical records cannot be split between CIs. This is not always the case in real systems where the same record may be split between several CIs, thus assuring that their capacity is fully used.

21.6 The main characteristics of disks

- The **linear density** or recording density: this is the number of bits per inch on a track. It is expressed in **bpi** (bits per inch) and goes up to 13 000 bpi.
- The **radial density**: this is the number of tracks per inch. It is expressed in tpi (tracks per inch) and goes up to 1100 tpi.
- The **speed of rotation**: this is the speed at which the disk turns and is expressed in revolutions per minute (**rpm**). It is of the order of 3600 rpm.
- The **access time:** this is made up of three elements, the seek time, the latency, and the transfer time, but manufacturers' literature usually ignores the latter.
- The **seek time:** this the time necessary to position the head over the required cylinder. The minimum seek time (5 to 20 milliseconds (ms) corresponds to the time required to move the heads to an adjacent cylinder, the maximum seek time (100 to 200 ms) corresponds to the time to traverse all the cylinders, the average seek time (10 to 80 ms) is the one usually quoted by the manufacturers.
- The **latency** or rotational delay: this the time necessary after the head is positioned on the correct track, for the data being sought to arrive under the head. The time can be zero or equal to the time for a complete rotation of the disk. On average it will require half a revolution which is of the order of 6 ms.
- The **transfer time:** this is the time taken to transfer data between the read–write head and the CPU.
- The **interleave factor:** hard disks are sometimes too fast for some computers. It is then necessary to slow down the transfer of data between the computer and the disk. For this reason data is not always written continuously but with an interleave factor. For example, if after reading sector 1, the system must delay a little before reading sector 2 (while the disk continues to turn), it is preferable not to place this sector immediately after sector 1 but a certain distance (from 3 to 9 sectors) away depending on the system.
- The **MTBF** or mean time between failures: this corresponds to the average time between one disk fault and the next, and is a point worth considering when buying a hard disk system. For certain disks this figure is currently greater than 100 000 hours.

The following figures are for a commercially available Winchester $5\frac{1}{4}''$ hard disk:

Number of disks	2
Number of surfaces used	4
Capacity before formatting	12·8 Mbytes
Maximum recording density	9074 bpi
Number of tracks	306
Radial density	345 tpi
Rotational velocity	3600 rpm
Seek time (adjacent tracks)	2 ms
Mean seek time	15 ms
Mean latency	8.33 ms
Mean access time using search buffer	85 ms
MTBF (in operation)	11 000 hours
Mean life of components	5 years
Software error rate	1 in 10^{10} bits
Hardware error rate	1 in 10^{12} bits

21.7 Exchangeable disks

Hard disks which are not exchangeable suffer from the disadvantage that in order to safeguard their contents one is obliged to copy them on to magnetic tapes, and if tape streamers using DAT are not available this takes a considerable time.

Hard exchangeable disks offer a solution to this problem. They use the same technology as fixed disks but the actual disks are contained in portable boxes (**disk packs**) which can be removed from one disk drive and placed in another drive. The capacity of such packs is currently of the order of 40 Mbytes with access times of approximately 19 ms.

EXERCISE

21.1 A hard disk has the following characteristics:

> Number of surfaces used: 5
> Number of sectors per face: 9
> Number of tracks per face: 612
> Number of bytes per sector: 1024

What is the capacity of the disk pack if information such as 'labels', etc., occupies 20% of the space?

Solution to SAQ

21.1 Calculate the amount of space reserved for a file on a theoretical machine assuming the following creation parameters:

(a) CR FIC1 – LRSZ 90 – CISZ 256
(b) CR FIC2 – LRSZ 90 – CISZ 512

(a) In a block of 256 bytes, it is possible to store two complete records. The space unused is therefore

$$256 - (90 \times 2) = 76 \text{ bytes}$$

i.e. a 'loss' of 29%.
(b) In a block of 512 bytes, it is possible to store five complete records. The space unused is therefore

$$512 - (90 \times 5) = 62 \text{ bytes}$$

i.e. a 'loss' of 12%.

Chapter 22

Floppy disks

Introduced by IBM in 1970, the floppy disk was used originally to load test programs into computers. That disk had an 8″ diameter and was coated with magnetic oxide on one side only.

In 1975 double-density (DD) recording was introduced by Shugart Associates. In 1976 IBM proposed double-sided disks with both surfaces coated in oxide. In the same year Shugart launched a mini-floppy disk with a diameter of $5\frac{1}{4}″$. The micro-floppy disk with a diameter of $3\frac{1}{2}″$ was introduced in 1981.

22.1 General considerations

The floppy disk (Figure 22.1) is one of the most widely used storage media due mainly to its ease of use and its low price. It comprises two parts.

22.1.1 The magnetic medium

The medium is made from a flexible plastic (mylar) disk with a hole at the centre to take the drive mechanism. It is covered in a thin layer of magnetic oxide, and can turn freely in a protective envelope.

A hole (index hole) punched in the mylar of 8″ and $5\frac{1}{4}″$ disks indicates the start of the first sector.

22.1.2 The protective envelope

Made in a rigid or semirigid plastic, the protective envelope coated inside with an anti-static and anti-dust lining, protects the disk from dust, finger marks or other impurities. The envelope is pierced with an oblong hole allowing access for the read–write heads

On the edge of $5\frac{1}{4}″$ and 8″ disks, there is generally a little notch which, by being covered or uncovered by a piece of adhesive, disables or enables the **writing** of data on to the disk. On $3\frac{1}{2}″$ disks this protection is afforded by a little plastic slider which covers or uncovers a hole to enable or disable writing. The envelope

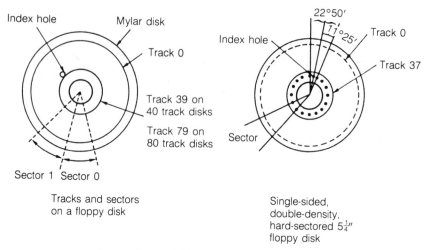

Tracks and sectors
on a floppy disk

Single-sided,
double-density,
hard-sectored $5\frac{1}{4}''$
floppy disk

Source: *Amstrad PC1512 User's Guide*.

Figure 22.1   Floppy disks

is pierced by one and sometimes two index holes for the 8″ and $5\frac{1}{4}''$ disks but not for the $3\frac{1}{2}''$ disk where the mark to indicate the start of a sector is written by software, as for hard disks.

22.2 **Recording methods**

Reading and writing of data is in one of three modes:

- FM or single density (**SD**).
- MFM or double density (**DD**).
- High density (**HD**).

Depending on whether two sides or only one side of the disk are used the disks are said to be either **double sided** or **single sided**. The single-sided disk is becoming less popular and is being replaced by double-sided disks. This depends not on the disks themselves but on whether the reading mechanism has two read–write heads or only one.

If you buy a single-sided disk it does not mean that you can only use one side of the disk but that only one side has been certified. You could use the second side 'at your own risk'.

As on hard disks, in addition to the user's stored data there is also the data used by the operating system for the management of the disks. This data and also the number of tracks and sectors are defined by the disk **format** and they are written during the **formatting** operation.

Sectors can be formatted in two ways:

- By **hard sectoring**: this method is less and less used because it offers no flexibility – the sectoring is defined by the presence of a hole at the start of every sector. The hole is detected by a photo-electric cell which gives rise to a signal called the 'sector clock'. The number of sectors per track cannot be altered but the method offers greater security.
- By **soft sectoring**, which is the method most often used at the present time because it allows the user to choose the number of sectors on a track. The sector formats are then virtually identical to those studied for hard disks.

A disk normally can be expected to have:

- 77 tracks and 26 sectors on an 8″ disk.
- 40/80 tracks and 8/9 sectors on a $5\frac{1}{4}$″ disk.
- 80/135 tracks and 8/9 sectors on a $3\frac{1}{2}$″ disk.

It will be recalled that the radial recording density is the number of tracks per inch: $5\frac{1}{4}$″ disks will have 48 tpi or 96 tpi depending on whether they are 40 track or 80 track disks. There are also $5\frac{1}{4}$″ disks with 135 tpi capable of storing 1.2 Mbytes. For the best results the higher recording densities require the best quality oxide. A disk with high density (HD) oxide which would normally be used to store 1.2 Mbytes, could equally well be formatted to store 360 kbytes; but used in this way it would not represent such good value for money. The diagram below shows a $5\frac{1}{4}$″ floppy disk:

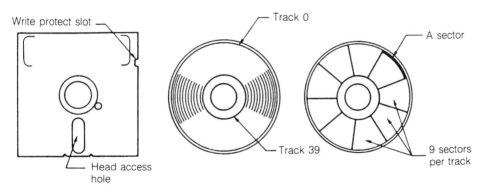

For the $3\frac{1}{2}$″ floppy disks, the battle continues and no universal standard has yet been defined; but at the present time it seems that it might be for 135 tpi having a capacity of 1.2 to 1.44 Mbytes.

22.3 **Capacities**

Depending on the recording technique used, and therefore on the computer, we have

- Single-sided/single-density ± 100 kbytes.

- Single-sided/double-density between 200 and 400 kbytes.
- Double-sided/double-density between 400 and 1400 kbytes.

Here again we have to consider capacities of formatted and unformatted disks. In $5\frac{1}{4}''$ disks the capacities when formatted are generally between 360 kbytes for 40 tracks DS/DD and 720 kbytes for 80 track DS/DD; there are also disks which store 1.2 Mbytes for DS/HD. The $3\frac{1}{2}''$ disks currently offer capacities varying between 720 kbytes and 1.44 Mbytes.

Storage capacities of floppy disks are likely to increase dramatically in the near future due to technological advances in recording methods (vertical recording) and magnetic media (use of barium ferrites). Certain manufacturers have already predicted floppy disks with unformatted capacities of from 3 to 25 Mbytes in the next few years.

22.4 **Software organisation**

As an example we will describe the way in which data is organised on a floppy disk for the IBM PC under MS-DOS.

Track 0 is partly used for information concerning the type of disk and its contents.

The first sector of this track is called the boot sector and it contains various details relating to the version of MS-DOS (the size of the sector, disk, etc.), while for a **system** disk there is also the system load program, from which the name 'boot' is derived. The data from this sector is loaded into read–write memory by the initial input program in ROM.

The second and third sectors store the file allocation table (FAT). Each element of this table indicates the state of an allocation unit (control interval, here called **cluster**) of two sectors, i.e. generally 1024 bytes. Thus the system knows if the cluster is available, occupied by a file, or faulty.

The files of programs and data are stored in data allocation units (clusters). When new files are created, MS-DOS has to allocate a certain number of clusters to them and must not reallocate a cluster already in use; equally MS-DOS must avoid allocating defective tracks. In addition, it is better to allocate clusters belonging to the same file so as to minimise head movements when reading and writing. For increased reliability the FAT is copied in sectors 4 and 5.

The file **directory** gives the names, size, creation date, and first cluster allocated to each of the files on the disk. It occupies sectors 7, 8 and 9 of side 0 and sectors 1 and 2 of side 1. Each element of the **root directory** is represented as a table occupying 32 bytes and represents either a file or a sub-directory. The information contained in the seven sectors allocated to the root directory is used by MS-DOS while servicing DIR commands to supply information such as the name, extension, size, dates and times of creation of the files. In addition it gives the address of the first cluster of each file.

A more detailed examination of these sectors is beyond the scope of this book. For further details students are advised to consult more specialised texts.

22.5 Reading floppy disks

This uses the same principles described earlier for reading hard disks but note that in the case of floppy disks, the head is in contact with the medium and in consequence there is more rapid wear of the surface. (There is also a 'flexible/hard' disk called a Bernoulli disk where the head floats above the surface.) The concept of a cylinder for a floppy disk is of course, limited to the two sides of the disk. The following diagram shows a floppy disk drive:

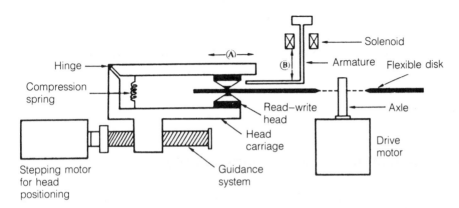

Unlike the hard disk the floppy disk does not rotate continuously in the reader because the permanent contact between the read–write heads and the surface would wear the surface too rapidly. Thus it rotates only when reading or writing is necessary. It is usually quite noisy.

22.6 The Bernoulli disk

The Bernoulli disk, named after the physicist, offers a combination of properties of the hard disk and the floppy disk. It is a flexible disk rotating at high speed whose read–write head avoids contact with the surface due to the operation of the venturi effect and thus avoids wear of the heads and the disk. In addition, the associated air-flow eliminates dust and so head crashes are also avoided.

The Bernoulli cartridge offers access times comparable to the Winchester disk and a capacity of up to 20 Mbytes on a $5\frac{1}{4}''$ format.

Chapter 23

New memory technologies

Constantly evolving, computer technology is preparing today the devices that will be in current use tomorrow. At a time when several types of memory are in the process of entering into common use, yet newer, still more revolutionary advances are being planned for the future.

Among the 'new' types of memory now to be found on the commercial market we will consider:

- Bubble memories.
- Optical stores.

23.1 Magnetic bubble memories (MBM)

First discovered in the early 1960s and then re-discovered in 1967, in turn thought to have a brilliant future and then abandoned by some developers to be taken up by others, magnetic bubble memories have had a very difficult birth and are still not firmly established.

23.1.1 General principles

The principle of the operation of magnetic bubble memories lies in the property possessed by some materials to become locally magnetised under the influence of an external magnetic field. These magnetic domains, several microns wide, are called **magnetic bubbles**. The presence or absence of a bubble represents the binary value 1 or 0.

Note that these bubbles are not distributed randomly through the material but are guided along carefully prepared routes by a magnetic field, as shown on p. 221. Let us look at how a bubble memory is constructed.

The memory comprises three parts:

- The thin film of material in which the bubbles are formed.
- Two coils which create a rotating magnetic field to govern the movement of the bubbles through the thin film.

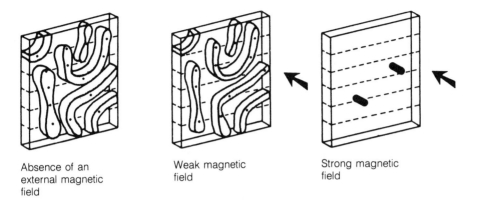

Absence of an
external magnetic
field

Weak magnetic
field

Strong magnetic
field

- Two permanent magnets which ensure the stability of the bubbles and thus the non-volatility of the data they represent, when the power supply is cut off.

The path taken by the bubbles as they circulate in the thin film is defined by some specially shaped strips of permalloy (a metal that is easily magnetised), placed on the surface of the film. The bubbles are constrained to move under the permalloy strips. Figure 23.1 illustrates the components of bubble memory.

We have seen in our study of codes, that data is translated in terms of words which for example may have a length of one or more bytes. Let us now see how to produce a memory word of one byte.

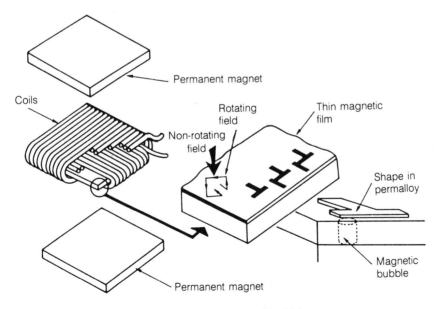

Figure 23.1   The components of bubble memory

23.1.2   *The architecture of bubble memories*

For storage purposes, the bubbles representing the data are channelled into special structures called **loops**. To store a memory word of 8 bits requires 8 loops.

Each of the 8 bits is represented by the presence or absence of a magnetic bubble. For example, if we wish to store the byte 10010111 we send the data at regular intervals to a particular circuit called a **bubble generator**.

The rotating magnetic field produced by the two orthogonal coils (whose fields are perpendicular), ensures that as the bubbles are being created they move one after the other in succession around the major loop to arrive after a given number of shifts, at the transfer gates.

At this point a control pulse causes them to pass through the gates from the major loop to the minor loops where, still under the influence of the rotating magnetic field, they continue to circulate but this time in parallel with only one bit circulating in each minor loop (see diagram below):

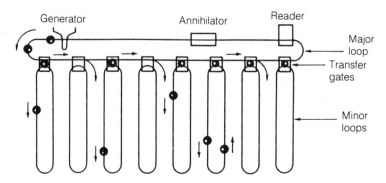

Other bytes can in their turn be written serially into the major loop to be gated at the appropriate moment into the minor loops. When we wish to read the first byte again we simply wait until the bubbles comprising it are positioned at the transfer gates. In fact since the circulation speed in the secondary loops is the same for all the bubbles, all the bubbles belonging to the first byte arrive at the transfer gates together. It only remains for them to be re-injected into the major loop where, under the effect of the rotating field, they will arrive successively at the reader.

Data is erased by activating the eraser in step with the bubbles as they pass below it. Bubbles which are not erased arrive again at their transfer gates where they can be reinjected into the minor loops. A loop made from permalloy shapes is shown below.

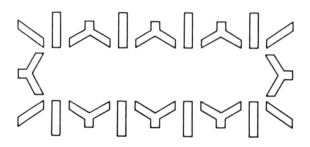

Some minor loops (not shown here) are reserved for addressing purposes and it is these that supply timing information for gating the required data out of the minor loops. Bubble memories enable large amounts of data to be stored in a small space but this is not their only characteristic.

23.1.3   *Characteristics of bubble memories*

Capacity/cm^2	1 million bits (data bits)
Volatility	None
Mechanics	None
Access time	< 11 ms
Cost per bit	Very low

These characteristics, and in particular the non-volatility of the data (it is claimed that data can be stored for as long as 20 million years), and the fact that they have no mechanical parts make these bubble memories very useful in difficult conditions. However they have a relatively small capacity (1 million bits).

Such memories are useful in difficult environments (e.g. factories, military uses) but, bearing in mind the low cost of storage, they can also be used for central memory, disk emulators, portable computers, etc.).

23.2   **Optical stores**

The optical disk store is the result of work carried out since 1970 by the manufacturers of videodisks. The optical disk store is known by several names CD-ROM (compact disc read-only memory), WOM (write once memory), WORM (write Once read many).

23.2.1   *General principles*

Optical disks are read using a laser beam which is reflected or diffused according to the state of surface of the disk, thus signifying a stored 1 or a stored 0. The purpose of the laser is to provide a very intense narrow beam of light allowing a precision of the order of a micron, to enable a high storage density on the surface.

For comparison with magnetic memories, consider the following table:

	12″ CD-ROM	Magnetic memory
Capacity (Mbytes/side)	1000	150
Density (Mbits/in^2)	225	20
Radial density	20000	1500
Linear density	35000	15000
Transfer rate (Mbytes/s)	3	3
Access time (ms)	<80	<20
Life in years	10	3
Error rate	10^{-12}	10^{-12}
Cost per Mbyte in pence	9.0	10

The distance between the optical reading head and the medium does not affect the quality of the reading or of the writing and thus, in contrast to magnetic media, the risk of a head crash can be avoided.

CD-ROMs are at present usually made from a very thin reflective layer on which the data is stored, sandwiched between two protective transparent surfaces of glass or plastic, as shown below:

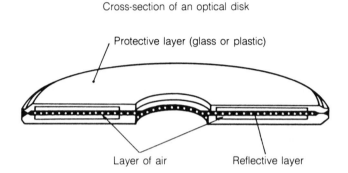

Cross-section of an optical disk

Protective layer (glass or plastic)

Layer of air   Reflective layer

There are several techniques for storing data.

23.2.1.1 Removal

Writing: under the effect of heat generated by the laser beam used for writing (stronger than the beam for reading), the chemical composition (an alloy of tellurium) melts, indicating the presence of a 0 (for example) (shown below):

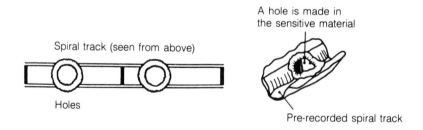

Spiral track (seen from above)

Holes

A hole is made in
the sensitive material

Pre-recorded spiral track

Reading: the distance between the reading head and the reflecting surface is increased where the surface has melted and so binary 0's and 1's can be distinguished by the presence or absence of a hole.

23.2.1.2 Distortion

Writing: heating the metallic layer by the writing beam causes a deformation (bubbling) of the reflecting surface, as shown:

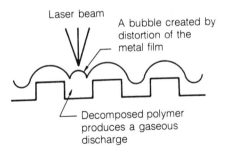

Reading: it uses a similar principle to that of the removal method described above and is based on the change of distance.

23.2.1.3 Amalgam

Writing: the writing beam melts the metallic layer which absorbs light, to reveal a second layer which reflects it, as shown in the diagram:

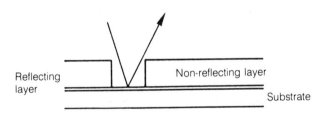

Reading: in one case the reading beam is reflected, in the other case it is absorbed.

23.2.1.4 Change of state

Writing: the strong laser beam causes the material to change from its amorphous state in which it absorbs light, to its crystalline state in which it reflects light, as shown in the diagram:

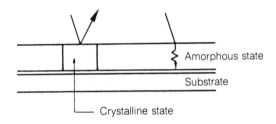

Reading: the principle is the same as that used for the amalgam described above.

23.2.1.5 Polarisation

In this method the reflective properties of the surface are altered as shown:

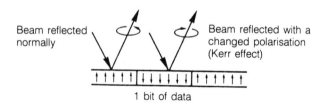

Writing: heat from the beam changes the magnetic properties of the metallic surface of the disk which is originally magnetised uniformly over its surface. When it cools again it can be locally remagnetised in the original sense (erasure).

Reading: light reflected from the surface is polarised in different ways depending on the direction of magnetisation of the surface (Kerr effect).

These two latter techniques (change of state and polarisation) offer the advantage of being able to erase the data (the techniques are not completely mastered at the present time) and therefore of reusing the media. Current research is leading towards an optical disc which can be written and read at will. This type of disc is about to appear on the market (D ONE, a $5\frac{1}{4}''$ disk with an access time of 60 ms using magneto-optical techniques).

23.2.1.6 Formatting

In some CD-ROM systems the disk has a single spiral track like that on a gramophone record; in others the format is based on that used for magnetic disks. In the latter case, an optical disk will be divided into:

● Tracks: from 32 000 to 40 000 tracks.
● Sectors: of the order of 24 to 50 sectors each of 1 kbyte.

These recording formats are not yet standardised but ATG (Alcatel Thompson Gigadisk) seems to be setting its own standard. In the ATG format each sector of a track contains 1 kbyte and each of the 4000 tracks has 25 sectors. On each track a number of bytes are reserved for the sector addresses and the control and management of errors. A certain number of synchronisation bits are pre-recorded. The format is shown in the following diagram.

The commercial marketing of optical disks has already begun even though they are still in their development stage. Their present faults are mainly that they cannot be erased and rewritten at will and that their access time is generally very inferior to that of magnetic disks; these are the problems currently being addressed by manufacturers at the present time. Because of their enormous storage capacity (20 000 A4 pages of text), their mode of access and a constant reduction in their cost they have a promising future in the field of archiving and may in the long term take the place of magnetic media.

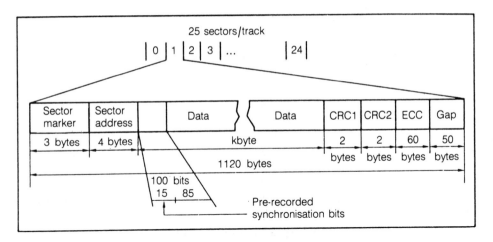

Format (not yet standardised) of an ATG optical disk

Chapter 24

Memory management

Two criticisms that are often levelled at central memories is that their capacity is too small and their speed is too slow, limiting the performance of the CPU. The solutions that can be suggested to these problems are:

- Extend the capacity of the memory by using large secondary memories.
- Increase the speed by using faster components (cache memories).

The progress made during the past few years in circuit integration and the reduction of manufacturing costs has been offset to some extent by an increase in the number of programs running concurrently and therefore placing heavier demands on the store. The problem of memory management is forever present in computer systems.

24.1 Management of central memory

From the foregoing discussion it will be clear that it is not always possible to place the whole of a program and its data in central memory at the same time. Instead it is necessary to perform a succession of transfers of program segments and data segments between central memory and secondary memory as the execution proceeds.

When a system of memory management called **virtual memory** is used, the operating system automatically performs the necessary transfers between backing store and main store. This enables programmers to use the whole of the available memory space, secondary memory (e.g. disks, tapes) and central memory (RAM) and treat it as though it were one large central memory.

As the memory requirements of a program in execution become known to the system, program instructions and data are brought from secondary memory and placed in central memory. These exchanges between backing store and main store are known as **swapping** (see p. 229).

In a multi-user or multi-tasking system it is important that memory areas attributed to one user or to one process are not encroached on by other users or processes present in the system.

To combat this, several techniques exist to enable the memory to be shared judiciously between users so that one user's area does not overflow into another's.

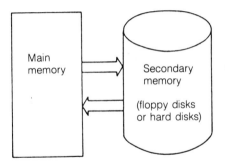

24.1.1 *Fixed partitioning*

This technique, also known as **static allocation** of memory, consists of arbitrarily dividing the central memory into a number of fixed partitions. The size of the partitions can differ from each other according to what they are to contain.

Processes will be loaded into the memory partitions in sequence as required. As one process is completed another will be loaded into the freed partition. The major disadvantage of this scheme is that some processes will be too large to fit into a single free partition. Another disadvantage is that space is often wasted because a process will usually not completely fill the partition to which it is allocated. Static memory allocation is illustrated in Figure 24.1.

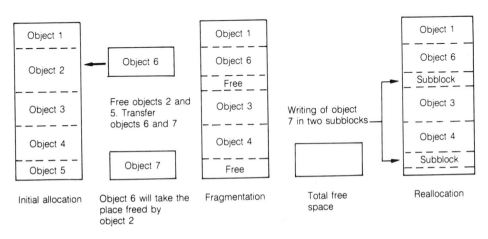

Source: M. Aumiaux, *Microprocesseurs 16 bits*, Editions Masson.

Figure 24.1 Static memory allocation

24.1.2 *Dynamic partitioning*

This technique, also called **dynamic allocation** of memory (see Figure 24.2), consists of loading the segments contiguously into memory one after the other. When a process finishes, its memory space becomes free. Each process has only as much memory as it needs and when it finishes it leaves a single contiguous segment of memory free. The remaining segments of memory are then moved to fill the vacant space (garbage collection). This movement of memory makes the technique costly in processing time.

24.1.3 *Paging*

This technique, which is not dissimilar to static partitioning, divides the memory into fixed size blocks (64 kbytes under MS-DOS) which are themselves divided into smaller fixed size blocks called **pages**. Paging thus avoids the problems arising when segments of different sizes need to be stored continuously, but requires a page table in the management of the paging process to reconstruct the logical order of the scattered pages comprising the original segment. It is illustrated in Figure 24.3.

24.1.4 *Segmentation*

In segmentation the memory space is divided into n segments of variable length, a number (the virtual address) being associated with each of the segments in the address space (virtual memory). The virtual address is translated into a physical

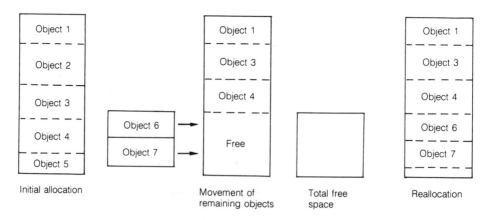

Source: M. Aumiaux, *Microprocesseurs 16 bits*, Editions Masson.

Figure 24.2 Dynamic memory allocation

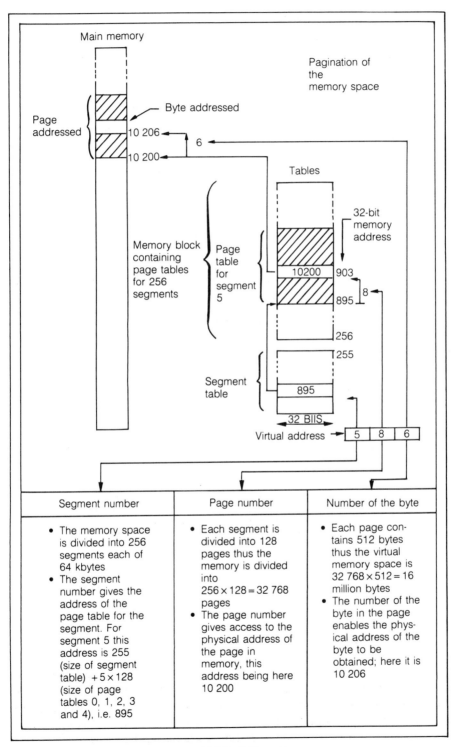

Source: M. Aumiaux, *Microprocesseurs 16 bits*, Editions Masson.

Figure 24.3   Page management in the NS16032

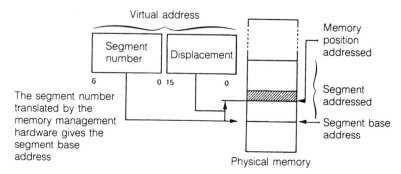

Physical address = base + displacement

Source: M. Aumiaux, *Microprocesseurs 16 bits*, Editions Masson.

Figure 24.4   Address translation

address by the calculation **base + displacement**. Address translation is illustrated in Figure 24.4. Each segment has certain attributes such as:

- Physical address of the base of the segment.
- Length of the segment.
- Protection class.

These attributes are stored in a segment descriptor which forms an entry in the segment table, a special area of the memory management unit (MMU), as follows:

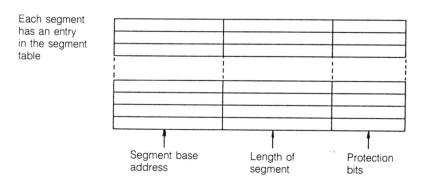

24.1.5 *Cache memory*

Some computers have, in addition to their main memory, a small (of the order of 32 kbytes but it can be as much as 1 Mbyte) very fast memory called a **cache memory** into which the operating system places the most frequently used instructions and data. Superficially, cache memory acts like a two-level paging system. Whenever a memory fetch operation takes place, the cache memory is first searched. If the item is not in cache the appropriate page in main memory is sought and, finally, if these searches have not been successful the required page is brought into main memory (swapped in or rolled in) from the auxiliary memory. This latter transfer may require that a page of main memory is moved out (swapped out or rolled out) on to backing store to make room for the new page.

24.2 Screen memory

Screen memory is an area of read–write memory (RWM) in which are stored one or more screen images enabling the screen to be changed quickly from one display to another. Each position on the screen has a corresponding position in the screen memory.

24.2.1 *Principle of operation*

When a key is pressed on the keyboard, for example an A, it generates the corresponding character code (65 in ASCII). The code is then placed in its correct position in a particular part of central memory called the screen memory. In

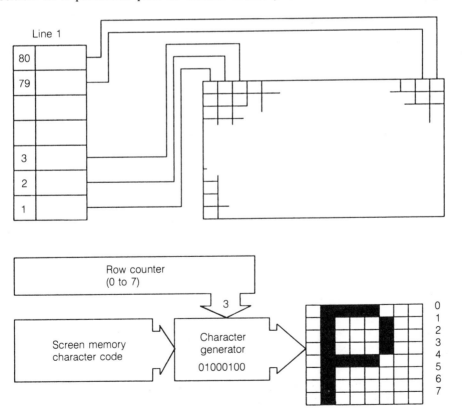

maintaining the screen display the system regularly scans the screen memory and the codes of the characters to be displayed are sent in sequence to the character generator. The character generator (normally stored in ROM) is a look-up table translating from ASCII code to screen pixels for displaying characters on the screen.

Each character is displayed as an array (e.g. 8×8) of pixels (points on the screen). The electron beam sweeps across the screen eight times (for an 8×8 array) to display one complete line of characters. On each sweep the sequence of characters from the line being displayed is read from screen memory and a row counter selects the correct row of pixels to read into a shift register. The row of pixels is output serially from the shift register to be displayed on the screen. Depending on the value of the pixel the electron beam is modulated to illuminate or not the appropriate points on the screen. The system is illustrated in the previous diagram.

Some systems avoid this repetitive translation from character codes to pixels every time the screen is refreshed, by storing the actual pixel values in screen memory.

Chapter 25

Peripherals

Peripherals is the name given to the collection of devices connected to the central processing unit. We distinguish two main types of peripheral: those which enable data to be entered into the computer, **input peripherals**, and those which enable data to be output from the computer, **output peripherals**. Some peripherals serve both functions.

25.1 Input peripherals

25.1.1 *The operator's console*

The operator's console is an essential part of a computer system. It is this console that enables the operator to interrupt the operation of the computer and give it instructions. Formerly operators' consoles were very elaborate, but now they are more likely to be just a keyboard and screen to input commands which enable, for example, the system to be started and stopped, or the state of various registers to be determined and their contents modified.

25.1.2 *Keyboards*

25.1.2.1 The composition of a keyboard
Unlike keyboards found on many simple home computers and games computers, normal keyboards are similar to those on typewriters but with more keys. In fact, computer keyboards have to offer more functions than are to be found on typewriters, (ESC, ALT, CTRL, etc).

The keys are generally grouped into blocks (or keypads) forming:

- Alphanumeric keys.
- Numeric keys.
- Symbolic keys.
- Function keys.

The number of keys, their position and their colour depend on the manufacturer; no true standard exists at the present time. There are, however, two types of keyboard which tend to be standard.

The first type (see Figure 25.1) provided for entry-level microcomputers and some terminals, is called **PC XT** (or 84-key keyboard) because its keys are arranged like those of the keyboard adopted by IBM for the IBM-PC microcomputer.

The second type, equipping middle- and top of the range microcomputers, and more rarely terminals, is called **PC AT** (or 102-key keyboard) because its keys are arranged like those of the keyboard adopted by IBM for the IBM-AT. This keyboard can easily be distinguished by the presence of a block of direction arrow keys separated from the numeric keypad.

Some keyboards are designed for specialised applications. This is the case for certain text processors (keys for changing from page mode to line or character, etc.). These keyboards, which are generally of good quality because they are needed for intensive and rapid typing, have been the object of advanced ergonomic studies and for this reason are often more pleasant to use (incurving keys, colours, touch, etc.). There are also industrial keyboards whose variety is equal to the number of possible applications (robots, process control, etc.).

25.1.2.2   The different forms of keyboard

Keyboard keys are constructed in different ways depending on how they will be used and how much they cost.

- **Membrane type:** the keys are screen printed on to a plastic film which completely seals banks of microcontacts. These keyboards are the least expensive on the market and the most resistant to ill treatment (spilt coffee, etc.) but they are often hard to use (e.g. poor contacts, repeated characters), and they have no specific applications.
- **Calculator type:** the keys are made of hard plastic and are mounted on springs. This type of keyboard has several disadvantages such as sensitivity to heavy-handed use, the fact that it is not ergonomic, the 'play' in the keys and unreliable contacts.

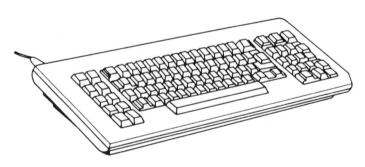

Source: *Amstrad User's Guide*

Figure 25.1   PC-XT keyboard

These two keyboard types are shown in the following diagram:

Membrane-type keyboard   Calculator-type keyboard

- **Rubber type:** these keyboards are only found on inexpensive home microprocessors because professional users would find the keys, which feel like rubber, too slow.
- **Typewriter type:** these keys are like those of the typewriter, with an ergonomic design for intensive use. The hardness of the keys, their 'professional feel' and sensitivity, varies from one model to another. This type of keyboard is one of the most expensive on the market and to replace it would cost from £100 for a bottom of the range 84-key keyboard to more than £1000 for a specialised one.

A diagram illustrating rubber and typewriter keyboards is shown below:

Rubber-type keyboard   Typewriter keyboard

- **Liquid crystal type:** these keyboards are not in widespread use. Each key can carry a pictogram of 20×8 pixels which can be altered to enable the keyboard to be used with several different alphabets (e.g. Hebrew, Arabic), or to display different symbols according to the mode (e.g. ALT, SHIFT, CTRL, normal).

25.1.2.3   The operation of a keyboard

General principle
The keyboard comprises a series of switches. Each time a key is pressed, the movement closes the switch corresponding to this key. The switches are placed in a matrix. Each row and each column of the matrix is connected to the computer via a conductor. The keyboard is perpetually scanned by software (usually part of the

operating system) to test whether a key has been pressed. This scanning is normally achieved by sending a signal down each column in turn and sensing whether it returns along one of the rows. If it does sense a signal in a row, the computer can identify the key by determining the position where the signal was switched from the column to the row, as the following diagram shows:

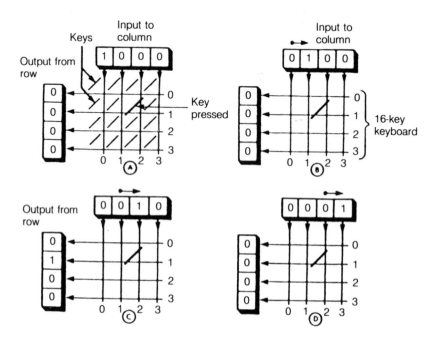

Identification of the key by scanning the columns

The contacts

Two types of contact are in current use, **resistive** and **capacitive**. They are shown in Figure 25.2.

In the resistive type the key is made from a simple switch which can be opened or closed depending on whether it is pressed or not. The connection is made when two gold-plated contacts touch (cross-point). In another resistive technique the contact is obtained by pushing a screen-printed membrane which then presses on a printed circuit which constitutes the base of the keyboard. Nowadays these two methods perform equally well but the membrane contact method is cheaper for large quantities.

The capacitive method consists of measuring the variation in the capacitance between two plates, one being joined to the moving part of the key, the other to the fixed part. Pressing the key brings the plates towards each other which causes a change in their capacitance. This method requires more electronics than the resistive one because the changes in capacitance have to be transformed into electrical signals. It is also more sensitive to electrical noise.

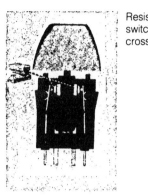

Resistive contact switch (gold) cross-point

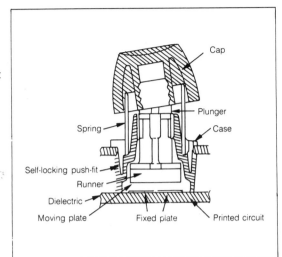

Capacitative contact switch

Source: *Minis et Micros*, No. 283/29, June 1987.

Figure 25.2   Types of switch contact

The contact bounce problem

In all switches using two electromechanical contacts, the true contact is only established after a period of oscillation of 10 to 20 ms between the instant when the key is pressed and the moment the contact is completely established. This is called **contact bounce**. It also occurs when the key is released.

A simple hardware solution to the problem consists of using a filter (e.g. a resistor and a capacitor of suitable size connected in parallel) or a flip-flop. This solution is normally used when the number of keys is small. Another solution, software this time, can be used to solve the problem by checking that the contact still remains closed at the end of a few milliseconds (5 to 20, according to the quality of the keyboard).

The transmission code

Once the mechanical to electrical conversion has been accomplished, the signal has to be coded so that the CPU can interpret the action. The standard code is ASCII but more and more use is being made of a **geographic coding system** first introduced by IBM for its PC. This encoding method consists of transmitting to the CPU a hexadecimal code, corresponding to the geographical position on the keyboard of the key being pressed and not to its identity. The same code plus 80H is transmitted to indicate the release of the key.

For example if the user presses the key corresponding to Q on the QWERTY keyboard, the key whose position number is 16, the code transmitted will be 10H if the keyboard is compatible with the PC. The CPU will later receive the code 90H, indicating the release of the key. Figure 25.3 illustrates this.

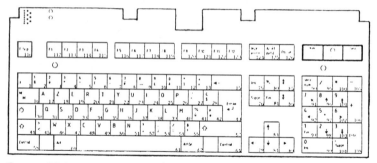

Source: *Minis et Micros*, No. 283/29, June 1987.

Figure 25.3 Key numbers for geographic coding

After switching on the computer, part of the start up procedure is to indicate to the operating system the type of keyboard (English, French, etc.). This is the purpose of the command KEYB UK or KEYB FR of MS-DOS). The central processor can then correctly identify the keys pressed. The advantage of this geographic coding compared with direct coding of the ASCII type, is that the values associated with the keys can be changed at will.

The qualities of a keyboard
The quality of a keyboard depends as much on its solidness as on the number and position of the keys. The position of the letters varies from country to country (in France there is the AZERTY keyboard where the first letters are in that sequence instead of QWERTY). There are (more or less recognised) standards concerning aspects such as the colour of the keys, the angle of the keyboard, the coefficient of reflection of light from the surface of the keys (which is why the surface of the keys is often lightly tinged with red). The top surface of each key can also be angled in relation to the base according to whether the plunger is straight or inclined: see Figure 25.4.

Keyboards are subjected to numerous mechanical shocks but they are fragile devices and should not be maltreated.

25.1.3 *The mouse*

The first mouse (Figure 25.5), devised by Professor Englebart of Stanford Research Institute, dates from the 1970s. Because of its ease of use, the mouse is the most popular interactive device after the keyboard. It offers certain advantages compared to the latter. It is, for example, more natural to associate the movement of the mouse with that of the cursor (generally shown as a little arrow), than with a combination of direction key presses on the keyboard. In the first case it requires only the user's automatic movements and does not involve any time delay, whereas

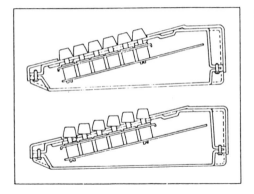

Keyboard with
straight plungers

Keyboard with
plungers inclined
at 10°

Source: *Minis et Micros*, No. 283/29, June 1987.

Figure 25.4   Keys are sometimes angled

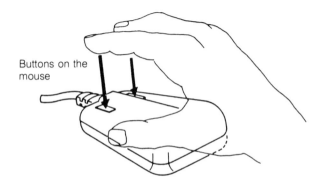

Buttons on the
mouse

Source: *Amstrad PC1512, User's Guide*.

Figure 25.5   The mouse is a popular interactive peripheral

to direct the cursor by the combined action of keys incurs an additional delay in execution.

A mouse is not only useful in moving the cursor but also serves to scan menus and make selections from them (or **click** on to them). In some cases it also serves as a drawing instrument. The favourite uses of the mouse are in the fields of publishing and computer aided design (CAD). They are increasingly being used with office software (word processing), and most notably software that has been written for graphic interfaces such as WINDOWS or GEM (Graphic Environment Manager).

25.1.3.1   The construction of a mouse
In one method of construction, the mouse is a case under which there is a metal ball covered in rubber. Movement of the case over a flat surface causes the ball to rotate, which in turn causes the rotation of two friction rollers mounted on spindles placed at right angles to each other. At the end of each spindle there is a coded disk.

In a mechanical mouse the coding is achieved by means of contactors, and contact points placed at regular intervals around the perimeter of the disks. The contactors detect the passage of the contact points indicating the direction and the degree of rotation. Whenever contacts are sensed, impulses are sent to the control card in the computer which translates them for the display screen. In an opto-mechanical mouse photo-cells and light emitting diodes (LEDs) are used instead of contacts. The disk is pierced with holes at regular intervals so that the beam from the LED is broken by the rotation of the disk and the photo-cells detect these changes which are transmitted to the controller. The diagram below shows an opto-mechanical mouse:

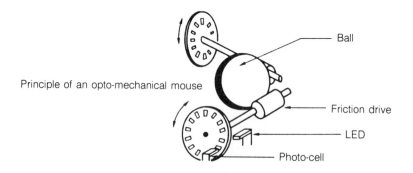

Principle of an opto-mechanical mouse

- Ball
- Friction drive
- LED
- Photo-cell

A method without moving parts requires the mouse to be moved over a special table which has a light reflecting surface divided by lines which absorb light. As the mouse passes over the surface, a light beam emitted by the mouse is reflected back except when the lines are crossed.

The mouse has one or more buttons on its upper surface. Generally there are one to three buttons but some manufacturers use more.

25.1.3.2 Using a mouse

A single button is sufficient for scrolling a menu, making a choice, starting an application or validating a command. A mouse with two buttons offers three possible combinations, a click on the left button usually selects a command, one on the right changes the choice. Two buttons pressed together correspond to an erase. A mouse with three or more buttons is mostly used in CAD applications.

25.1.4 *Graphics tablets*

Graphics tablets (digitising tablets or writing tablets) create a familiar working environment for designers that is similar to a drawing board. They are an interesting alternative to a mouse and to other interactive tools whenever graphic information has to be converted into absolute coordinates for the computer.

There are two ways of coding the coordinates: a digital system where each position of the pen is logged by a string of digits; and an analog system requiring the conversion of analog data collected by the pen.

25.1.4.1   Operation of a digital coding system

The digitising table is in the form of a flat surface (a drawing board) on to which a sheet of paper is placed. Set inside the surface of the tablet are two sets of conducting wires (1024 or more) insulated from each other and laid orthogonally like X and Y coordinates. There are two registers, one for the X-wires and one for Y-wires.

The circuit thus created is like a capacitor with one of the plates formed by the tablet and the other formed by the stylus. At regular intervals each set of wires receives a series of pulses enabling the position of each wire to be identified. The position of the stylus is then obtained by reading the contents of the registers associated with the X and Y coordinates at the instant when the stylus senses pulses via its capacitive linkage. The resolution obtained can be 0.025 mm and the frequency of readings can be higher than 200 coordinates per second. A graphics tablet is shown below:

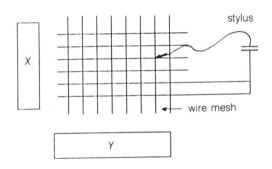

25.1.4.2   Operation of an analog coding system

The analog coding table looks like a digital coding table. It is made of an insulating layer covering a thin conducting layer, the whole being protected by an insulating cover (e.g. glass). An electric voltage is applied to the conducting film and the high impedance stylus is connected to a winding. A voltage potential is developed across the tablet in the X direction, and the X coordinate of the stylus position is obtained from the voltage measured at the stylus tip. The Y coordinate is obtained in a similar way from the voltage gradient developed in the Y direction. The X and Y voltages are applied alternately.

A variation of this method uses the properties of acoustics. Sound sensors are placed round the edge of the drawing surface. When the stylus is positioned in the required spot a switch is pressed and the stylus emits an ultrasonic pulse which is detected by the sensors. The time delay between the sound being emitted and being received by the sensors determines the position of the stylus.

25.1.4.3 Criteria for choosing a graphics tablet

There are two important factors in the choice of equipment of this type: the tablet and its pointer. The pointer can be either a stylus or a cross-wire with buttons (usually provided with a magnifying glass). The stylus is used to draw and to select commands from a menu. It can also be provided with an ink cartridge so that it leaves a visual trace on the paper. The cross-wires (cursor) with buttons is said to be much more accurate than the stylus. It can be positioned very finely, being again helped by an integral magnifying glass. Designers working with CAD equipment prefer to use a cross-wire because it can be manoeuvred more easily than a mouse and with more precision.

25.1.5 *Scanners*

The basic principle of the scanner consists of capturing the image on a page, and converting its contents to a computer file. The operation is relatively simple and generally based on the same technology as that used in photocopiers, using the principles of light and reflection.

The system therefore has a light source. The darker the area of the document illuminated, the less light it reflects. By means of a mirror and a lens, a row of CCD (charge coupled device) photo-cells collects light reflected from the document. Each point of the document can thus be analysed and its grey-level determined as a function of the light received by the photo-cell. The diagram below illustrates the mechanism:

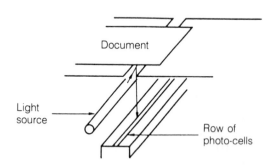

The row of photo-cells which currently contains from 1700 to 5000 cells, enables a resolution of 400×400 dots per square inch (dpi^2) with possibly 256 grey-levels. In the case of **true grey-levels**, several bits must be coded to record the brightness of each point, which could require a megabyte per page. When **pseudo grey-levels** are used, each point is converted into black or white only and it is the closeness of adjacent points which simulates a grey-level (as in a photograph in a newspaper or printing by laser); the resolution is not as good (but the price is not as high either).

Scanners are used mainly in desk top publishing (DTP) and CAD, but also in the optical archiving of documents in association with videodisk CD-ROM because scanning allows the 'look' of a document to be preserved.

25.1.6 *Optical and magnetic character recognition*

Data can be captured automatically with devices using the principles of optics **OCR** (Optical Character Recognition), or magnetism **MICR** or **MCR** (Magnetic (Ink) Character Recognition).

25.1.6.1 Magnetic readers

Magnetic character recognition is mostly used by banks. The characters found along the bottom edge of cheques are written in a font called E13b. On the continent a font called CMC7 (*Caractères Magnétisables Codés à 7 barres*) is used. Characters are printed using a special ink loaded with magnetic oxide. The document is passed through the reader where the documents are magnetised so that they can then be read by passing them under an elongated reading head.

CMC7

Each character is formed from a group of seven vertical lines of variable length, and each line is divided into sections to produce a visual image which can be easily recognised by humans. Each line is printed in magnetisable ink and is separated from the following line by a distance which can be either wide (binary 1) or narrow (binary 0). There are six intervals separating the seven lines and each can take one of two values giving 64 possible combinations of which 41 are used (see the following diagram):

E13b

This font, first used in the United States, has ten numbers and four special characters. Each character is scanned by a narrow scanning coil like an elongated magnetic reading head, which produces a signal whose amplitude is proportional to the quantity of magnetised ink under the coil. Each character generates a unique shape — see the diagram below:

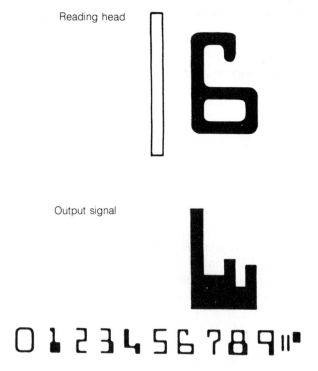

Reading head

Output signal

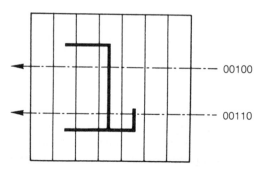

The major disadvantage of this method is the need to use magnetisable ink, but reading is very fast (1000 to 1500 documents per minute for cheques). In the UK CMC7 is now mostly used in optical character recognition and can be seen for example on postal orders.

Optical readers

Optical readers recognise characters written in standard fonts by illuminating them with two parallel beams of light which examine two particular areas of the character, the presence of ink causing the intensity of the reflected light to vary — see the diagram below:

Documents to be used in Optical Character Recognition (OCR) have tended to replace the CMC7 character font with fonts which, while being just as easy to read (for machines and humans) do not have the disadvantages associated with the complexity of the CMC7 font. However, for the time being, the size and the shape of the characters do have to conform to quite rigorous standards. There are two standard fonts for character recognition, OCR-A and OCR-B, shown below:

OCR-A

space	0		P
	1	A	Q
"	2	B	R
£	3	C	S
$	4	D	T
⁒	5	E	U
&	6	F	V
'	7	G	W
{	8	H	X
}	9	I	Y
*	:	J	Z
+	;	K	
	♪	L	
−	=	M	
	;!	N	
/	?	0	

OCR-B

space	0	@	P	'	p
!	1	A	Q	a	q
..	2	B	R	b	r
£#	3	C	S	c	s
$¤	4	D	T	d	t
%	5	E	U	e	u
&	6	F	V	f	v
'	7	G	W	g	w
(	8	H	X	h	x
)	9	I	Y	i	y
*	:	J	Z	j	z
+	;	K	[	k	{
,	<	L	\	l	l
−	=	M	]	m	}
.	>	N	^	n	~
/	?	0	_	o	

The main advantage of optical reading is that it does not require special ink. The printed document is very easy for humans to read and provided the standards are adhered to even handwritten characters can be read by machine.

Character recognition is currently receiving much attention, and research is developing new techniques enabling machines to *learn* to recognise ordinary handwritten characters. It is expected that these techniques will develop in a spectacular fashion in the next few years.

25.1.7 *Bar codes*

Bar codes, now widely employed in retailing, use a different system of representing data. Characters are coded as groups of bars of varying thickness, separated by spaces of varying widths, as shown:

3 109550 016701

There are several codes used for these characters. The standard UPC, (Universal Product Code), used in United States and Canada, like the EAN (European Article Number) used in Europe, has seven fields for coding a character, i.e. 128 combinations.

25.2 Output peripherals

25.2.1 *Screens*

The computer screen can be incorporated into the computer itself (portable computers, laptops), or the choice of screen can be left to the user. Since, as far as the user is concerned, the screen is one of the main pieces of the computer (it is the only part whose quality can be appreciated by a non-expert), it is important to pay it particular attention. A professional user should have a **video monitor**, specially constructed to give a stable and high definition image which allows work for several hours at the keyboard without producing excessive eye strain.

25.2.1.1 The cathode-ray tube (CRT)

Monochrome screens
The screen is made from a cathode-ray tube (similar to those used in oscilloscopes, and televisions) covered with a uniform layer of phosphorescent material in the case of a monochrome screen (generally white, green or amber). A beam of electrons is emitted by the cathode and deflected by deflection plates according to signals received from the character generator, to form the character at the correct position on the screen. The display rate can be as high as 100 000 characters per second. Screens are usually divided into rows (24) and columns (80). A CRT screen is illustrated below:

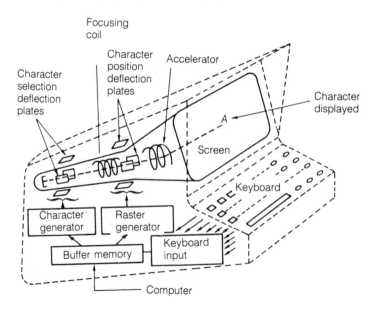

Colour screens
There are currently two types of colour consoles; the most common are based on standard colour television technology the others are based on penetron tubes.

Standard colour consoles
Screens based on television technology, use the same principle as monochrome consoles. Screens comprise **pixels** (the smallest addressable area on the screen), which are groups of three different coloured phosphor dots (generally red, green and blue, known as RGB).

With these three colours all the other shades can be generated, the three dots of phosphor in a pixel being sufficiently small to be confused by the eye as a single point. The definition depends directly on the diameter of the pixel and for colour the diameter varies between 0.25 and 0.4 mm.

There are two distinct systems for sweeping the screen with electrons. One system uses three electron guns where the electrons emitted excite the three dots of phosphor grouped on the screen. Holes in a shadow-mask disk direct the beams to select the correct dot, as shown in the following diagram:

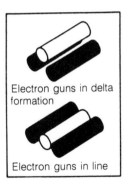

Electron guns in delta formation

Electron guns in line

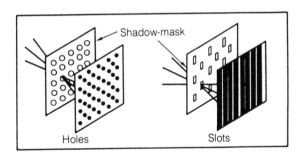

The other system, currently more commonly used, produces 4096 different colours. It uses only one gun and deflects the beam using horizontal and vertical deflection plates.

Penetron tubes
In this type of display the screen is coated with three layers of phosphor, each layer can be excited independently of the others by varying the power of the beam of electrons emitted by a single electron gun.

25.2.1.2   Characteristics of monitors
To form an image the beam must cover the screen line by line, exciting or not exciting each photosensitive element as it passes. Provided that the screen is covered (refreshed) repeatedly more than 25 times per second, the eye has the illusion of a stable image. The frequency with which the beam covers the screen is called the

raster frequency (between 45 and 75 Hz for multifrequency monitors). If the raster frequency is too slow the picture has a disagreeable judder.

The sweep of the electron beam may be interlaced. In interlacing the beam traces every other line (the odd lines) and on a second pass traces the even lines. This technique allows twice the definition for a given raster frequency. The results are satisfactory provided the screen has a longer remanence than average. A non-interlaced sweep gives better results in animation applications, for example, when a high remanence can be disagreeable.

Line frequency

Another characteristic of monitors is their line frequency. This parameter is a function of the time it takes to sweep across a line of the screen. If the number of lines is to be increased while the raster frequency remains constant, each line must be traced faster by increasing the line frequency. Currently line frequencies vary between 15 kHz and 40 kHz.

Resolution and band-pass

The resolution of a monitor determines the number of pixels that can be displayed in an image: the more pixels the better the definition. The resolution depends not only on the tube but also on the associated circuitry and in particular on the band-pass circuit. The band-pass corresponds to the number of points that can be shown on the screen per second. For example, to obtain a resolution of 640×350 points in non-interlaced mode, with a raster frequency of 60 Hz, requires $640 \times 350 \times 60 = 13\,440\,000$ points, i.e. a band-pass of at least 18 MHz (a margin of 20 to 30% being desirable). In fact, most good monitors have a band-pass of up to 20 MHz.

Input signal: digital or analog

The input signal to a colour monitor can be digital or analog. The disadvantage of digital input lies in the limited number of colours that can be used. Monitors using digital input are generally limited to 64 different colours of which only 16 can be shown at a time.

An analog input can take any value between 0 V and 0.7 V, which in theory offers an infinity of possible colours. But note that in practice the voltages are produced by a microcomputer and can therefore only take a finite, though very large, number of values. Some systems offer a choice of 262 144 colours (VGA standard).

25.2.1.3   Modes of display

Monitors are controlled by electronic circuit boards called control cards. There are many different types of control cards and in general they are incompatible with one another. At the present time, four systems dominate the market: CGA, EGA and VGA for colour and Hercules for monochrome. However, VGA will undoubtedly dominate in the years to come.

MDA, HGA Hercules, CGA

For monochrome, the MDA (Monochrome Display Adapter) card, which originated with the IBM PC, offers no graphics and only allows a display of 25 lines by 80 columns in 750×350 pixels. Each character is defined by a 9×14 dot matrix.

Without doubt it was the poor quality of MDA which led to the initial success of the Hercules mode (Hercules Graphic Adapter, HGA). Text format appears the same as MDA, but it allows graphic images at a resolution of 750×350 points. A variation of the Hercules is the monochrome HGCP (Hercules Graphics Card Plus). Compatible with Hercules, it offers an extended graphics mode and uses the Ramfont mode which allows the creation of character fonts and the definition of up to 3072 different characters. The user-modifiable character matrix is 4 to 16 pixels high and 8 or 9 pixels wide. This mode is now used less and less frequently.

The CGA mode (Colour Graphics Adapter) of IBM was the first graphics mode for PC microcomputers. It offered 320×200 pixels with four out of sixteen possible colours, or 640×200 pixels with a single foreground colour. Characters are composed of an 8×8 matrix of pixels.

EGA and PGA

EGA (Enhanced Graphics Adapter) mode was proposed by IBM in 1984. Its better resolution gave users a colour monitor of a professional standard. This graphics card enables the display of from 25 to 43 lines and 40 or 80 columns with a resolution of 640×350 pixels in text mode and a choice of 4 or 16 colours from 64.

At the same time as EGA, IBM also proposed the PGA (Professional Graphic Adapter) standard intended essentially for CAD applications. While offering a resolution of 640×480 pixels, the display of text or graphics in 256 colours chosen from a palette of 4096 colours, its high cost and its slow drawing speed prevented it from dominating the market.

VGA and MCGA

In 1987 IBM defined the display modes MCGA (MultiColour Graphics Array) and above all VGA (Video Graphics Array). The first emulated the CGA mode and some aspects of EGA to give a resolution of 640×480 pixels in two colours, while the second completely emulated EGA and offered additionally 640×480 pixels in graphics mode and 30 lines of 80 characters of text, in 16 colours chosen from 262 144. This latter mode has been proposed for the new PS/2 from IBM and will certainly dominate in the future.

The choice of definition of 640×480 pixels has not been made at random. It is the same ratio as that of the width and height of a standard video screen. It enables truly round circles to be produced easily, and preserves correct proportions, the screen faithfully reproduces what will finally be printed out. This is known as WYSIWYG (What You See Is What You Get).

High definition cards

A certain number of firms produce high definition cards emulating several modes (PARADISE, EIZO, etc.). One of the most impressive cards is without doubt that of AT&T, the vista videographics adapter. Provided with a 32-bit processor, it offers:

- 1024 × 1024 pixels in 16 million (!) colours.
- 2048 × 1024 pixels in 32 000 colours.
- 2048 × 2048 if 256 colours are sufficient.

25.2.1.4   Choosing a monitor

The monitor should be chosen carefully because a poor choice can have serious consequences. During an international colloquium devoted to the problems of working at a screen in Paris 1984, specialists estimated that regular work in front of an ill-adapted screen could be the source of migraines, eye strain, etc. While it is admitted that monitors do not by themselves provoke loss of visual acuity, they do often reveal weaknesses or badly corrected defects of vision.

The Health and Safety Commission has recently issued draft regulations and guidance on the safe use of computer screens. They were issued to help users implement regulations outlined in a recent European Community directive on the minimum safety and health requirements for work with VDUs. Some of the proposals are as follows:

- Employers must assess their display screen population to identify possible risks.
- Users are entitled to eye and eyesight tests and any costs relating to tests or corrective measures are to be covered by employers.
- There are to be breaks or changes of activity to interrupt display screen work.

The first criterion to be considered in choosing a monitor is its size. This is traditionally given by the length of the diagonal of the screen in inches. A monitor should not be too small and it is not by chance that some workstations use screens up to A3 format. A screen which is too small will cause a user unnecessary fatigue. The larger a screen the more obvious are its faults. A good size for a screen of medium quality would be 12–14 inches.

Depending on the application, colour can be indispensable or merely attractive. For office work and for DTP a large monochrome screen will usually be quite suitable, although the use of colour can enhance the application. In contrast certain CAD applications require colour; without it complex drawings quickly become difficult to read.

Monochrome screens of standard size (from 12–14 inches) pose the problem of background colour (green, amber or white). Black writing on a white background is the most readable and the most restful according to the specialists, but the screen has to be of good quality because juddering is most distracting. The choice between green and amber is, according to specialists, only one of personal preference.

Conclusion

The foreseeable evolution of monitors leads naturally to multifrequency models the price of which will noticeably fall in the years to come. It is equally likely that with the increasing use of DTP, A3 and A4 monochrome screens will extend their market share.

25.2.1.5   The flat cathode-ray tube

The flat CRT, while offering the advantage of reduced size over normal screens, nevertheless has certain disadvantages. The principle of the flat tube is, like that of the normal CRT, to send a beam of electrons on to a screen covered with a layer of phosphor. But in the case of the flat CRT the trajectory of the beam has to be curved by means of an additional field pulling the electrons on to the screen. The flat screen, although having a reduced thickness, has almost double the width to accommodate the electron gun – see the following diagram:

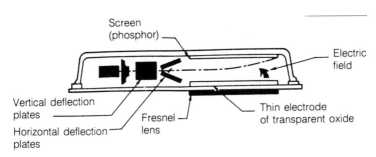

The image produced by such screens suffers from fluttering and instability due to the screen scan; at the same time the corners are rounded and there is distortion and a lack of sharpness at the edges of the screen.

25.2.2   *The interactive display console*

This is the name given to a console which enables data to be captured at the screen by using a stylus (a light pen), as shown in the following diagram:

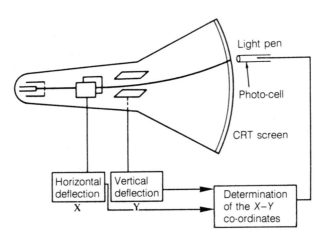

When the photo-cell of the light pen is positioned on the screen, the light beam sweeps across the screen and reaches a given $X-Y$ position. The cell is excited and initiates a reading of the values appearing at that instant on the $X-Y$ deflection plates. The knowledge of this data gives the exact position of the light pen. However, because the screen is slightly convex errors can appear at the edges.

There is another system which allows data to be captured at the screen; this uses a tactile screen. In one method the user has only to point to the required spot on the screen with a finger, the position of the finger being noted by a collection of photo-cells forming a grid in front of the screen, as shown below:

25.2.3 *Matrix screens*

Unlike cathode-ray tubes, matrix screens are naturally flat. A network of two sets of conductors laid orthogonally to each other, closely spaced (several tens in a few hundred microns), is connected to integrated circuits that send them electrical signals. To address a point with coordinates X, Y on the screen, a difference of potential is applied between the conductor of row X and the conductor of column Y, an electro-optic substance then reacts.

25.2.3.1 Electroluminescent screens
Electroluminescent screens are made from a bed of electroluminescent phosphor sandwiched between two sheets of glass supporting two networks of electrodes laid orthogonally. The point selected emits light when voltage is applied to the two electrodes positioned one above the other.

They offer the advantage of a great resistance to mechanical shock but are tiring to use because of their brightness.

25.2.3.2 Plasma screens
Plasma screens use a technology which offers a performance approaching that of cathode-ray tubes. They are made from three layers of glass sealed hermetically around the edges. The middle layer is pierced by holes filled with gas (neon, argon,

etc.). The gas reacts under the effect of an electric field, to glow at the points which form the characters. In fact the voltage applied at the electrodes ionises the gas which then becomes a plasma, that is it becomes a mixture of ions and electrons. The following diagram illustrates the construction:

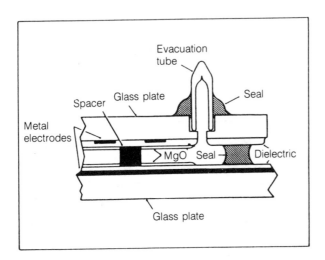

The image on the plasma screen does not need to be refreshed, unlike those produced on CRTs which have to be refreshed constantly, occasionally producing an annoying flicker of the screen. The resolution varies according to the panel. The distance between the cells can be as little as 0.46 mm allowing resolutions to attain 260 000 points. An additional advantage is that the screens can be read from any position in front of the panel. Their price remains, however, quite high and the only colours available at the moment are the orange-red of neon and green.

25.2.3.3 Liquid crystal screens
Liquid crystal screens are passive screens because they need to have an external light source in order to see them, unlike the screens studied above which are active screens because they give off their own light. Mechanically the crystals behave like liquids but their molecular structure gives them certain optical properties. There are two types of liquid crystal:

- **Nematic:** these are normally 'transparent' but become opaque under the effect of a magnetic or electric field.
- **Cholesteric:** they change colour with temperature or under the influence of an electric or magnetic field.

The following diagrams show the composition of a liquid crystal display, and its principle:

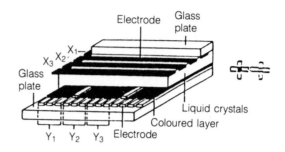

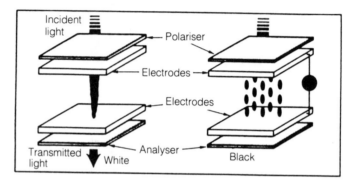

A coloured mosaic filter can be superimposed on to the device to obtain a colour screen. The intensity will depend on the amount of light passing through the filter, but even so the colours are less bright than those produced by a cathode-ray tube.

25.2.3.4 Conclusion

In the presence of so many variables it is difficult to predict which of these technologies will become dominant in the years ahead. The main obstacle is the well-established position of the cathode-ray tube. In order to compete with that, other devices will not only have to match its price but will also have to achieve a comparable quality in terms of the complexity of its displays, its responsiveness and its colour.

It is probable that rather than displace the CRT, the new flat screens will find applications in other parts of the market (for example, portable microcomputers); liquid crystal displays are already widely used in pocket calculators and laptops.

25.2.4 *Terminals*

Terminals are the means of access to remote computers to which they are connected via a data transmission line.

25.2.4.1   Non-specialised terminals

These can be divided into 'light' terminals which function in a connected mode, and 'heavy' terminals which, equipped with input and output devices and a control unit, enable local processing of data sent to them. When the processing power of a 'heavy' terminal is quite well developed, it is called an intelligent terminal.

25.2.4.2   Specialised terminals

A **point-of-sale** terminal is used in place of the standard cash register. It acts as a calculator and provides for on-line stock management, the calculation of tax and discounts, and the recording of the value of sales.

These terminals use built in microprograms and have numeric keyboards, optical readers for capturing data directly from bar-coded labels, and one or more visual displays allowing the operator and the customer to verify the captured data. Some are even equipped with speech output to announce the item and its cost.

Specialised **banking terminals** such as bank note distributors generally comprise magnetic badge readers, simple function keys, an alphanumeric keypad and a screen. Some also have printers and some have facilities for accepting envelopes to enable cheques, etc., to be deposited.

By following instructions displayed on the screen and typing in at the keyboard it is possible to perform many of the normal banking transactions (withdraw money, deposit cheques, obtain the current balance of the account, order a bank statement, etc.).

25.2.4.3   Industrial terminals

The importance and widespread use of computing in commerce and industry whether for management or process control means that industrial terminals are very diverse and constantly evolving.

They are found in many applications such as timekeeping, stock control, order capture, quality control, etc. They appear in many forms such as badge readers and keyboards, keyboards and screens, optical readers and screens with keyboards. They tend more and more to be stand-alone models, with diskette backing storage.

Chapter 26

Printers

Paper documents remain up to the present time the medium most acceptable to people. The printer is therefore, with the visual display console, the output peripheral *par excellence*. There are numerous types of printer functioning in different ways depending on the technology employed; but it is possible to distinguish four criteria for classifying them.

26.1 Classification criteria

26.1.1 *The technology*

- **Impact:** the image is formed by hammering the character against an inked ribbon placed in front of the paper.
- **Non-impact:** characters are formed by squirting ink, or by applying heat, or by an offset transfer process.

26.1.2 *The print head*

- Pre-formed character: the image is formed using an embossed inverted character carried on a print head.
- Dot matrix: the character is formed from a matrix of points:

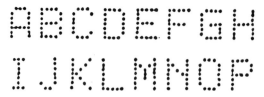

Magnified dot-matrix characters

26.1.3 *The print mode*

- **Character mode:** characters are printed one after the other.
- **Line mode:** a complete line is printed at a time.

26.1.4   *The paper movement*

- Friction: the paper is moved by a rubber friction roller.
- Traction: the paper is moved by sprockets engaging with sprocket holes punched in the edges of the paper.

26.2   **Printing mechanisms**

26.2.1   *The band (or belt) printer*

A metal band carrying several copies of the character set moves horizontally and continuously in front of the paper. Between the band and the paper there is an inked ribbon. A row of hammers, placed behind the paper, fires against the required character as it passes the desired position in the line.

Although relatively slow (300 to 2000 lines per minute or lpm) this system is reliable and gives good alignment of characters on the same line. It is used mostly on mainframe systems, and is illustrated below:

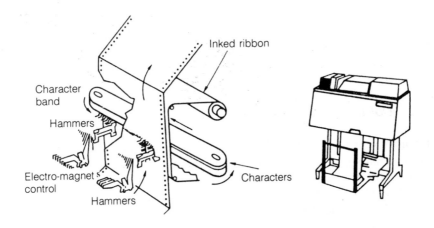

26.2.2   *Drum or barrel printer*

The complete character set is embossed on the rim of a disk and several disks are then mounted on the same axle to form a cylinder, the number of disks depends on the length of the line (mostly 132 characters).

The position on the barrel of the character to be printed is determined by a device which detects the coincidence between the angular rotation of the barrel and the character sent from the computer to be printed. This coincidence simultaneously fires the hammers in all positions where the character is to appear in the line. Thus all the A characters appearing in the line are printed and then all the B, etc. After a complete revolution of the barrel, all the line will have been printed. This printer is illustrated in the following diagram:

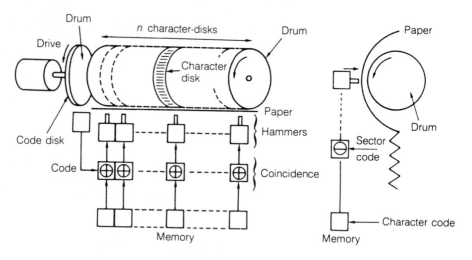

Note: the inked ribbon is placed between the paper and the barrel

This method of printing gives speeds of between 300 and 2000 lpm and produces a good print quality; however, it is difficult to arrange for the characters to be perfectly aligned and it can have only one character font. It is used on mainframe and mini-computers but is rapidly going out of use.

26.2.3   Dot matrix printers

In dot matrix printing, which is currently the most common form, a character comprises a matrix of points, some of which are printed and others not. For several years the most common matrix sizes were 5×7 or 7×9 but they have recently improved to 18×21, 18×24 and even 18×48. The diameter of the needles has meanwhile been reduced by 50% to 200 μm for 24-pin heads.

There are three techniques of matrix printing: impact, thermal transfer and ink-jet. This latter technique will be considered separately.

26.2.3.1   Dot matrix impact printing

Printing is on ordinary paper using an inked ribbon struck by a needle. The ribbon can be monochrome black, as is often the case, but it is equally possible to print in colour. For this a ribbon with four colours, one of which is black, is used. The other colours which can be mixed to give a larger palette of colours are yellow, magenta and cyan (YMC).

There are two main problems associated with colour printing. Firstly, depending on how much the individual colours are used, some parts of the ribbon wear out much faster than the others (particularly the yellow). Secondly, during intensive use of the printer there can be slight irregularities in raising and lowering the ribbon to the extent that neighbouring colours run together.

The needles are arranged in a head which in low specification printers consists of 9 needles, and in high specification printers consists of 24 or, more recently 48, needles. The principle is illustrated in the following diagram:

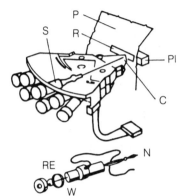

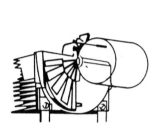

The principle of the operation of a dot-matrix print head

C: capillary guide tube   N: needle
P: paper   PI: platen
R: ribbon   RE: return spring
S: solenoid   W: winding

26.2.3.2   Dot matrix thermal printing

Two techniques are used for thermal matrix printing: either printing on special thermosensitive paper or employing a thermal transfer inked ribbon.

With thermosensitive paper, the needle is heated and its contact with the specially treated paper initiates a chemical reaction causing a blue or black image to appear at the point of contact.

With a thermal transfer ribbon the matrix is made from tiny elements which when heated melt a special wax to release particles of coloured ink from the polyester ribbon. Using RGB or YMC ribbons it is possible to obtain palettes of up to 100 colours. Such printers require particularly smooth paper but ensure better quality printing than do impact printers (resolutions of up to 400 dots per inch (dpi) are possible). The diagram below shows the mechanism:

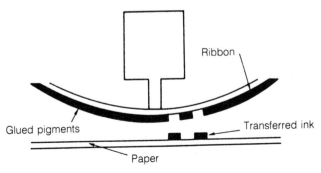

Ribbon

Glued pigments   Transferred ink

Paper

26.2.3.3 Conclusion

Dot matrix printing is relatively reliable and can be of fairly good quality when each character is struck twice with a very slight shift (letter quality printing or **LQ**). It is often slow (especially in letter quality mode), of the order of 120 to 400 characters per second (**cps**), i.e. about 40 to 150 lpm (however, some printers of this type reach 850 cps and 600 lpm). Dot matrix printing can also be used to draw graphs or diagrams.

This printing technique is widely used at the moment because of the low cost of the printers. However it is noisy and will very probably be replaced in the coming years by ink-jet and laser printers.

26.2.4 *Ink-jet printers*

In this type of printer the character is still formed by a matrix of dots but this time they are obtained, not by impact, but by squirting a microscopic droplet of ink at the surface of the paper. There are two printing techniques using the ink-jet.

26.2.4.1 Continuous jet

This type of printer is illustrated in Figure 26.1. A series of nozzles emit the ink in a continuous jet. A converter using high frequency oscillations transforms the jet into droplets. The droplets pass through a charging electrode where they collect an electric charge. The deflection plates deflect the unused droplets into a collector where they are gathered for recycling. There are two methods of positioning the droplets on the paper:

- A **digital** method where the charged droplets are deflected and the others are projected on to the paper without deflection.
- An **analog** method where the charged droplets are deflected by the deflection plates (horizontally and vertically).

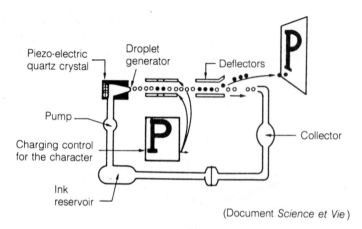

(Document *Science et Vie*)

Figure 26.1 An ink-jet printer

The frequency with which the drops are emitted from the nozzle is 100 000/s or greater which gives a resolution of 240×240 dpi^2.

26.2.4.2 Drops on request

In this system (shown in Figure 26.2) the ink is maintained at low pressure, which keeps the droplets in the charger. On request from the print controller, an impulse is sent to the nozzle causing a droplet to be projected on to the paper. The frequency of emission of the drops reaches 5000/s and there is no need to collect surplus drops.

26.2.5 *Electrographic and laser printers*

The basic principle used in this technology, also called **xerography**, is that used in electrostatic photocopiers. A drum covered in a layer of photosensitive selenium, is positively charged. The image of the character to be printed is then projected photographically on to the drum. Under the effect of the light the selenium loses its positive charge and only the image of the character, which has stopped the light, remains positively charged. A powdered ink (toner), carrying a negative charge, is then attracted to the positively charged image of the character on the selenium drum. This powder is then transferred on to the paper by contact and fixed to the paper by heating. This mechanism is illustrated in Figure 26.3.

The image of the character can be generated by a cathode-ray tube, by masks placed in front of a light source, by a matrix of light emitting diodes or by a laser beam guided by a character generator. In the case of a **laser** printer, the laser beam scans parallel to the axis on the photosensitive cylinder. The light beam is projected by a polygonal mirror turning at high speed. As the beam strikes one facet of the mirror, the movement of the mirror causes one scan across the cylinder. The mirror and the cylinder are continuously turning in synchronisation so that the beam scans

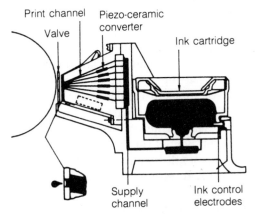

Figure 26.2 Drops on request

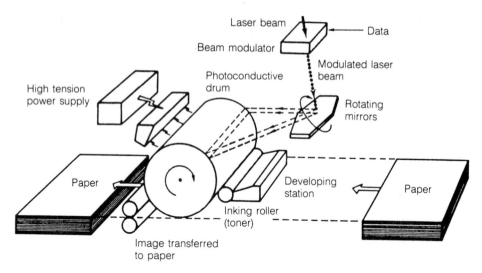

Figure 26.3 An electrographic printer

the whole of the surface of the cylinder. The character is therefore formed from successive lines of points.

The advantages of these printers lies principally in their high transfer rates (up to 20 000 lpm), and very good resolution (from 300 to 400 dpi) on average, being able to attain 1200×600 dpi^2. On the other hand they are relatively expensive and their complex technology makes them a little fragile.

26.2.6 *Embossed-head letter quality printers*

This category of printers – daisy-wheel, tulip, ball-head – produce the best quality print. Originally they were simple electronic typewriters attached to computers.

The first employed a ball or a sphere (IBM golf-ball) on which the characters were inscribed in relief. In printing, the ball is turned to place the desired character in position, then the head is thrown against an inked ribbon which it pushes on to the paper. The maximum speed for this type of printer is of the order of 15 cps.

The tip of each petal or spoke of the daisy-wheel carries a character in relief. During printing, the wheel is turned and when the desired character is in position a hammer strikes the petal against the ribbon.

The tulip is an infrequently used variant of the daisy-wheel in which the petals are folded to form a tulip shape; the hammer now being placed inside the 'flower'.

These printers, illustrated in Figure 26.4, while producing an excellent quality of print, are very slow and very noisy and are therefore not used very much in computer applications where large quantities of printed output are often required.

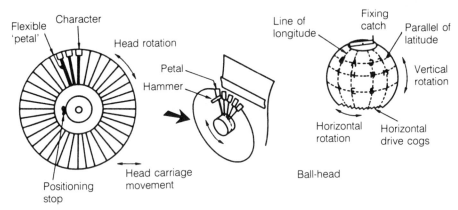

Figure 26.4   Letter quality printers

26.3   **Printer interfaces**

There are two methods of transmitting characters between cpu and printer:

- **Serial:** the bits forming the characters are sent one after the other down a transmission line with just a few wires. This technique, which allows transmission over longer distances, is known as an RS 232 or a serial connection. The connector is usually a 25-way or 9-way cannon type.
- **Parallel:** the bits forming the characters are transmitted simultaneously over sufficient separate wires. This technique, which only allows transmission over short distances, is known as a centronics interface or a parallel connection. The connector can be a centronics connector or a 25-way cannon type.

    It is important when buying a printer to know if it has one or the other (or both) types of connector and to know that the computer has at least one of the appropriate outputs. Both types are shown in Figure 26.5.

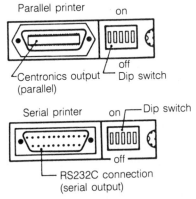

Source: I; Virgatchik, *Comment choisir votre micro ordinateur*, Marabout.

Figure 26.5   Computer output connectors

26.4 **Criteria for choosing a printer**

There are numerous criteria for choosing a printer and they depend on the type of use envisaged.

- **Interfacing:** parallel or serial. It must match that of the computer to which it will be connected.
- **Quality:** dot matrix printers do not in general give such good results as laser printers or letter quality printers, although for 24-pin print heads this is not necessarily the case.
- **Changing fonts:** changing the font can be achieved by changing the print head for letter quality printers, or by 'switching', normally under software control, to a different character generator for dot matrix or laser printers.
- **Number of columns:** this is usually either 80 or 132 but some printers can print more than this in 'condensed' mode.
- **Printing speed:** the printing speed for microcomputers varies between 100 and 400 cps. Printers at the top of the range (lasers) reach speeds of up to 200 pages per minute (ppm).
- **Choice of paper:** thermal printers need a special, more expensive paper. Dot matrix and laser printers sometimes require paper of a particular weight.
- **Paper format:** this is limited to the largest size of page that can be fed into the machine (A4 format (21×29.7 cm), listing (80 or 132 columns) pages (11″ or 12″ long)).
- **Ink source:** mylar ribbons are generally more expensive and less durable than inked fabric ribbons. The size and type of the ribbon depends on the printer. Cartridges of toner for laser printers are relatively expensive.
- **Noise:** impact printers are noisy, especially large machines, but sometimes sound-proof covers are available. Lasers and ink-jets are quieter (but more expensive).

26.5 **Other hard-copy output devices**

26.5.1 *Flat-bed plotters*

Flat-bed plotters are used to produce graphs, drawings, maps or plans. They have a horizontal table supporting the paper, a track which runs over the surface of the paper, and a pen carriage which moves backwards and forwards along the track allowing pens of various colours to be positioned anywhere over the paper. The selected pen is positioned above the point where it is to draw and then lowered on to the paper. Movements of the carriage and the track cause the required line to be drawn and then the pen is raised. Very accurate drawings can be made because the pen can be placed to within 0.05 mm of the actual position required (see the diagram below):

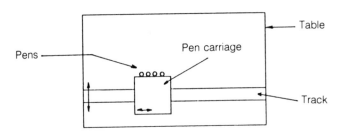

26.5.2 *Drum plotters*

Drum plotters produce the same types of drawings as flat-bed plotters. A drum driven by a stepping motor moves the paper quite quickly up and down. A pen carriage moves back and forward across the paper and orthogonal to the direction of paper movement (see below):

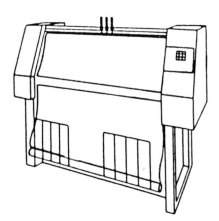

A variant of the drum plotter is the electrostatic plotter in which electrodes at a high potential leave a static charge on special dielectrically coated paper. The image is revealed when the paper is passed through a bath of toner containing carbon particles in suspension which are fixed to the charged areas.

26.5.3 *Computer output on microfilm*

Use of computer output on microfilm (COM) is increasing in office applications. It offers an interesting alternative to the superabundance of paper and finds a role whenever normal media do not offer solutions appropriate to the nature of the problem. Microfilming has two different branches:

- **Archiving:** providing flexible and inexpensive access to archived data.
- **Information processing:** stemming from the liaison between computers and microfilming.

Microfilming produces two types of media collectively called microforms: **microfiches** and **microfilms**.

26.5.3.1 Microforms

Microforms appear either as microfiche in A6 format (105 mm × 148 mm), or as microfilm in rolls of 16 mm or 35 mm. The choice between microfiche and microfilm depends on several criteria such as storage space, methods of access, and costs.

Capacity

Microfilms generally allow 2500 exposures (films 30 m long 16 mm wide) or 600 exposures (for 35 mm). The current standard for microfiches is 98 archive document exposures but it is possible to attain 600 exposures.

Mode	Archive documents	Information processing
Film 16 mm	2500 exposures	2500 exposures
Microfiches		
A6	98 exposures	270 exposures

Reading methods

Microfilm has the advantage of grouping together a larger quantity of data, thus reducing handling, losses, etc. In contrast it has the disadvantage that the data can only be read by one person at a time. The user's choice of microfiche or microfilm must therefore take into account the nature of accesses (frequency and volume) and the facilities available for reading the two types.

Cost

While microfilms are cheaper to produce than microfiches for the same quantity of data, the price of microfilm readers can be up to five times greater. The choice may therefore be decided by the cost of recording cameras which, for microfilm, can be more than £80 000.

26.5.3.2 Microfilms

Microfilm printers allow data to be transcribed at high speed directly on to microfilm from computers or from magnetic tapes, with speeds varying from 8000 to 50 000 lines per minute. If microfilm were to replace paper and become the normal output medium, the relatively slow printing of conventional printers could be avoided as well as the need to handle the impractical bulk of many computer listings.

Operation of COM printers
Data is input to the COM printer either from a computer output channel (on-line COM), or from magnetic tape (off-line COM). In the latter case data coming from the magnetic tape is first decoded, then interpreted, and finally converted to images that are recorded by the COM camera. There are several techniques for forming the images, the oldest being to use a cathode-ray tube. Characters are drawn by an electron beam on the screen. A page is drawn character by character, line by line. When the page is full it is photographed, and the film advanced to the next frame. The screen is then cleared and the cycle begins again as follows:

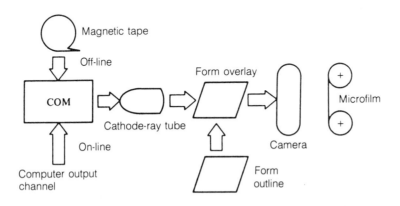

In a variant of this technique, a beam of electrons records directly on to the film:

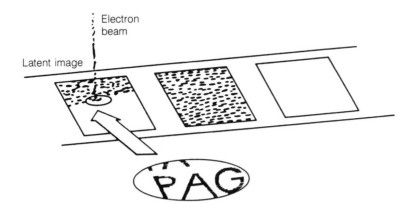

A more recent technique using fibre optics, produces the exposure not page by page but line by line. Each coded character prompts the excitation of certain light emitting diodes from a matrix of 35. The excitation of each diode causes the transmission of light along an optical fibre. The character is thus drawn as a pattern of dots on a 5 × 7 matrix at the ends of the optical fibres. Each line can contain 205 characters. A mask in front of the camera lens enables the characters to be recorded one after the other in step with their formation, as shown below:

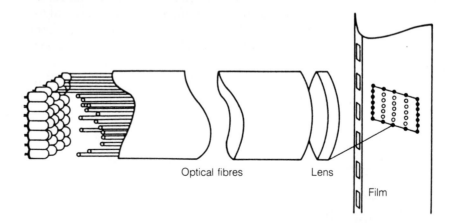

Optical fibres   Lens

Film

Some printers offer several fonts in lower case, upper case and bold.

Indexing

To facilitate and speed up searching for particular frames on the microfilm, manufacturers have derived different automatic indexing systems. A little mark can be recorded in the margin at the side of each frame to count the exposures and thus enable the required frame to be accessed quickly.

Chapter 27

Data communications and teleprocessing: basic ideas

Teleprocessing can be defined as remote computer processing using telecommunications devices. In a teleprocessing system, two (or more) elements of the system, possibly hundreds of miles apart, function as if they were side by side. By eliminating intermediate data handling, this technique makes an important contribution to reducing turnround time.

Data communications puts the power of computers at the disposal of a large number of users. Beyond simple integrated company management uses there are numerous applications of data communications (e.g. sales, data banks, telematics) to be found throughout a company.

27.1 Principles of data transmission

Data is transmitted character by character between the different parts of a computer so it is possible to have as many lines in the data paths between units as there are bits in a character. Such a transmission mode is called **parallel transmission**, but this type of transmission is normally only used over very short distances (of the order of a few dozen metres); it is costly and unreliable over longer distances.

Over longer distances, a single line is used down which the bits of a character are sent one after the other in serial transmission. The following diagram shows both types of transmission:

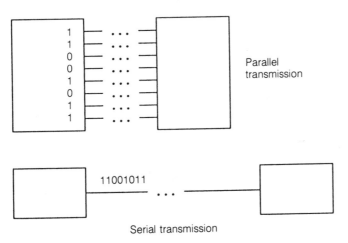

Parallel transmission

Serial transmission

In serial transmission, time is divided into intervals of equal length, a bit being transmitted in each interval. The basic principle is that a voltage $+V$ is applied during an interval to represent a 1 bit and a voltage 0 to represent a 0 bit. At the receiver the values of the voltage are observed at appropriate moments. Thus serial transmission requires: the provision of a clock at the transmitter and at the receiver to divide the time into regular intervals; and synchronisation between the transmitter and the receiver so that the latter knows the correct instant to observe the voltage level.

27.1.1   *The signals used*

Digital signals are very difficult to transmit over long distances and therefore analog signals which can be more easily transmitted are normally used. The simplest analog signal is the sinewave with the equation:

$$\alpha(t) = A \sin (\omega t + \phi)$$

$\alpha(t)$ = voltage at time t
A = amplitude of the wave
ω = 2f where f is the frequency (the number of periods or oscillations per second) in Hertz
t = time in seconds
ϕ = phase (shifting of the wave with respect to the origin)

A, F and ϕ are the three fundamental characteristics of a sinewave. If such a wave is a carrier of binary data, one or several of these characteristics must be altered to indicate the logic states 1 and 0 being transmitted.

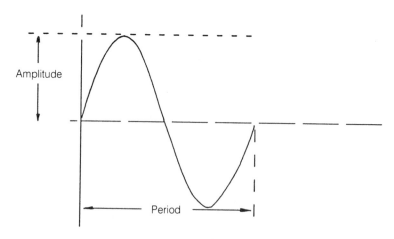

Figure 27.1   A sinewave

The modification of the characteristics to indicate the binary values being transmitted is made by reference to a **carrier wave** (or **carrier signal** or simply **carrier**). The time between successive modulations of the carrier wave is called an **elementary interval**. The number of elementary intervals transmitted in a second is the **modulation rate** (R). This modulation rate is expressed in **bauds**, after the engineer Baudot, who invented the Baudot code used in data transmission.

It is important to appreciate the difference between modulation rate and the number of bits transmitted per second. During one elementary interval it is possible to code a variable number of bits depending on the nature of the modulation. For example:

Consider the case where in one elementary interval a 1 or a 0 can be coded:

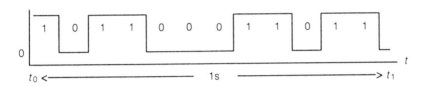

Two levels of amplitude are employed here and therefore only one bit (0 or 1) can be transmitted in each elementary interval. The rate of modulation being 12 elementary intervals per second (12 bauds) the transmission rate is 12 bits per second.

Consider now the case where in one elementary interval two bits can be coded simultaneously:

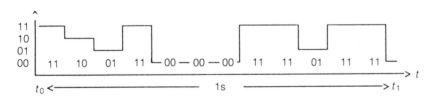

The rate of modulation still being 12 elementary intervals per second (12 bauds) the transmission rate here will be 24 bits per second because now two bits can be coded in each elementary interval.

From these two examples we can see that in the general case the relationship between the data transmission rate D, the modulation rate R, and the number of bits, V, coded in each elementary interval is given by:

$$D = R \times \log_2(V)$$

27.1.2 *Bandwidth and pass band*

The range of frequencies used by a signal is called the **bandwidth**. It can be seen intuitively that the greater the bandwidth, the greater will be the transmission rate. The bandwidth depends not only on the way in which the signal is transmitted but also on the quality of the line. But, since no transmission line is perfect it will only allow a certain range of frequencies to be transmitted correctly; this range is the **pass band** (or bandwidth of the medium). For example, the telephone network uses frequencies between 300 Hz and 3400 Hz, for voice transmission, i.e. a pass band of 3100 Hz

The pass band has an important bearing on the modulation rate. The mathematician Nyquist has shown that the number of pulses that can be transmitted and received in a unit of time equals twice the pass band of the channel, i.e. $R = 2 \times W$ where R is the modulation rate and W is the pass band. For example, a telephone line with a pass band of 3100 Hz can transmit signals at 6200 bauds.

27.1.3 *Distortions of the transmitted signals*

- **Attenuation:** when the signal is transmitted with a certain strength and is received as a weaker signal. Attenuation can distort the transmitted signal and the degree of attenuation is a characteristic of the data transmission lines.
- **Distortions:** there are two types of distortion, amplitude distortions which increase or decrease the normal amplitude of the signal at an instant t, and distortions of phase which cause untimely phase changes relative to the carrier.
- **Noise:** there are three types of noise, thermal noise, from the thermal agitation of the electrons, cross-talk from signals on adjacent lines, and impulse noise from switches and lighting, etc. The maximum capacity of a noisy channel is determined by Shannon's formula $C = W \log_2(1 + S/N)$, where W represents the pass band, S the power of the signal and N the power of the noise. As an example, for a telephone line of pass band 3100 Hz with a signal/noise ratio of the order of 1000, the maximum capacity is approximately 31 000 bits/s.

27.2 **Signalling methods**

Several different methods of data transmission are in use.

27.2.1 *Baseband*

Baseband transmission transmits a digital signal, that is a signal without any modification except possibly amplification (to avoid attenuation problems) and some encoding to ensure good transmission of long strings of 0's or of 1's (e.g. NRZ code, Manchester encoding).

Attenuation of the signals caused by characteristics of the data transmission line, limits the use of this technique to a theoretical maximum distance of 50 km.

27.2.2 *Frequency modulation*

In this type of transmission, the frequency of the signal indicates the value of the bit being transmitted.

Two common methods of frequency modulations are illustrated in the two following diagrams:

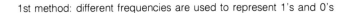

1st method: different frequencies are used to represent 1's and 0's

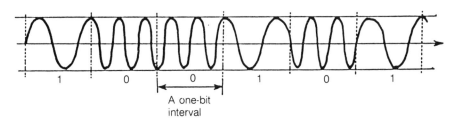

2nd method: a change in frequency or no change in frequency represents the value of a bit

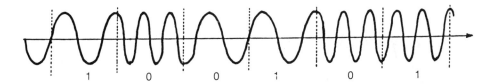

This modulation technique requires simple hardware, but due to the effect of frequency on bandwidth, it is only used for low speed transmission (up to 2400 bits/s).

27.2.3 *Amplitude modulation*

In this type of transmission, one amplitude is used to transmit a 1 and another amplitude is used to transmit a 0.

The main disadvantage with this method of modulation is that data is sent twice, in the sense that the upper lateral band is a reflection of the lower lateral band

and thus half of the transmission is wasted, as seen in the following diagram:

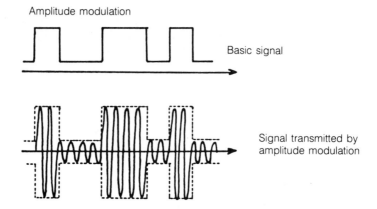

Amplitude modulation

Basic signal

Signal transmitted by amplitude modulation

Techniques exist to limit this constraint.

27.2.4   *Phase modulation*

In this type of transmission, the modulated signal is obtained by changing the phase. Thus it is possible to associate a phase change of $180°$ with a logic 1 and a phase change of zero relative to the carrier to represent a logic 0, as below:

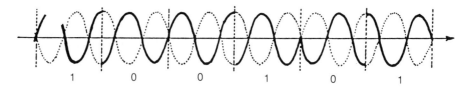

1st method: each phase represents a bit value

A modulation is **coherent** when it is the absolute value of the phase which represents data, and **differential** when the data is represented by changes of phase between two successive instants, as below:

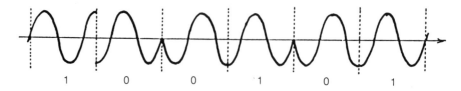

2nd method: a change of phase or no change of phase gives the value of the bit

Amplitude modulation and phase modulation are currently used for faster transmission rates (above 2400 bits/s).

27.2.5   *Multiple bits*

In the preceding modes the time was divided into intervals of equal duration and in each interval a bit could be transmitted. Instead of one bit it is possible to send several bits in each elementary interval. Each of the preceding methods can be used in this way. Signalling may be:

- Multilevel in amplitude modulation.
- Multifrequency in frequency modulation.
- Multiphase in phase modulation.

The following diagram is an example of multiphase signalling:

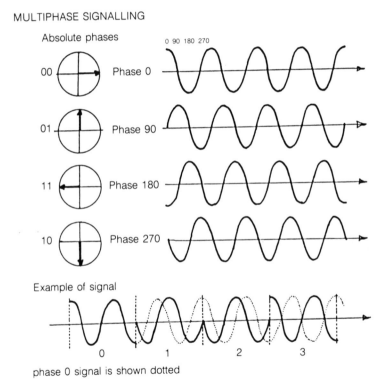

MULTIPHASE SIGNALLING

Absolute phases

Example of signal

phase 0 signal is shown dotted

Another technique is used in practice, combining amplitude modulation and phase modulation to obtain higher transmission rates. For example, a signal with two amplitude levels and 8 phases allows a transmission of 9600 bits/s.

27.2.6   *Pulse code modulation (PCM)*

A signal bandwidth W can be represented by a train of samples of the signal taken at a frequency of $2W$. A transmission with a bandwidth of, for simplification, up to 4000 Hz, can be reconstructed from samples taken at a frequency of 8000 Hz, that is with samples taken every 125 μs, each sample being taken over several μs.

The amplitude of the original signal, read during the sampling, is then coded as eight bits using a 256 point scale. Thus a byte is transmitted every 125 μs allowing an increased transmission rate of $8 \times 1s/125\,\mu$s, i.e. 64 kbits/s. The bytes representing the signal are then transmitted via baseband transmission (digital transmission) which requires repeaters to be placed every 2 km or so along the line. This is illustrated below:

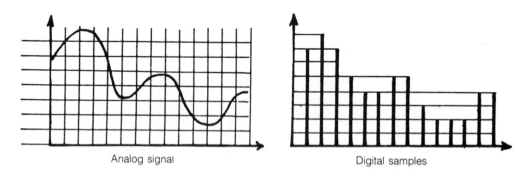

Analog signal   Digital samples

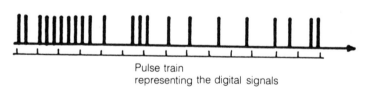

Pulse train
representing the digital signals

Several transmission signals can be combined (**multiplexed**) along one line. The time interval (120 μs approximately) between two consecutive samples from one signal can be used to send samples from other signals.

27.3 **Transmission modes**

Messages transmitted from an information source are built up from alphanumeric characters (letters, or figures) represented by a string of bits in a precise sequence, or from strings of independent binary digits.

The most commonly used codes for representing characters as strings of bits are **Telex** or **CCITT No 2** and **ASCII** or **CCITT No 5**.

A message arriving at the receiver can thus be regarded as a succession of characters, either text or control characters. This poses two problems at the receiver: to divide the received signal into characters (i.e. **character synchronisation**); to divide each character into binary elements enabling the character to be identified (**bit** synchronisation). Bit synchronisation can be achieved in three ways:

- Throughout the duration of the connection between the various components of the network. This is **synchronous** transmission.
- Only during the transmission of the message. This is **synchronised-asynchronous** transmission (but is often simply called synchronous transmission).
- Only during the transmission of each character. This is **asynchronous** transmission or **start–stop** transmission.

27.3.1 *Asynchronous transmission*

When the source produces characters at random intervals (e.g. characters typed in at the keyboard of a terminal), they are often transmitted independently of those preceding or following. To ensure synchronisation between the transmitter and the receiver, each character is preceded by a **start** bit which is in fact a transition from the idle state (1 state) to the 0 state, and is followed at the end by a **stop** ($= 1$) which has a minimum duration of 1, $1\frac{1}{2}$ or 2 bits depending on the system used.

The synchronisation at the bit level is achieved with the aid of local clocks of the same nominal frequency. At the receiver, the start signal sets off the local oscillator which enables the individual bits of the character to be sampled. Any slight drift in the sample time away from the ideal is of no consequence over such a brief interval.

This transmission mode which is usually restricted to speeds of 1200 bits/s or less is called **asynchronous** or **start–stop**, and is illustrated below:

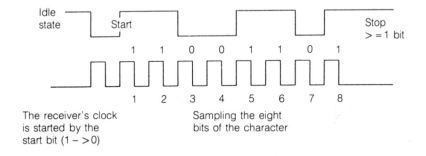

27.3.2 *Synchronous transmission*

In synchronous transmission bit synchronisation must be permanently assured, that is, not only during actual transmission but also during periods of 'silence'. Time is therefore continuously divided into elementary intervals at the transmitter, intervals which must then be passed to the receiver. This poses some problems. In fact, the use in the receiver, of a local clock differing only slightly in frequency from that of the transmitter would lead, because of the length of transmitted blocks of characters, to errors in recognising characters.

In order to avoid this, the receiver clock must be resynchronised frequently with that of the transmitter. This can be done by ensuring that there are sufficient transitions from 1 to 0 and from 0 to 1 in the transmitted message. If the data to be transmitted consists of long strings of 1's or of 0's these have to have suitable transitions inserted to resynchronise the clocks.

Such techniques are difficult to implement and so usually a technique called synchronised-asynchronous (often simply called synchronous) transmission is used instead.

27.3.3   Synchronised-asynchronous transmission

This transmission mode is characterised by the fact that, even though the message is transmitted in a synchronous manner, there is no synchronisation during the interval of time between two messages. In order to readjust the local oscillator at the start of a message, the message is preceded by a number of special synchronising characters (for example SYN in ASCII).

27.4   **Multiplexing techniques**

In order to increase the capacity of communication lines, it is useful to be able to send several messages down a line at the same time; this technique is called **multiplexing**.

27.4.1   Frequency division multiplexing (FDM)

Frequency multiplexing employs amplitude modulation and consists of using a different frequency for each channel. Several channels can then be combined for transmission down the same line. This system has a relatively low capacity (from 50 to 200 bauds) since, to avoid cross-talk between channels, the frequency bands are separated by wide unused 'margins':

27.4.2 *Time division multiplexing (TDM)*

The principle of **time division multiplexing** consists of allocating a time quantum to each input channel in turn.

In time division **multiplexing by character** the message is divided into **frames** (collections of bits or characters), comprised of subblocks called **time intervals** (TI), each containing a character and one other bit to indicate the nature of the TI (message character or control character). Each input channel (subchannel) is allocated a TI in the frame so that each frame is made up of one character from each subchannel, as shown below:

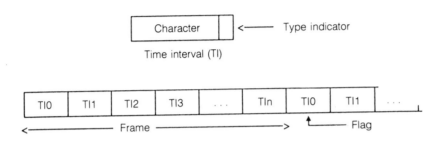

In order that the multiplexer can recognise the sequence number of the TI in the frame, it must be able to recognise the beginning; for this purpose at the head of the frame there is a special binary combination called a **flag**.

Time division **multiplexing by bit** is most often used for slow speed transmission. The principle is based on that of the character multiplexer but the TIs only concern bits.

Statistical time division multiplexing (STDM) is a technique of allocating dynamically the TIs of a frame only to those input channels which are currently active and not to all inputs as in the preceding methods, which results in better use of the line. The following diagram illustrates:

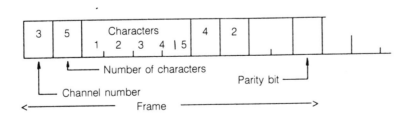

This type of multiplexing offers a good efficiency but may be unacceptable when all the channels are active at the same time because this will produce saturation.

27.5   **Different types of connection**

27.5.1   *Terminology*

Data terminal equipment (DTE) processes transmitted data (e.g. a computer or a screen/keyboard terminal). Data circuit-terminating equipment (DCE) performs line interfacing functions such as signal conversion between a DTE and a data transmission line.

    During data communication, a connection is established between two DTEs via a data transmission line, as shown below:

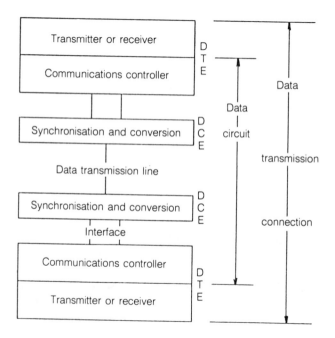

This connection can be made in different ways.

27.5.2   *Simplex*

In a simplex connection, data always passes in the same direction from the transmitter towards the receiver (radio for example):

27.5.3   *Half-duplex (HDX)*

In a half duplex connection, each DTE functions alternately as a transmitter then as a receiver (walkie-talkie, for example). A single data transmission line (two-wire) is sufficient for such a connection:

Transmitter/receiver   Transmitter/receiver

27.5.4   *Full-duplex (FDX)*

In this type of communication, data passes simultaneously in both directions (a telephone conversation for example). The full-duplex connection normally requires two transmission lines (four wires), even though it is technically possible to make it with only one:

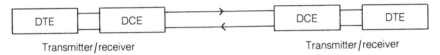

Transmitter/receiver   Transmitter/receiver

27.6   **Network topologies**

There are numerous ways of interconnecting DTEs but they can be classified into a few major types of configuration.

27.6.1   *Star configuration*

The simplest connection between two DTEs is one with only two ends. Such a connection is called **point to point**. A group of several point-to-point connections, centred, as is often the case, around a central DTE (a small computer for example) forms a star configuration:

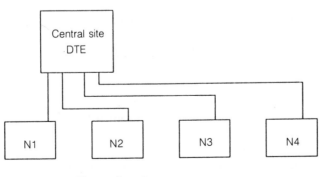

Star configuration

This type of configuration has the advantage of simplicity (the DTE is connected directly); but is costly because of the amount of cabling required.

27.6.2   Multipoint or BUS configuration

In this type of connection, the interconnected DTEs share the same data transmission line, as below:

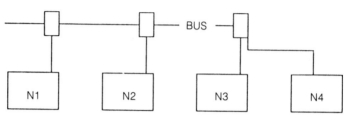

BUS configuration

As a general rule, in a multipoint connection, the transmission line comprises four wires. One pair of wires is used to connect the master DTE to the slave DTEs (remote stations), and the other pair to connect from the slaves to the master. In such a configuration it is therefore only possible to have a single station transmitting at any instant if two transmitters are not to interfere with each other's transmissions. It is sometimes possible for the controller and one or more remote stations to attempt to transmit at the same time; this is called **contention**.

If the line is to be shared without contention between various users, the following procedures can be used.

27.6.2.1   Polling and selecting

In **polling** the controller asks each remote station in turn in some predetermined sequence if it has some data to send and will give it temporarily the status of master. The remote station may simply acknowledge the polling message or if it has data to send, it will send it.

In **selecting**, the controller asks the terminal if it is ready to receive a message which is waiting to be sent.

These procedures will be studied in more detail in a later chapter.

27.6.2.2   Broadcast

This technique is based on the principle of broadcasting the data to all remote stations. Only the station whose address is transmitted will take any notice of the **message**.

27.6.2.3   Advantages and disadvantages of multipoint connections

In a multipoint connection, terminals cannot communicate simultaneously which limits the response time. The line is optimised, i.e. it is used at a minimum cost. However, there is a physical limitation which prevents more than three branches off the main trunk and prevents more than eight DTEs per access point. If a branch is defective, communication with all the DTEs on that branch is lost.

27.6.3 Token ring configuration

The **ring** topology comprises a sequence of point-to-point connections arranged in a ring:

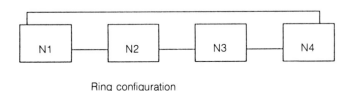

Ring configuration

Access to the ring is managed by passing a **token** from station to station. In such a configuration a terminal is only allowed to transmit if it is in possession of the token. If it has nothing to send it passes the token to the next station. If it has a message to send, it puts a header on to the ring, then the message itself and then the token. The header contains the address of the destination. All stations on the ring are listening for their own address and when a station recognises its address it copies the message and retransmits it on to the ring with a flag to indicate that the message has been received. When the message returns to the transmitter with its flag set it is removed from the ring, if its flag is not set it continues to circulate (but only for a limited number of times).

27.6.4 Mesh configuration

Made from a series of point-to-point connections between several DTEs, the network is said to be a strongly connected or a less strongly connected mesh according to the number of connections established.

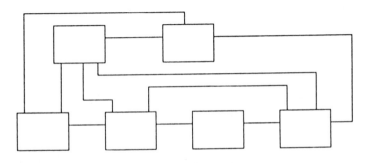

Mesh configuration

As a general rule such configurations are reserved for connections between computers (for example, the computers of the JANET network).

27.7 Switching

To establish a connection the components of the network must be physically connected by means of communication channels. This is known as switching and there are various ways of doing it.

27.7.1 Circuit switching

This technique is the oldest and the simplest. It consists of establishing **on request** the circuit joining two stations, by connecting partial circuits end to end, **before** the communication starts (this is still in use for voice communications over the telephone network). The circuit, once established, remains connected for the duration of the call.

27.7.2 Message switching

This technique enables messages accompanied by their destination address to travel independently from node to node on the network along a predetermined route to their destinations. This allows the use of the network to be optimised.

27.7.2.1 Advantages and disadvantages

- A single message can be distributed to several destinations (electronic mail) and it can be kept waiting if a destination is not ready to receive it.
- The time for a transmission to reach its destination is variable and depends on how busy the network is.
- The technique requires the nodes to have capacity for the temporary storage of messages.

27.7.3 Packet switching

Packet switching, used by British Telecom's PSS (packet switchstream service), allows the transmission through the network of small packets of data. Messages transmitted by a DTE are split into small units provided with the sender and receiver addresses, to form a **packet**. Such networks offer a service called **virtual circuits** which form a **logical** connection between two DTEs. The packets circulating on the line maintain their order of transmission and the network can decide, in the case of a broken or blocked line, to send the packets on different routes, which will not necessarily be the most direct. Such a computer network is illustrated in Figure 27.2.

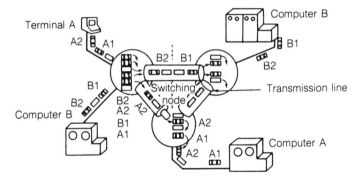

Figure 27.2   A computer network

These virtual circuits can be established on request (switched virtual circuits), or they can be permanently established (permanent virtual circuits). Two circuits are shown below:

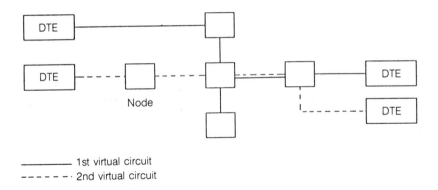

——————— 1st virtual circuit
– – – – – –· 2nd virtual circuit

The introduction of packet switched and virtual circuit techniques, has led manufacturers and international standards organisations to define standard network architectures:

- The DSA architecture of BULL.
- The SNA architecture of IBM.
- The OSI model of ISO (ISO–OSI).

27.7.4   *The ISO-OSI seven-layer model*

The ISO (International Standards Organisation) OSI (Open Systems Inter-connection) model is a network architecture defined in layers (ISO seven-layer model), each layer having a specific function:

Application	7	Storage and processing systems
Presentation	6	
Session	5	Intermediate systems for packet transmission
Transport	4	
Network	3	
Data link	2	
Physical	1	

Physical transmission media of the open systems

Level 0, also called the **media** level, indicates the physical transmission media (e.g. copper, optical fibre).

Level 1 (physical) is concerned with the form taken by the elementary data (digital or analog signal).

Level 2 (data link) defines point-to-point logical routes and is responsible for error detection, flow control and link management.

Level 3 (network) is responsible for setting up and maintaining connections across the whole network using address information.

Level 4 (transport) enables the operation of further error control protocols for verifying and correcting data.

Level 5 (session) fulfils the functions for connecting one terminal with another.

Level 6 (presentation) ensures that data is in a form which is accessible to the user (code conversion).

Level 7 (application) is concerned with the user interface to the seven-layer model.

The diagram on p. 289 illustrates exchanges between and within layers.

27.8 **Protection against errors**

Signals transmitted along a data transmission path risk, as has already been mentioned, being distorted by noise, attenuation, etc. For the human voice such distortions are not very serious but it is a quite different matter for binary signals. Hence special codes are used to help to avoid most of the errors and redundant data is added to the transmitted messages (e.g. parity, VRC, LRC, polynomial codes).

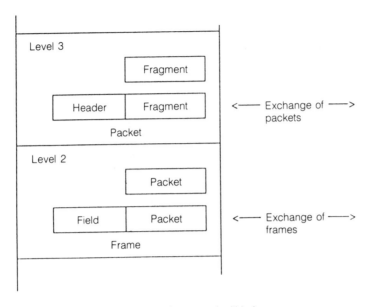

Example of exchanges between layers and within layers

Example 27.1   Calculation of a BCC (Block Check Character)

A computer wishes to transmit to a terminal with address 00, the message
'A B C D E'. It will send the following sequence of characters: 'SOH 0 0 STX
A B C D E ETX' and a BCC calculated as follows:

Message	ASCII	Parity	7	6	5	4	3	2	1
0	30	0	0	1	1	0	0	0	0
0	30	0	0	1	1	0	0	0	0
STX	02	1	0	0	0	0	0	1	0
A	41	0	1	0	0	0	0	0	1
B	42	0	1	0	0	0	0	1	0
C	43	1	1	0	0	0	0	1	1
D	44	0	1	0	0	0	1	0	0
E	45	1	1	0	0	0	1	0	1
ETX	03	0	0	0	0	0	0	1	1
BCC		1	1	0	0	0	0	0	0

The BCC is found to have the value 40 which in ASCII corresponds to
the character @. The BCC which is transmitted by the computer immediately
after ETX will therefore be @.

27.8.1 *The correction of errors*

The correction of any errors will in general be achieved purely and simply by the retransmission of the message. The transmitter sends a message and then waits for the return of an acknowledgement. If the signal is a NAK (negative acknowledge), the message is retransmitted. If the returned signal is an ACK (acknowledge), the next message is sent. If the return signal is slow to arrive (Time-Out), the unacknowledged block is retransmitted, possibly a limited number of times. This type of retransmission, although fairly old, is still very much in use and is often called ARQ–ACK (automatic repeat request–acknowledge).

Another method does not require the transmitter to wait for an ACK, it only interrupts transmission of the blocks when it receives a NACK in which case the incorrect block is retransmitted. This method is called ARQ–NAK (automatic repeat request–no acknowledge).

Chapter 28

Data transmission: procedures and protocols

Communication between the various constituents of the data transmission network is not made haphazardly but is governed by rules which enable different types of equipment to communicate under optimum conditions. These rules are formulated in terms of **procedures** and **protocols** which regulate the exchanges of data and control information necessary for the proper functioning of the network.

28.1 Procedures

Procedures govern all teleprocessing communication, from the time when the link between the constituent parties is established, up to the time when the connection is severed. Procedures can be divided into five phases.

1. **Establishment:** establishes the connection between the different equipments to be linked together. This phase includes, for example, the switching in of the various circuits to make the connection.
2. **Initialisation:** establishes the logical connection between the equipment, verifying that it is indeed linked together. It makes sure that both pieces of equipment are in fact capable of recognising each other and of 'talking the same language'.
3. **Transfer:** ensures the transfer of the data which must be exchanged between the parties.
4. **Termination:** ends the logical link, ensuring that the connection is terminated correctly.
5. **Release:** relinquishes to other users the physical circuits borrowed for the communication.

Example 28.1   A telephone conversation

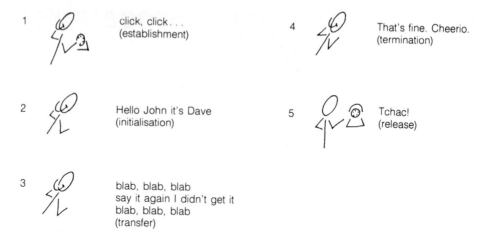

1   click, click . . .
    (establishment)

4   That's fine. Cheerio.
    (termination)

2   Hello John it's Dave
    (initialisation)

5   Tchac!
    (release)

3   blab, blab, blab
    say it again I didn't get it
    blab, blab, blab
    (transfer)

The management of these five phases requires the application of some precise rules of communication or **protocols**.

28.2 **Protocols**

Protocols depend mainly on the mode of synchronisation adopted in the connection between the DTEs participating in the teleprocessing link. There are two main groups of protocols: asynchronous and synchronous.

Asynchronous protocols: in asynchronous mode, since characters are transmitted independently of each other, no particular protocols have been developed.

Synchronous protocols: in synchronous transmission, the protocols can be of two types, they can be **synchro-character** (COP, Character Orientated Protocol), if the data is represented as characters; or they can be **synchro-bit** (BOP, Bit Orientated Protocol), if the data is considered to consist of simple binary strings.

28.2.1   *Character orientated protocols (COP)*

After making their first appearance in the 1960s these protocols are now very numerous. They include:

- BSC (Binary Synchronous Communication) developed by IBM and introduced in 1964.
- VIP (Visualising Interactive Processing) developed by Bull.
- DDCMP (Digital Data Communication Message Protocol) developed by Digital Equipment in 1974.

We will study one of the most widespread of these character orientated protocols, BSC.

28.2.1.1   BSC in point-to-point connections

The basic element of BSC protocol is a block of data (text), which is transmitted down the communication line preceded by the transmission of an STX character (Start of TeXt, coded 02H in ASCII), and followed by the transmission of an ETX (End of TeXt, coded 03H in ASCII) character to indicate the end of the data message.

The message to be transmitted is often quite long and is then divided into several blocks only the last of which is followed by an ETX; the end of each intermediate block being indicated by an ETB character (End of Transmission Block, 27H in ASCII), followed by a BCC (Block Check Character). To ensure the synchronisation of characters between the transmitter and the receiver, each block is preceded by at least two synchronisation characters: SYN (26H in ASCII).

Since the characters at the beginning and end of the transmission are the most prone to deteriorate, at least one SYN character is generally sent preceding the message and the byte FF is usually sent at the end.

When a block is transmitted, the receiver has to reply with an acknowledgement, positive or negative (ACK or NAK). If a block is rejected with a NAK it is retransmitted. In addition, to ensure that all the blocks have been properly received, positive acknowledgements are indicated by ACK0 or ACK1 characters alternately. In this way if the transmitter receives two ACK0 characters or two ACK1 characters in sequence, it knows that there has been a transmission error.

SAQ

28.1 Is it possible to use the BSC protocol for a polling/selecting procedure in a point-to-point connection? Explain.

Example 28.2   Dialogue between two stations A and B, using the BSC protocol for a point-to-point link

Station A (master)   Station B (slave)

Request to transmit	SYN...SYN ENQ FF	
Transmit		SYN...SYN ACK0 FF Ready
	SYN...SYN STX Text ETB BCC FF	
		SYN...SYN ACK1 FF No errors
Transmit	SYN...SYN STX Text ETB BCC FF	
		SYN...SYN NAK FF Error
Retransmit	SYN...SYN STX Text ETB BCC FF	
		SYN...SYN ACK0 FF No errors
End	SYN...SYN EOT FF	

Station A can then become the slave and station B the master if necessary

28.2.1.2 BSC in multipoint connections

In multipoint connections, the BSC protocol is used together with the cyclic interrogation of the stations using a polling/selecting technique described in the preceding chapter.

The following example is based on a primary station with three secondary stations A,B,C each of which may have several DTEs. So as not to complicate the diagram, SYN characters, BCC and the FF bytes have not been shown, their use being identical to that described in the example above:

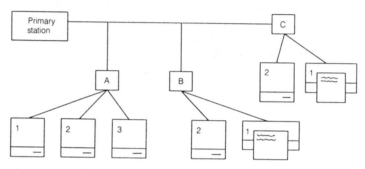

The polling/selecting sequence is as follows:

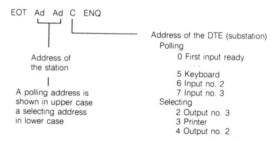

EOT Ad Ad C ENQ

Address of the DTE (substation)
Polling
   0 First input ready
   . . .
   5 Keyboard
   6 Input no. 2
   7 Input no. 3
Selecting
   2 Output no. 3
   3 Printer
   4 Output no. 2

Address of
the station

A polling address is
shown in upper case
a selecting address
in lower case

Example 28.3 Polling

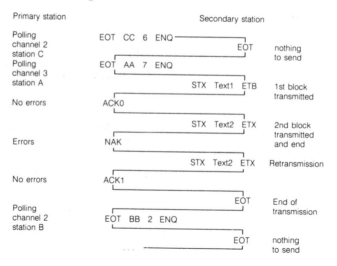

SAQ

28.2 Why is selecting not used in the sequence but only polling?

Example 28.4   Selecting

```
Primary station                              Secondary station

Selection of        EOT  cc  3  ENQ
printer                                      NAK       Not ready
station C
Selection           EOT  aa  4  ENQ
channel 2
station A                                    NAK       Not ready

Try again           EOT  cc  3  ENQ

                                             ACK0      Ready

Send 1st            STX  Text1  ETB
block
                                             ACK1      No errors

Send 2nd            STX  Text2  ETX
block
                                             ACK0      No errors

End                 EOT
transmission
                                             ACK1      No errors
```

The BSC protocol has other possibilities which we will not consider here, except to mention the conversational mode where the reply to a block is another block, and the transparent mode, where any binary pattern whatsoever can be transmitted.

28.2.1.3   Limitations of synchronous COPs

Although they are often used, synchronous character orientated protocols, such as BSC have certain limitations:

- The dialogue is limited to half-duplex connections because of the nature of the invitations to transmit and receive.
- Control information is transmitted separately, which wastes transmission time.
- The block check character (BCC) is not used for control messages.

28.2.2   *Bit orientated protocols (BOPs)*

The principal bit orientated protocols are at present:

- **HDLC** (High Level Data Link Control) standardised by ISO.
- **SDLC** (Synchronous Data Link Control) developed by IBM.

- **ADCCP** (Advanced Data Communication Control Procedure) standardised by the American National Standards Institute (ANSI).

These very similar protocols have a number of features in common:

- Simultaneous bidirectional communication (full-duplex).
- Messages, called **frames** can combine text and control data such as acknowledgements of previous frames.
- Frames, even those carrying control data only, are all protected against transmission errors. In addition they all have the same format and include a unique **flag** (a delimiter) at the beginning and the end.
- An acknowledgement is not expected for each frame and several frames can be sent in sequence without a separate acknowledge being sent.
- During transmissions of binary strings instead of characters, the transfer proceeds without any translation of the contents, which ensures the complete transparency of the codes actually used.

28.2.2.1 The HDLC protocol

There are different types of link under HDLC:

- **Unbalanced:** such a connection, whether it be point to point or multipoint, has one primary station (host) whose purpose is to control the link, and one or more secondary stations (slaves). The frames transmitted by the host are **commands**, those transmitted by the slaves are **responses**.
- **Balanced:** such a connection, which must be point to point, has stations which can both send or receive, commands or responses.

The stations have different operating modes:

- **Normal response mode (NRM):** in this mode which is only used in unbalanced systems a slave station can only transmit if it is invited to do so by the host. When it has finished it gives control back to the host.
- **Asynchronous balanced mode (ABM):** in this mode, a secondary station can transmit at any time without having to be invited by a primary station.

HDLC thus defines three classes of procedures:

- UNC, unbalanced normal class.
- UAC, unbalanced asynchronous class.
- BAC, balanced asynchronous class.

Structure of the HDLC frame

In HDLC protocol, all transmissions use a frame with a specific format irrespective of whether they contain data or control information. This is shown below:

Flag 1	Address 2	Control 3	Data 4	FCS 5	Flag 6

Flags (1 and 6) begin and end every HDLC frame and are used for bit synchronisation within the frame. They have the defined binary pattern of 011111110. Hence strings of six 1's appearing in a message must be avoided and therefore a 0 is systematically inserted after every string of five 1's.

The **address** (2) identifies the destination of the message.

The **control** field (3) defines which of three possible types of frames (I, S or U) it is, and also gives the sequence number of the frame.

The **data** field (4) contains the data to be transmitted. It can contain any binary pattern except those which look like flags (six 1's sandwiched between two 0's).

FCS (5) this frame check sequence contains the CRC (cyclic redundancy check) in two bytes – the remainder of the division of the transmitted message (address + command + data) by the generator polynomial.

Information frame (I) is used to transfer data:

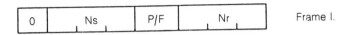

| 0 | Ns | P/F | Nr | Frame I.

Ns is the sequence counter of the transmitter and indicates the number of the frame of type I transmitted, Nr is the sequence counter of the receiver and indicates the sequence number of the next frame I expected, and P/F is a bit called P (Poll bit) in commands and F (Final bit) in responses.

When bit P is a 1 it is a command to all secondary stations to reply. Bit F indicates that a station in NRM has finished transmitting.

Acting as a sort of token, this bit gives the station that receives it the right to transmit (P = 1, the secondary station has the right to transmit; F = 1, the right is restored to the primary station).

Supervision frame (S) used to acknowledge the receipt of a frame and thus to aid the flow of data over the link:

| 1 | 0 | S | S | P/F | Nr | Frame S.

The two supervisor bits S specify four types of supervisory functions:

- 00 Receive Ready (RR).
- 01 REJect (REJ).
- 10 Receive Not Ready (RNR).
- 11 Selective REJect (SREJ).

RR is used by a station to indicate that it is ready to receive data.

REJ is used by a station to request the transmission or the retransmission of data frames, starting with the frame numbered Nr, which confirms the error-free reception of frames up to Nr-1.

RNR is used by a station to indicate that it is, temporarily, not ready to receive data frames but confirms the error-free reception of frames up to Nr-1.

SREJ is used by a station to request the transmission or the retransmission of the single frame numbered Nr, and confirms the error-free reception of frames up to Nr-1.

Unnumbered (U) used to define the mode of response of a station, to initialise it or disconnect it.

The five bits labelled M are used to code 32 types of commands or supplementary responses.

| 1 | 1 | M | M | P/F | M | M | M | Frame U. |

Frame abandon

It is possible to terminate a frame prematurely by transmitting an abandon signal, formed of at least seven consecutive 1's. Thus, while a frame is being received, if a succession of five 1's is detected, the following cases can arise:

- If the 6th bit is a 0, it is eliminated and the five 1 bits are considered to be data.
- If the 6th bit is a 1 and the 7th bit a 0, it represents the end flag of a frame.
- If the 6th and 7th bits are both 1, it is an abandon signal. The frame is terminated prematurely and considered invalid.

Use of HDLC frames

Frames of type I: this type of frame can be a command or a reply, carrying data. The HDLC protocol offers the advantage of being able to accept several consecutive frames without requiring separate acknowledgement of each. Only frames of this type are numbered and stations have to keep a count of the number of frames received or transmitted.

Ns holds the number of frames transmitted, from 0 to 7.
Nr holds the number of frames received, from 0 to 7.

If a frame is incorrectly received, the counter Nr is not incremented. To avoid errors a station must not have more than seven frames waiting to be acknowledged; the number of frames waiting is called the **frame credit** or **sliding window**.

Frames of type S: this type of frame does not carry data but is used for supervising the communication. An S frame could signal to the transmitter that the receiver has a full credit and it cannot accept any more data frames for the time being (role of the S bits).

Frames of type U: these unnumbered frames are used to define the response mode of a station, to disconnect a station, to indicate procedure errors, or to test stations.

Example 28.5 Dialogue between two stations in NRM

Station A Ns Nr	Frame exchanged Type Ns P/F Nr	Station B Ns Nr	Observations
	—— U (SNRM) ——>		Set in NRM mode
0　0		0　0	
	<—— U ————		No errors
0　0		0　0	
	—— I　0　p0　0 ——>		Send frame A0
1　0		0　1	
	—— I　1　p1　0 ——>		Send frame A1
2　0		0　2	
	<—— I　0　f1　2 ——		Reply B0
2　1		1　2	Received error-free by A
	—— I　2　p0　1 ——>		Send frame A2
3　1		1　3	No errors
	—— I　3　p0　1 ——>		Send A3 (error)
4　1		1　3	Nr does not change
	—— I　4　p0　1 ——>		Send A4
5　1		1　3	Ignored (3 not received)
	<—— I　1　f1　3 ——		Reply B1
3　2		2　3	No errors
	—— I　3　p0　2 ——>		Retransmit frame A3
4　2		2　4	No errors
	—— I　4　p1　2 ——>		Retransmit frame A4
5　2		2　5	No errors
	<—— I　2　f1　5 ——>		Reply B2 (acknowledge A4)
5　3		3　5	No errors
	—— I　5　p0　3 ——>		Send A5
6　3		3　6	No errors
	—— I　6　p0　3 ——>		Send A6
7　3		3　7	No errors
	—— I　7　p0　3 ——>		Send A7
0　3		3　7	Full (credit of 3)
	—— I　0　p1　3 ——>		Send A0
1　3		3　7	Full, frame ignored
	<—— S RNR f1　7 ——>		Receiver not ready
7　3		3　7	Reset state Ns
	—— S RR　p1　3 ——>		Is B ready?
7　3		3　7	
	<—— S RR　f1　7 ——>		B is ready
7　3		3　7	
	—— I　7　p0　3 ——>		Retransmit frame A7
0　3		3　0	
	—— I　0　p1　3 ——>		Retransmit frame A0
1　3		3　1	No errors
	<—— I　3　f1　1 ——>		Reply B3
1　4		4　1	
	—— I　1　p1　4 ——>		Send frame A1
2　4		4　2	No errors
	<—— S RR　f1　2 ——		No errors B has nothing else to send

28.2.2.2   X25 protocol for packet-switched transmission
This protocol governs packet transmissions and is used in numerous networks:

- Packet SwitchStream Service in the UK.
- TRANSPAC in France.
- EURONET in the EEC.
- TYMNET, TELENET in the USA, etc.

The X25 protocol covers the first three layers of the OSI standard:

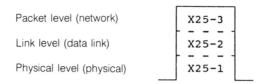

The X25-1 layer, conforms to recommendation V24 (essentially the same as RS-232-C) concerning the **physical** interface between DTE and DCE. The layer X25-2 defines the **link** and corresponds in fact to the HDLC class BAC protocol. The X25-3 layer, the **packet** level, manages connections (virtual calls) between pairs of DTEs by:

- Establishing connections to the public network and releasing them.
- Addressing the parties concerned.
- Transfer of packets.
- Management of errors and incidents.

Formation of packets
The data to be transmitted from one DTE to another is split into **fragments** of 32, 64, 128 or 256 bytes. A packet consists of a fragment provided with a header containing control information. There are also control packets containing only control information such as the request to establish or free a connection.

Packet headers require three bytes and are formed as in the following example of an X25 packet header:

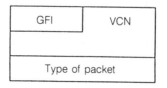

The General Format Identifier (GFI) indicates the size of the sliding window. The 12-bit Virtual Circuit Number (VCN) identifies the destination of the packet.

The type of packet indicates whether it is a data packet or a control packet. The following diagram shows the formation of packets under TRANSPAC:

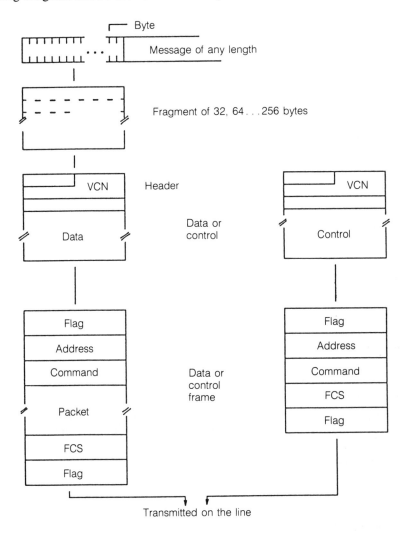

Establishing and releasing a virtual call
When DTE A, for example, wishes to communicate with DTE B, it first establishes a **virtual call** connecting them both. Such a circuit is established by means of a special packet called a **request packet**. DTE A builds up a request packet and sends it to its DCE which delivers the packet through the network to the destination DCE. DCE B then selects a free path and presents its DTE B with a packet called an **entry request**.

DTE B inspects the packet and either accepts the communication or rejects it. If it is refused, DCE B sends over the network a **clear request packet**; if it is accepted, it sends a **call accepted packet**.

Example 28.6   Establishing and releasing a virtual call

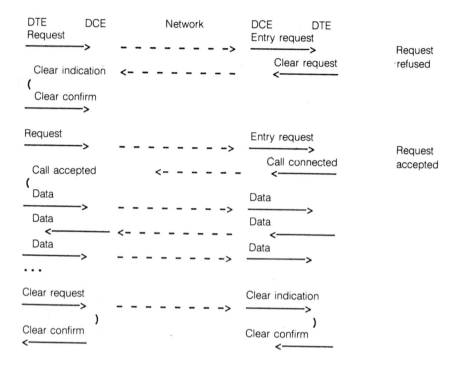

Data transfer

Once the virtual call is established (or the connection could be via a permanent virtual circuit which is permanently connected), the DCEs exchange packets of data in full-duplex mode. A bit in the GFI transmitted in each header indicates whether or not the packets have been received error free, in the same way as when frames are exchanged under HDLC.

Flow control

The flow of packets on a virtual call is limited, partly by the speed of the network, and partly by the abilities of the sending and receiving equipment (e.g. size of buffer memory). It is important that the flow from the transmitter is absorbed by the receiver. This can be done by sending packets to authorise a transmission; but it is also possible to send a certain number of packets without waiting for a confirmation by using a sliding window as described above for HDLC.

Solutions to SAQs

28.1   It is possible to use the BSC protocol for a polling/selecting procedure in a point-to-point connection? Explain.

No, the BSC protocol cannot be used for polling/selecting in point-to-point because the technique is only used in **multipoint** where it allows the selection or polling of a particular DTE; the question does not arise in point-to-point where only two DTEs are linked.

28.2 Why is selecting not used in the sequence but only polling?

There is no selection procedure because it is only a polling sequence and not a selecting sequence.

Chapter 29

Teleprocessing: composition of networks

As we have seen in preceding chapters, teleprocessing networks can take numerous forms, not only in their physical configurations but also in the means of communication used to link their DTEs. In addition, the telecom service offers the user numerous alternative services.

In the first part of this chapter, we shall study the component parts of networks; we will then introduce several networks which are available to users, and finally examine a concise method of creating a network.

29.1 The constituent elements

The physical realisation of a network requires a number of important and often complex installations. We will look briefly at their composition and function. The diagram below shows the constituent elements:

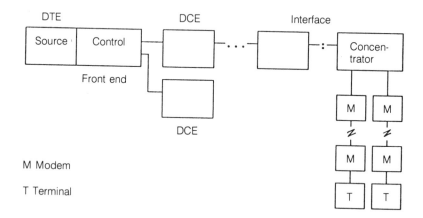

29.1.1 Terminals

Terminals are so diverse that it is virtually impossible to classify them. They vary not only in their processing power but also in their 'intelligence'. A computer used in connection with another master computer to execute batch programs could be called a terminal; so too could a remote teleprinter. More generally, a heavy terminal can be defined as a terminal capable of performing some processing of the data received, and a light terminal as a terminal which can, for example, only receive or transmit data.

29.1.2 *Standard interfaces*

In order to connect a terminal or DTE with the DCE, it is necessary to establish an interface which governs the communication and which can ensure:

- The setting up of the data circuit.
- The preparation of the data.
- The transmitting and receiving of data.
- The release of data circuits.

These interfaces are covered by certain CCITT recommendations, some of which have become standards.

Recommendation V24 is one of the best known interface standards. The basic idea of recommendation V24, better known by its American name of RS-232-C, lies in the use of distinct physical circuits for each type of command or signal, as shown below:

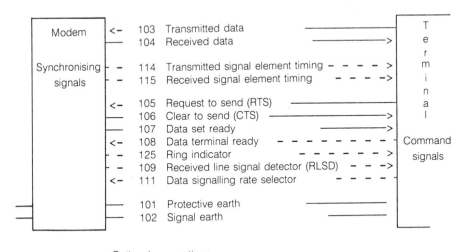

Modem

| <- | 103 | Transmitted data |
| | 104 | Received data |

Synchronising signals

-	114	Transmitted signal element timing
-	115	Received signal element timing
<-	105	Request to send (RTS)
	106	Clear to send (CTS)
	107	Data set ready
<-	108	Data terminal ready
-	125	Ring indicator
-	109	Received line signal detector (RLSD)
<-	111	Data signalling rate selector
	101	Protective earth
	102	Signal earth

Terminal

Command signals

– – – – Optional connections

The connection between the DTE and the DCE is achieved by means of a cable (of maximum length 100 m), containing as many wires as there are circuits. The connector at the end of the cable has been standardised by ISO; the latest comprises 25 pins and is generally known as a serial RS-232-C output or as a CANNON 25-way.

29.1.3 *Modems*

As we saw in the section on signal theory, it is usually necessary to transform the digital signal transmitted by the DTE into a modulated signal for transmission down the line. Conversely, at the other end of the line, it has to be demodulated. This function of MOdulation and DEModulation is performed by a special piece of equipment called a MODEM, which might be just a single board in a computer or it might be in a separate box. Modems are also standardised by CCITT recommendations.

29.1.3.1 Principles of operation

We will consider modems functioning in frequency modulation. The implementation of the modulator is rapidly being taken over by voltage-controlled oscillators (VCO). The frequency of a voltage-controlled oscillator is determined by the passive components and by a control voltage. Logic signals can therefore be applied as control voltages causing the output frequency of the VCO to vary directly.

In simple demodulators the received signal is applied to two selective filters; according to the frequency received, the comparator outputs a logic 0 or a 1. This technique is also being superseded by demodulators using VCO.

29.1.4 *Transmission lines*

The various pieces of equipment that have just been described are connected together by: wires, coaxial cables, optical fibres, lasers, infrared radiation, microwave radiation and satellites.

Wires, generally in the form of twisted pairs are used by the public telephone system for connecting subscribers' telephones to exchanges. The wires are twisted to reduce capacitive interference between lines.

The twisted pairs can be grouped together into cables with as many as 2600 pairs in a single cable but there can then be problems with cross-talk.

Coaxial cables used for long-distance transmissions are made of two cylindrical conductors separated from each other by an insulator. They are used for frequencies up to 60 MHz. The outside conductor serves to shield the inner one. They are much less subject to interference than are twisted pairs.

Optical fibres enable connections to be made over great distances and offer the advantage of being insensitive to electrical or magnetic environments. In addition they form very slim fibre cables that can be used for frequencies up to 140 MHz. The cost of optical fibres is very low and their use is becoming more widespread, particularly in large networks. British Telecom are not installing any new coaxial cables but are using optical fibres instead.

Line-of-sight transmission connections include infrared, lasers, microwave and radio. They enable transmissions of up to 40 GHz in the case of microwaves and can be used for distances of tens of kilometres, but they require the transmitter and receiver to be in line of sight.

Although directly related to microwave links **satellites** differ in several respects from line-of-sight transmission systems. Satellites introduce a longer transmission path and result in longer transmission delays, they actually broadcast their transmissions which can then be received by all stations under their downward beam with or without permission.

29.2 **Public networks**

The Public Switched Telephone Network (**PSTN**) in the UK was largely installed by British Telecom when it was part of the General Post Office. The Telecommunications Act of 1981 gave other licensed bodies, such as Mercury Communications Ltd, permission to become public telephone operators (PTOs) and some cable companies have licences to provide local loop networks linking users with wider telephone networks.

During recent years, British Telecom's old analog telephone network comprising switching exchanges, manual switchboards and thousands of miles of copper wire and cable has been largely replaced by modern computer-based equipment and optical fibre transmission lines carrying digital signals.

The new system comprises:

- The bearer network;
- The local distribution network (local loop);
- The functional networks

as shown below:

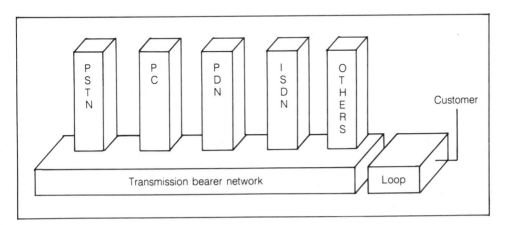

29.2.1 *The BT bearer network*

The bearer network interconnects the functional networks. It uses copper cables, fibre optics and radio links for digital transmissions, and it also carries a steadily diminishing volume of analog transmissions.

At the centre of the bearer network is a large capacity core, capable of transmitting 565 Mbits/s, which is connected to smaller and smaller trunks of progressively reducing capacities down to 2 Mbits/s.

The separate functional networks, each having its own processing and switching capability, share the bearer network.

29.2.2 *The local distribution network (local loop)*

The local distribution network connects user's equipment into the bearer network. Most users gain access to the bearer network via a simple analog link connecting their premises to the exchange where the analog signals are converted to digital form.

Other users may be provided with **Integrated Digital Access (IDA)** and have a digital connection directly into the network.

Some high volume users have **Flexible Access Systems (FAS)** providing an optical fibre connection directly into multiplexing equipment installed on their premises.

29.2.3 *The functional networks*

These can be divided into:

- Public switched telephone network.
- Public data network.
- Integrated services digital network.
- Private circuit digital (and analog) network.
- Other networks.

The latter category, other networks, includes networks lying outside the scope of this text, such as visual services networks, concerned with the transmission of television signals; derived service networks, concerned with specialised network services such as the 0800 automatic freephone facility; telex networks, providing a low-speed 50 baud telegraphy service, still widely used for national and international business transactions and in the process of being modernised; administration networks, used solely for the management and maintenance of the complete network system.

29.2.4 *Public switched telephone network*

This represents the most important part of British Telecom's business. The network is currently being converted to digital working but it will be some time before the conversion is complete. The local analog networks are being replaced by Digital Local Exchanges (**DLEs**) consisting of processors, central digital switches and concentrators. The concentrators can be positioned close to the DLEs or placed remotely in users' premises. Remote Concentrator Units (**RCUs**) are connected to the digital switch via 2 Mbit/s links.

The trunk network has a number of fully interconnected exchanges or **DMSUs** (Digital Main Switching Units). The DMSUs have completely replaced the analog trunk network.

Digital international gateway exchanges provide digital connection via DMSUs to the international networks.

Figure 29.1 shows how these elements link up.

29.2.4.1   Transmission rates

The permitted transmission rates are:

- 300 bauds in full-duplex (CCITT V21).
- 600/1200 bauds in simplex or half-duplex (V23).

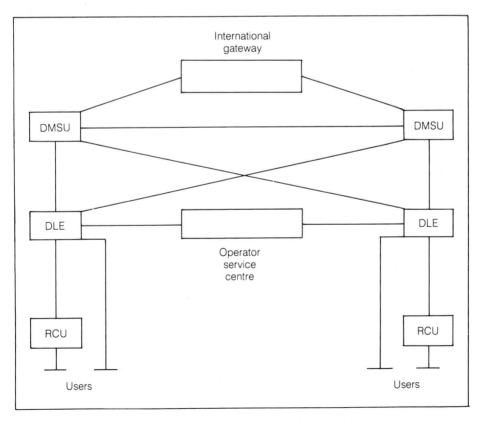

Figure 29.1   A digital switched network

- 1200/2400 bauds in simplex or half-duplex (V26 bis).
- 2400/4800 bauds in simplex (V27 ter).

Measurements have shown that at these rates the errors produced by the network remain at an acceptable level for most transmissions. It is important to remember that there are so many possible routes that the transmission characteristics cannot always be guaranteed.

29.2.4.2 Charges
Data transmission does not, at present, attract any additional charge associated with its use. A connection charge is always payable on installation and there is also the quarterly rental charge, clearly calls have to be paid for but the cost depends on the time of day and the zone being called.

29.2.4.3 Advantages and disadvantages
The telephone network has the advantage of being easily accessible for all users by means of a modem. Additionally it gives access to the Packet SwitchStream Service. This is the network used, for example, by videotext users and by retailers for credit card checking. In contrast the network also presents some disadvantages. The transmission rate is limited to 9600 bits/s in full-duplex, the connection and disconnection times are not guaranteed and the line characteristics can vary from one call to another which implies the need to use high quality and therefore expensive modems and, finally, communication costs become prohibitive for calls to destinations outside the local zone.

29.2.5 *Public data network (PDN)*

The public data network carries BT's **Packet SwitchStream Service (PSS)** used in business applications for file transfer, electronic funds transfer, accessing databases and messaging.

The network uses large computer-controlled digital exchanges, known as **System X**, connected via 64 kbits/s data channels multiplexed into 2 Mbits/s channels.

Access to the PSS is generally via a dedicated link called a **dataline** from the user's premises to a **packet assembler/disassembler (PAD)**. Several user datalines can be linked together to form a **multiline** so that calls can be shared between users.

Access to the PAD can also be made via the public telephone network using a dial-up line or a leased line.

If the terminal is a character terminal transmitting at 300/1200 bits/s, the PAD assembles the characters it receives from the terminal into packets for onward transmission through the network. If the character terminal is a receiving terminal, the PAD recovers characters it receives in packets from the network and sends them to the terminal.

PADs are also used to interface packet terminals working at 2400/9600/48 000 bits/s, to the public data network.

The virtual circuit (or VC) forms the basis of the service offered by PSS. Recall that this is a 'connection' between two subscribers allowing the transmission of data without restriction on its length or its nature, and with a high degree of security. It is called a virtual circuit because the physical circuits used by the packets of one subscriber are shared by other transmissions. The circuits are switched (SVC) that is, set up and released at the request of one of the parties to a communication, and offering therefore the possibility for every subscriber to communicate with every other subscriber on the network.

Additional services are offered by PSS, in particular reversed charge calls where the receiver pays for the call; fully itemised billing.

29.2.5.1   Charges
A connection charge is always payable on installation and there is a monthly rental charge, clearly calls have to be paid for but the cost depends on the time of day and the zone being called.

29.2.5.2   Advantages and disadvantages
The PSS network offers numerous advantages and enables in particular the exchange of data between users in any part of the country even when they are equipped with hardware having different characteristics. It is a network conforming to the international standards of ISO, offering transmission rates of up to 48 kbits/s (which may prove to be a limitation), having a great reliability and relatively good security. It is generally less expensive than a leased line.

29.2.6   *Integrated services digital network (ISDN)*

For a long time it has been recognised that there was a need for an integrated network that could offer end-to-end switched transmission of voice, computer data, viewdata, telex, video and fax. In response to this need, CCITT has defined a class of telecommunication service known as ISDN which is supported by many of the public telephone operators throughout the world and has recently become widely available in the UK.

29.2.6.1   Access rates
There are two types of service defined for ISDN: Basic Rate Access (BRA) and Primary Rate Access (PRA). BT's primary rate access service, ISDN 2, provides the user with two channels enabling full-duplex working at 64 kbits/s. For its primary rate access service, ISDN 30, BT provides thirty 64 kbits/s channels.

29.2.6.2   Charges
There is an installation charge and a quarterly rental charge. Within the UK, voice

calls and data calls are all charged at the normal telephone rates, but international call charges are based on four charge-bands depending on the destination.

29.2.7 *Private circuit networks (PC)*

Private circuits (leased lines) are for the use of a particular subscriber, and are no longer available to be switched as they are in the PSTN or PDN networks. Leased lines are organised according to the same principles as switched lines. There are several types distinguished by the service they offer.

29.2.7.1 Transmission rates

Leased-line telegraphic connections: the need for this type of connection is rapidly declining for data transmissions.

Leased-line telephonic connections: a line is called telephonic when it transmits signals in the telephone frequency band, i.e. between 300 and 3400 Hz. Such a service can be achieved:

- By two-wire links, of normal quality (2QN), giving rates of 2400 bits/s in full-duplex and 4800 bits/s in half duplex.
- By four-wire links, of normal quality (4QN) or of superior quality (4QS), giving rates respectively of 4800 and 9600 bits/s in full-duplex.

Special base band connections: a leased line is called a baseband line when it allows transmission of an electrical signal in its original frequency band (baseband transmission). These connections allow transmission rates of 72 kbits/s but within the local exchange area.

The **KiloStream** service is a range of digital private circuits used to transmit large volumes of data between fixed points. It provides full-duplex, synchronous connections at a range of speeds from 2.4 kbits/s to 64 kbits/s.

The **MegaStream** service is similar to KiloStream but offers very high-speed links that can carry data and speech combined. Typically it is used at speeds of 2 Mbits/s and at 8 Mbits/s.

29.2.7.2 Charges

Leased lines have the advantage of a tariff which is independent of the use made of the line, but depends on the length, characteristics and the quality offered. An installation fee is charged at each end of the connection.

29.2.7.3 Advantages and disadvantages

Leased lines have the advantage of offering subscribers a certain security of communication, in the sense that they are the only ones using the leased lines; the cost is relatively small over short distances. In contrast the cost is high if the lines are not used very frequently or if they are only used for small volumes of data, because the charge is independent of the amount of traffic.

29.2.7.4   The KiloStream and MegaStream services

Access to the Kilostream service is through a network terminating unit on the user's premises, which is linked to a KiloStream multiplexer at the local exchange. The KiloStream Plus service provides a dedicated 2 Mbits/s path directly into the user's premises enabling up to 31 individual circuits to be carried from a central mainframe to a number of terminals at separate locations. KiloStream Plus also offers separated routing. Where there are two KiloStream Plus installations at a single site, it is possible to separate the two bearer links so that if one link fails, only part of the transmission capacity will be lost.

By using the MegaStream standby option with the MegaStream service, it is possible to arrange for two separate routes to be installed between the user's premises and the exchange. Should a breakdown occur in one of the routes, automatic switching equipment switches to the alternative route. This safeguards against loss of service due to physical damage in the local section of the link.

Charges
There is an initial charge for the installation of equipment at each end of the link. There is a connection charge for making the initial connection; the cost depending on the length of the link, and there is an annual rental which also depends on the length of the link.

Advantages and disadvantages
The networks offer a number of advantages, in particular:

- Digital transmissions giving high transfer rates.
- Reliable connections, using the option to duplicate the connection between the DCE and the access point to the network.
- Multiline connections which allow, for security reasons, two subscribers to be connected by several independent physical circuits.
- The capability to link into the International SwitchStream service and thus gain access to the international X25 packet networks.

29.3   Network design principles

Because of the complexity and the extent of knowledge necessary to design a network from first principles, networks in small to medium sized firms are often designed empirically; nevertheless we present here a first approach to such a problem. The preliminary study of the design of a network must cover the following points:

- Determination of the volume of transactions.
- Determination of the duration of a transaction.
- Deducing the number of terminals required.
- Deducing the required transmission speed of the line.

After this first approach, a network configuration has to be chosen and that will depend not just on geographical criteria but also, inevitably, on economics.

29.4 **Case study**

GML, a company whose head office is in Tamworth currently has its accounts processed at a processing centre in Lichfield to which it is connected by means of a two-wire 4800 bits/s leased line of normal quality. GML receives the accounts of its branch offices by post and is responsible for data capture. It decides, in view of the increasing work load, to free itself from the work of data capture and to reduce the processing time by connecting the branch offices direct to the processing centre at Lichfield.

The branches are situated respectively at:

Tamworth	6 km
Stafford	26 km
Leicester	30 km
Derby	35 km
Crewe	80 km
Chester	100 km
Winchester	160 km

The studies made on site at Tamworth indicate an average of 5000 transactions (a page of writing) per site per month (20 working days), each, transaction lasting one minute on average and consisting of 1.2 kbytes. The hardware, situated at Tamworth can manage synchronous half-duplex transmissions.

The problem is to decide which type of connection to establish in order to obtain an efficient network, capable of expansion in the future, and for which the cost is the most 'reasonable' possible.

29.4.1 *An outline solution*

The first thing it is important to know, in such a situation, is the number of terminals necessary at each site and the data rate emitted or received at each of the sites. First of all let us determine the number of terminals necessary.

We know that we have 5000 transactions/site/20 days, say 250 transactions per day. But each transaction lasts one minute, i.e. 250 minutes in total, which comes to approximately five hours with a margin of safety. Therefore it would seem that, since a working day is seven hours, one terminal per site is ample for the present needs.

Let us now determine the speed of transmission which will be required. Each transaction is 1.2 kbytes, i.e 9830 bits to be sent in one minute. Therefore a rate of 163 bits/s is necessary. This is very slow.

Now we have to cost the various possible solutions (charges as of 1992).

29.4.1.1 1st proposal

The first solution to be proposed makes use of the Packet SwitchStream Service on the public data network. We know intuitively already that this solution (five hours of communication per day) is not going to be cost-effective.

If we choose the case of direct access via a dataline, at a rate of 2400 bits/s (looking to the future), we will have for each site:

Rental: £5.00/month
Connection: 20 days/month × 5 hours/day × 60 minutes × £1.90/minute
               = £11 400 per month

i.e. a total of £11 405 per month per site, which gives a total cost for the whole network of £79 835 per month.

29.4.1.2 2nd proposal

The second proposal makes use of the public telephone network. The calculation is similar to that used in the first proposal but the connect time is less costly and varies between 5p per minute and 20p per minute depending on the distance and the time of day.

If we assume the worst case charge of 20p per minute, in contrast to the charge of £1.90 in the first proposal, the total cost would amount to, approximately, only one-tenth of the cost of using the Packet SwitchStream Service, say £7900 per month.

In the case of Tamworth, it would be feasible to use a baseband link at a cost of £735 + (77 × (6 − 5 km)) = £812 per year, plus the cost of renting the terminating equipment (£250 at each end).

29.4.1.3 3rd proposal

The third proposal makes use of leased lines. Suppose we choose to use a four-wire normal quality line in full-duplex. The current scale of charges gives us, for distances more than 15 km (i.e. five of the six sites), an annual charge of:

$$£1505 + (12 \times (D - 15))$$

(where D is the distance 'as the crow flies' between the extreme DTEs), i.e.

Stafford	1505 + (12 × (26 − 15 km))	= £1637
Leicester	1505 + (12 × (30 − 15 km))	= £1685
Derby	1505 + (12 × (35 − 15 km))	= £1745
Crewe	1505 + (12 × (80 − 15 km))	= £2285
Chester	1505 + (12 × (100 − 15 km))	= £2525
Winchester	1505 + (12 × (160 − 15 km))	= £3245

The connection from Tamworth (6 km) would cost £812.

The annual bill in such a case totals £13 934, say £1160 per month, plus the cost of renting the terminal equipment.

This price is very much better than the earlier proposals but at this stage, we can suggest that the connection between Winchester and Lichfield is not direct but is made via Tamworth (the connection between Tamworth and Lichfield is already in existence and the new work sharing will lighten the load): see Figure 29.2. The connection from Chester could also be envisaged as being made via Crewe and that from Crewe can be made via Stafford (in fact a four-wire link can be used at rates of up to 4800 bits/s in half-duplex, but we only need approximately 200 bits/s).

Chester–Crewe	1505 + (12 × (18 − 15 km)) = £1541
Crewe–Stafford	1505 + (12 × (40 − 15 km)) = £1805
Stafford–Lichfield	1505 + (12 × (26 − 15 km)) = £1637
Derby–Lichfield	1505 + (12 × (35 − 15 km)) = £1745
Leicester–Lichfield	1505 + (12 × (30 − 15 km)) = £1685
Winchester–Tamworth	1505 + (12 × (154 − 15 km)) = £3173

The connection from Tamworth (6 km) would cost £812, i.e. a total cost of £12 398 approximately per year or just over £1000 per month.

This last proposal is clearly the best of those considered so far.

29.4.1.4   4th proposal

Up to this point in the analysis we have not considered using processors at the

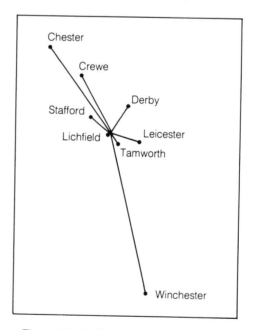

Figure 29.2   The sites on the network

remote sites. If processors were used to store a day's input, say, on a hard disk, it would be possible to transmit the day's accumulated data, using the ISDN 2 service, at 64 kbits/s. This would reduce the transmission time for each site from 5 hours/day to approximately one minute (250 transactions $\times$ 1.2 kbytes/transaction $\div$ 64 kbits/s = 46 s/day). It would also be possible to transmit the data at a time of day when the tariff was least costly thus reducing the cost of transmission still further.

29.4.2   *Decision*

The choice of a solution begins with an analysis of the configuration and the volume of traffic expected on the network. The choice can be influenced by the type of protocol accepted by the host processor; in fact, depending on whether or not it accepts HDLC or BSC protocols there could be a need for full-duplex or half-duplex channels. If a leased line solution is selected it will be necessary to decide whether a four-wire link is needed or whether a two-wire link would be sufficient.

Once these criteria are decided, there remains to consider the charges which apply and to determine the type of network which offers the most suitable performance at the lowest cost. Account must also be taken of the various network components such as modems, concentrators, multiplexers . . . which may or may not be included in the service offered with the chosen network, and which can increase the initial cost. The general approach to network design is therefore guided by:

- Research into performance (e.g. response times).
- Research into the level of security required in the transmissions.
- Attempting to minimise network costs in particular by concentrating the traffic.

Such studies cannot be carried out without a good knowledge of the range of network facilities made available to the user by the network operators.

Chapter 30

Data transmission: local area networks

A preliminary definition of a local area network (LAN) might be the following: a local area network is a combination of hardware and software which physically interconnects computers and their peripherals within the geographical confines of a single site. Its purpose is to share common resources between several users.

In practice the notions covered by the term local area network, or more simply **network**, are manifold. The term is applied to simple office networks built around a PC/XT and including several work-stations; it is applied to networks of clusters organised around mini-computers, and including numerous work-stations on which applications can be developed and run; and extends to industrial networks, capable in some cases of collecting data in real time.

The work undertaken on a local area network can be assessed on a scale of increasing complexity. At the bottom of the scale, the exchange of files between work-stations calls for a network of only modest capability. In this type of application, when a work-station requests a program, a text file or a spreadsheet, the data is transferred from the server to the work-station and the processing is then performed locally. When the processing is finished, the results obtained are sent to the server to be saved and/or printed. There is thus only need to use network resources at the beginning and end of the session and in limited amounts.

In the middle of the scale of complexity is work on shared databases that requires permanent access to common resources. Processing remains modest in the case of data capture, updates, and searches but the demand on the servers increases for sorting, indexing and complex printing requirements.

Finally at the top of the scale activities such as program compilation or reading and copying of large volumes, can quite quickly saturate a host.

The majority of local networks perform the following functions:

- Sharing files, that is, working with several other users simultaneously and without interference on the same database, on the same files, or with the same program (e.g. word processor, spreadsheet).
- Attributing rights of access to files, from no access, through read only access, to access permission for file creation and updating.
- Passing messages (electronic mail).
- Management of files waiting for the printer or printers.

30.1 **The topology of local networks**

The specific topology adopted for a particular network will depend on where the work-stations have to be positioned. The topologies of local area networks are in principle the same as those described for wide area computer networks.

30.1.1 *Linear bus*

The **linear bus** is one of the most common configurations for a local network:

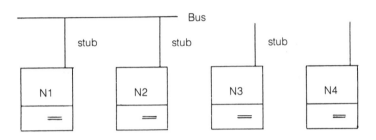

A linear bus topology

It is formed from a single length of cable to which stations are generally connected by **stubs** (connecting cables with a length of 2 m maximum) and some T connectors (the point of connection is often known as a node). If stubs and T connectors were not used, the length of the cable would have to be increased thus increasing the cost of the network.

An advantage is that the network can support several hosts (servers), and that should any stations break down they will not affect the operation of the remaining network. The network does, however, have a disadvantage; if the main cable fails then the whole network fails. What is worse, if such a cable is buried under the floor, the whole cable very often has to be uncovered since it is not easy to diagnose the exact location of the fault.

30.1.2 *Star*

In a **star** topology each station is connected by cable to a central host (the main computer system), (see next page).

Because an individual cable connects each station to the host, the cost of installation may be particularly high. This cost can be reduced by using twisted pair connections but then the transmission rates are also reduced.

As a general rule star configurations can be recommended for up to ten stations provided that disk accesses are not too frequent.

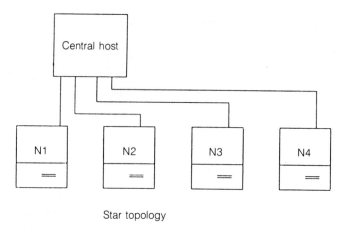

Star topology

Distributed star is a mixed topology which enables stations to be connected to a central point via a dedicated cable. This central point is a junction box (called a hub) capable of supporting 4 to 16 stations. Each hub is attached to the bus:

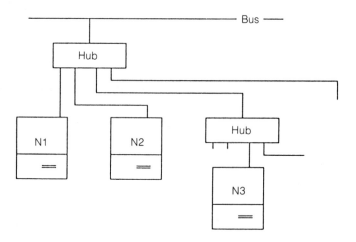

Distributed star topology

It is therefore easy to adapt this topology to different sites. The detection of faulty cables is easy because each station is connected by its own cable and the hubs are all connected to the same bus.

30.1.3 Ring

The **ring** appears in the form of a closed bus, each stub connects one station to another, the controller can be in any position. One of the stations usually acts as controller:

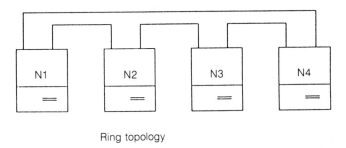

Ring topology

30.2 **Transmission modes and access modes**

Two modes of transmission are currently used in local area networks:

- Baseband, in which signals are transmitted in their digital form.
- Wideband, which uses frequency modulation to transmit the signals. It requires more complex techniques than baseband and uses coaxial cables or fibre optics; it is not used very much at the present time.

Two messages cannot be allowed to interfere with each other as they circulate through the network. A protocol must therefore be established which determines the rules of access to the network. The most commonly used modes are the contention mode and token passing.

30.2.1 *Contention mode*

In a contention protocol (CSMA, Carrier Sense Multiple Access), generally associated with bus topologies, each terminal 'listens out' for (senses) other transmissions and can itself transmit when it can no longer hear the carrier signal. It is always possible that two stations, listening to determine if the bus is free, decide to transmit at the same moment, in which case the two messages are said to **collide**. To resolve matters after a collision:

- Either allocate fixed time slices to the different stations (CSMA/CA – CSMA with collision avoidance or TDMA, Time Division Multiple Access).
- Or stop the transmission from the two stations momentarily and allow them to retransmit after a random time interval (CSMA/CD – CSMA with Collision Detect).
- Or use a combination of the two systems.

30.2.1.1 Principle of CSMA/CD

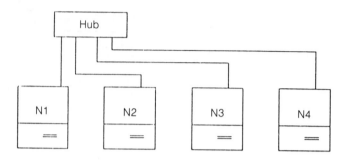

Suppose that station N1 wishes to send a message to station N3 and that N2 wishes to send a message to N4. Stations N1 and N2 will 'listen' to the line and if the line is free will send their messages.

The hub therefore detects two active transmissions and sends a collision signal to all stations. Stations N1 and N2 will detect this special signal and will stop transmitting. At the end of a random period the transmission restarts. It is very unlikely that the two stations will decide to retransmit simultaneously. If such were the case the waiting cycle would begin again.

Other methods which can be mentioned here are: CDMA (Code Division Multiple Access), FDMA (Frequency Division Multiple Access), SRMA (Split-Channel Reservation Multiple Access) or GSMA (Global Scheduling Multiple Access). The detailed study of these is beyond the scope of this book. They are used mostly in industrial local area networks.

30.2.2 *The slotted ring*

One or more empty packets circulate around the ring. A station transmits data in the form of standard packets with a header, a central zone (the actual message) and an end. A special bit (the marker bit) is found in the header. It is set to 1 if the packet is currently carrying a valid message or to 0 if it is free.

A station wishing to transmit does so only when the marker in a passing packet indicates that the packet is free. All stations will receive the packet in turn and read the header in which is written the address of the destination. The receiver can thus recognise its address, read the message and retransmit the packet on to the network. When the packet arrives back at the sender the sender can validate the message and free the packet by resetting the marker. The packet is freed and sent on its way to prevent the sender using it exclusively. The following diagram illustrates this:

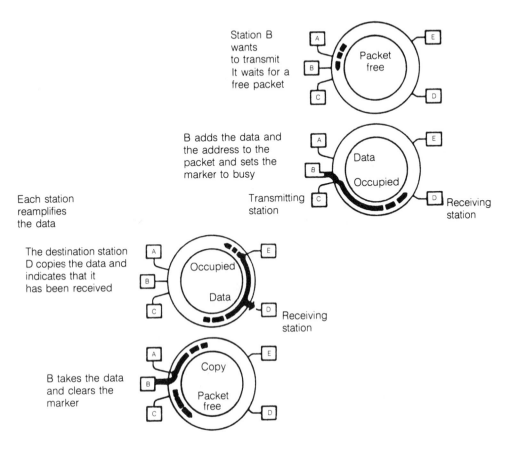

Station B
wants
to transmit
It waits for a
free packet

Packet
free

B adds the data and
the address to the
packet and sets the
marker to busy

Data
Occupied

Each station
reamplifies
the data

Transmitting
station

Receiving
station

The destination station
D copies the data and
indicates that it
has been received

Occupied

Data

Receiving
station

B takes the data
and clears the
marker

Copy

Packet
free

30.2.3 *Token passing*

In the token passing technique, developed by IBM and used both in ring and in bus networks, a control token is passed between stations. Any station which has the token is allowed to transmit on to the bus. The control token is a packet which contains no data except for the token (a bit pattern) which gives the right to transmit. When a station wishes to transmit, it must wait until the token is passed to it before it can transmit its message. The token only confers the right to transmit for a limited time. When the end of the message is reached or when the time interval has expired, the node transmits the token to the next node that has the right to transmit.

30.3 **The hardware components**

30.3.1 *The cabling*

The cabling is very often the first element to be considered in the hardware installation of a local network. The fact that the network may have a long life (of the order of ten to fifteen years) should always be kept in mind and the technical problems when installing cabling in an existing building or in a building to be built in the future should not be overlooked. In addition, its cost can vary from £50 to £600 per station, which may represent a substantial part of the total cost of the installation. The types of cable most widely used are the twisted pair, the coaxial cable and the fibre optic cable.

The twisted pair is the ordinary telephone wire. Whilst being inexpensive and easy to install it nevertheless possesses the great disadvantage of being susceptible to electrical and magnetic noise.

Coaxial cable ensures a much faster transmission rate. Made from an internal conductor surrounded by an external shield, it can carry up to 10 Mbits/s. However, it is more expensive than the simple twisted pair.

The optical fibre, much more sophisticated than previous media, has total immunity to ambient electromagnetic interference, and offers high data rates on a large number of channels. Unfortunately it is still costly and technically difficult to install, particularly at junctions.

The following table summarises the respective characteristics:

Media	Speed of transmission	Length of run	Support of multipoint	Relative cost	Applications
Coaxial in baseband	Up to 50 Mbps over a short distance in half-duplex	2.5 km and less	Yes up to 100 nodes	21 p/m to 36 p/m	Station to station all types of application
Coaxial wideband	Up to 150 to 200 MHz full-duplex	320 km	Yes several thousand nodes	31 p/m to 60 p/m	Networks with many distributed systems, multipurpose systems
Optical fibre	Up to several thousand bits per second half-duplex	320 km	Repeater necessary at each node	£3.60 m to £4 m regardless of the number of fibres per cable	Communication between central computers, office applications necessitating a high degree of noise immunity and large volumes of data to transmit

The speed of data along the cable is only one of the performance measures applied to local area networks. It cannot by itself determine the performance of the network. The host's disk transfer rate (approximately 800 kbits/s), can create a bottleneck, even in a network capable of transmitting 10 Mbits/s along its cables. The role of the operating system in optimising disk accesses is of prime importance in determining performance.

30.3.2 *Servers*

Servers manage the common resources of the network for the work-stations. Each server has, in principle, a large mass memory, which contains all or some of the data files and programs shared by the users. Generally it is equipped with one or several printers. The server receives requests to use the resources that it controls, processes the requests, and then issues responses to the requesters. When the server receives simultaneous requests from different stations it must place them in a queue. Briefly, the server has to manage the printer queues (spooling), the disk directory and the file allocation tables.

A server that is concerned only with managing the network and its common resources, is said to be a dedicated server; a server can at the same time also be a work-station, but this is only sensible if the activity of the network is very low, otherwise the effect on the response time would be very noticeable.

30.4 **The software components**

Standard protocols aim to make the software independent of the hardware in the interests of the user. This independence enables communication (bridges) between networks of different types, and at the same time allows existing networks to evolve while ensuring the continued use of previous applications.

The first standard to meet in the design of network software is that of the OSI (Open Systems Interconnection) seven-layer model. The higher layers have given rise to Net-BIOS, a standard recently adopted by most manufacturers of PC networks. Each local network of microcomputers has its own operating system covering the OSI levels: transport, session and presentation.

Net-BIOS (Network Basic Input/Output System) consists of a collection of software interrupts and function calls to establish sessions, to send data packets, and to allocate names to enable stations on the network to be identified. Covering OSI layers 4 and 5, it provides the interface between the network and applications and allows the network to be connected to other types of network.

The standard 'presentation' layer assumes the use of MS-DOS 3.1, which was the first version of DOS to include file locking functions, and the control of accesses to files by applications software. The network operating system must therefore be compatible with DOS 3.1.

The combination of software with hardware can be achieved in two ways: when a manufacturer develops all the components of a network and markets the complete network, the network is said to be generic. In contrast networks can be produced from a combination of components from several sources. Two principal ranges seem to lead the market at present.

30.4.1   *The Ethernet range*

Ethernet is a standard developed more than ten years ago by Digital Equipment, Intel and Xerox. The interest created by this product has resulted in it being emulated by numerous manufacturers who have adopted it as a standard. Ethernet is characterised in particular by its use of:

- A bus network.
- Coaxial cable (or fibre optic link).
- CSMA/CD protocol.

This standard has been validated by ISO under the reference 802.3. The networks 3Com-Ethernet and Net-One belong to this range.

30.4.2   *The Starlan range*

The Starlan range was developed by AT&T and represents an alternative to both the Ethernet range and to IBM's Token Ring.

The key difference between this network and the others is that it is not limited to a particular topology. It can use a bus, a star or a distributed star architecture, and can use ordinary telephone cables so that even in the middle of a factory it can be connected directly to the internal telephone network without having to lay any additional cables. The data output circuit is distinct from the data input which means that a double twisted pair is needed.

Starlan networks support transmission rates of 1 Mbit/s with a CSMA/CD protocol on runs of up to 300 m. Each run can have seven stations.

The Micral-Net belongs to this category.

30.5   **A brief presentation of several LANs**

30.5.1   *The Bull Micral-Net*

There are two versions of Micral-Net, each using the Starlan standard for interconnection (twisted pair, baseband, star and CSMA/CD). The first version uses MS-Net software. The second uses the software of 10-Net, modified to be compatible with Net-BIOS. Interestingly, Micral-Net can use a tree topology starting with nodes connecting clusters of eight stations or other nodes. This tree topology of the distributed star type can have five levels of nodes (hubs) starting from a central node. In theory this enables up to 32 768 stations on the same network. The maximum distance permitted between a node and a station or other node is 250 m; however, the greatest distance between two communicating stations is 2 km.

30.5.2   The 3Com Etherlink

This is one of the most widely used networks. It employs CSMA, transmits in baseband at 10 Mbits/s down coaxial cables, in a linear bus topology. The network interface card (transceiver) is of the Ethernet type and does not incorporate a processor (that is on the Ethernet controller board connecting the terminal which is usually some distance from the cable). The 8-bit bus uses the input/output ports to transfer data. A high data rate can quickly saturate the buffer, once it becomes full, the interface card cannot accept any more data until it has been emptied. In this case, data transmitted must be retransmitted. A new interface card, Etherlink Plus, resolves most of these problems. It is equipped with an 80186 processor which has a 128-kbyte memory and a 16-bit bus.

30.5.3   The Corvus Omninet

Created by Corvus in 1981, Omninet is a widely used local network for microcomputers. The Omninet protocol and its interface cards often form the basis of other nets running under different software (Usernet, GoupilNet, VictorNet, etc.). It is a bus network that allows different types of microcomputer (PC, Macintosh, etc.), to be connected together and share the same printers or hard disks or exchange files. The data rate is 1 Mbit/s along a simple twisted pair allowing up to 64 stations to be connected. It has a maximum length of 1200 m and uses a CSMA/CA protocol.

30.5.4   IBM token ring

The IBM Token Ring has two versions. The first can interconnect up to 260 stations (PC, XT or AT) at 16 Mbits/s along a twisted pair. The second interconnects only 72 stations but at 4 Mbits/s. Each node of the network consists of a Multistation Access Unit (MAU) to which up to eight stations can be attached. These stations can be up to 100 m away from the MAU in the first version and up to 45 m in the second version.

30.5.5   Novell

At the current time this is one of the main local networks favoured by commercial users. Novell networks use the NetWare Operating System (NOS) on the controller which indicates that the controller must be dedicated to the network, but MS-DOS can be used on the stations. In fact the NetWare software has to be adapted to each type of hardware, which implies that the stations must be strictly homogeneous (PC). The network is limited to fifty stations. NetWare is the basis for numerous other local networks (ArcNet, 3Com-Ethernet, G-Net, etc.).

Index